TRANSISTORS HANDBOOK

TRANSISTORS HANDBOOK

By

WILLIAM DEALTRY BEVITT

Transistor Applications Engineer, Commercial Engineering Department, CBS-Hytron, A Division of the Columbia Broadcasting System

PRENTICE-HALL, INC.

Englewood Cliffs, N. J.

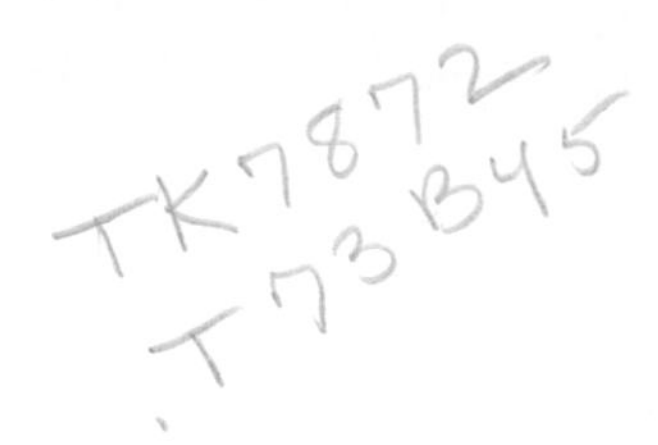

Library of Congress Catalog Card No.: 56-8057

First printing .... March, 1956
Second printing .... September, 1956
Third printing .... April, 1957
Fourth printing .... September, 1957
Fifth printing .... November, 1958
Sixth printing................June, 1959
Seventh printing........September, 1962

PRINTED IN THE UNITED STATES OF AMERICA

93018–C

To my father,

Edwin Dealtry Bevitt

PREFACE

This book presents a survey of the field of transistor circuits and applications. It has been my objective to summarize significant technical articles on the subject and to cover the major contributions of the companies which have developed transistors and their circuits. Examples of good practice in the design of transistor circuits are given by showing tested circuits with typical values of the circuit elements where possible. The methods of analyzing and applying transistor circuits to many different devices are also explained. The reader is referred to the Table of Contents and to the comprehensive Subject Index for a detailed list of specific applications.

Our concern here is with the practical aspects of transistors: what the transistor is doing toward making electronic circuits simpler, more efficient, more compact, as well as making possible new circuits. In short, the book seeks to tell what is being done with transistors, and how it is being done.

The first half of the book deals with fundamental concepts, the different types of transistors, their characteristics and their measurements, and the circuit properties and behavior of transistors. The last half of the work covers practical applications and circuits of transistors.

The book does not cover the physical theory of transistor electronics as described in the journals of physics. Such studies involving quantum mechanics are better left to the solid-state physicists. Likewise, the work does not deal with the design of transistors. Rather, its purpose is to show how to utilize transistors effectively.

Although many new developments and improvements of the transistor will doubtless take place, the basic nature of the device most likely will remain the same, just as the fundamental principle of the vacuum tube has not changed since DeForest invented it. Likewise, the basic circuits of the transistor probably will not change; this is indicated by their general similarity to vacuum-tube circuits. The network theory, on which transistor circuits are based, is firmly established in electronic science. Therefore present transistor circuits undoubtedly will be important for many years to come. Although the reader may wish to develop a new transistor circuit, he will always want to know what has already been accomplished in his particular field.

The book is intended for all who are associated with the electronics field, not only practicing engineers, but experimenters, radio amateurs, radio and television servicemen, engineering students, and graduate students. All of these are interested in tested transistor circuits. Throughout the book the main emphasis is on specific transistor circuits which can be read and understood by practically all persons connected with electronics.

The reader should note that many of the circuits described in this book are patented. No commercial use of any circuit should be made without investigating its patent status and securing the appropriate licensing agreement if such is required. No responsibility is assumed by the author, his employer, or the publisher for any infringement of patent or other rights of third parties which may result from the use of circuits, systems, or processes described or referred to in this book.

Finally, I convey my deep appreciation to my wife, Dorothy Whitsell Bevitt, who illustrated and typed the manuscript.

William Dealtry Bevitt

CONTENTS

5. *Power Transistors* *61*

6. *Measurements of Transistor Characteristics* *87*

7. *Methods of Analysis of Transistors and Transistor Circuits* *108*

8. *Tetrode and Pentode Transistors* *133*

Chapter 1

INTRODUCTION

In 1948 a revolutionary concept was introduced to the electronics world: Bardeen and Brattain of the Bell Telephone Laboratories announced the invention of the transistor, a crystal which amplified. Nothing like this had happened in electronics since DeForest discovered the triode vacuum tube in 1907; some years later radio tubes replaced the crystal detectors of the wireless era. Now a crystal amplifier, the transistor, challenges the vacuum tube because transistors are smaller, simpler, more efficient, more rugged, and longer lived. Already transistors have replaced tubes in hearing aids, with unheard-of battery economy. Moreover, many transistor circuits have fewer components than the vacuum tube circuits which perform the same functions. For example, in switching circuits, such as multivibrators, one point-contact transistor will do the work of two triode tubes. More importantly, transistors make possible new circuits for which no vacuum tube counterparts exist. An example of this is the complementary symmetry, class-B, push-pull amplifier. Other than the four transistors, this requires no circuit elements; it has no input transformer or phase inverter circuit, no output transformer, and no power switch. The amplifier consumes negligible standby power, and yet with only small junction transistors develops half a watt of output power across the 500-ohm voice coil of a special loudspeaker.

The transistor is a current-operated device, whereas the vacuum tube is a voltage-operated device. The transistor seems destined to become a relatively high-current, low-voltage device, although the vacuum tube is a high-voltage, low-current device. The transistor in a grounded-emitter circuit has a low input impedance, but a vacuum tube in a grounded-cathode circuit has a high input impedance. Nevertheless, some vacuum tube circuits will operate if the vacuum tubes are replaced by suitable transistors after the bias voltages and their polarities have been properly adjusted.

As good as present transistors are, a large amount of research and development is being carried on by the Armed Forces and private enterprise to improve them. In particular, it is desired to raise the high-frequency limit, to make them less temperature sensitive, to increase the maximum temperature of operation, to develop higher power transistors, and to decrease the noise figure.

Several methods have been proposed to extend the high-frequency range. One is the interposition of a layer of high-purity germanium between the base and collector,[1] which reduces the effective base-collector capacitance and increases the mobility of current carriers through this region. Such transistors are known as P-N-I-P or N-P-I-N units. A second method is the surface-barrier transistor[2] produced by precise electrochemical etching and plating techniques. This transistor employs a new mode of hole injection produced by a broad-area metal electrode in intimate contact with a single crystal of N-type germanium. A third method is to construct point-contact transistors with P-type germanium[3] instead of N-type germanium. This takes advantage of the greater mobility of electrons, which are injected into the emitter, as compared with holes in an N-type point-contact transistor. A fourth method is to utilize a thick wafer of low-resistance germanium and to place the active junctions on a thin section produced by drilling a well into the wafer.[4] This reduces the resistance-capacitance low-pass filter effect in the base-emitter input.

Most germanium junction transistors have maximum ambient temperature ratings of about 50°C, and germanium point-contact units have a range from 40°C to 60°C. Several companies have developed experimental silicon transistors, and one company is producing five types of silicon transistors on a commercial basis. Types 903, 904, 904A, 905, and X-15 silicon grown junction transistors[5] have a maximum ambient temperature rating of 150°C. For the grounded-base connection, the maximum collector dissipation is 100 mw at 25°C and 50 mw at 100°C. Research to develop materials for high-temperature operation of transistors is being carried on with compounds such as gallium antimony, and aluminum antimony.

There are several power transistors on the market with collector dissipations of 1 to 2 w, and one transistor with a 20 w collector dissipation. Work is being done to develop much higher power transistors.

The average point-contact transistor has a noise figure of about 48 db at 1000 cps, whereas the average junction transistor has a value of about 22 db. Low-noise junction transistors are available with a noise figure of about 15 db; these are usually selected from a production run. Research is under way to produce transistors with noise levels as low as those of vacuum tubes.

Intensive laboratory study is being made on self-powered transistors with built-in radioactive materials to supply the power.

No man can predict the ultimate future of transistors with certainty. However, it would seem that transistors are destined to have a great future. There are a number of interesting possibilities in the foreseeable future.

Transistors, because of their desirable properties, shortly may replace electron tubes to a large extent in communication equipment, computers, radios, and television receivers.[6] As improved types of transistors are put on the market, it will be possible to replace more and more electron tubes in equipment. However, it is not expected that a complete replacement of electron tubes by semiconductor devices will ever be technically possible or economically practical.

As one writer[7] has stated, the transistor makes the fully automatic factory a much more immediate prospect.

An automatic pilot for automobiles has been investigated.[8] It steers itself over a prescribed route, stops when it approaches another motor vehicle, or turns out of its lane to pass the slower vehicle. This electronic control of automobiles depends on the ultimate availability of transistors in tremendous quantities at a few cents apiece.

In airborne equipment[9] transistors have increased the performance of the AN/AIC-10 intercommunication system, a fuel-measuring system employing 20 w power transistors has been developed, and a transistorized digital computer has been designed. Estimates already indicate that junction and surface-barrier transistors can handle 75 per cent of present vacuum tube operations within the near future. This will bring about a major drop in total power consumption. In communication systems for commercial as well as military aircraft, essentially all functions except transmitter output theoretically can be transferred from vacuum tubes to transistors. Transistors can also take over a major load in information-handling equipment, high-speed computers, navigation and radar systems, autopilots, and control and servo systems.

Several important industrial applications of the transistor have been proposed. For example, the operation of certain types of switchgear which are utilized in the distribution of electric power[10] conceivably could be improved or simplified by transistors. Because the transistor should have indefinitely long life and freedom from burn-out, it may well be applied to those industrial fields where reliability is of prime importance. It should be possible to make the transistor mechanically very rugged for applications where severe mechanical vibrations or shock are encountered.

Dr. Alexanderson[11] has suggested several control applications of the transistor. A main transistor controlled by auxilary transistors could perform in a way resembling the phase-controlled rectifier. It could be energized from an a-c power supply and operate with an efficiency which approaches that of the rectifier. The suggested applications include the remote control of a d-c motor, and a frequency changer for operating an induction motor. These applications await transistors of higher power.

It has been predicted [12] that the ability of the transistor to control power flow with an over-all efficiency of 98 to 99 per cent will lead to extensive application of transistors in the power control field in general and the machine tool industry in particular.

The employment of the transistor as a substitute for the vacuum tube in electronic machines may permit such machines to grow to levels of complexity now unattainable.[13] At a conservative estimate transistor electronics may allow a hundredfold increase in complexity over vacuum tube machines. The Eniac computer, containing about 10,000 basic on-or-off elements, is a million times less complex than the human brain, which is estimated to have about 10,000 million neurons. However, the unit operations of the Eniac are accomplished about a thousand times faster than those of the brain. Hence if a figure of merit is established for comparing the competence of man-made and natural machines, taking into account both complexity and speed, the Eniac, for those operations fitted to its low complexity, is only about one thousand times less competent than the human brain. Thus transistors should permit the building of a device only 10,000 times less complicated than the brain in no greater space and with smaller power requirements than are now required for vacuum tube computers. Since it will operate a thousand times faster, such a transistorized device, for those problems suitable to its low complexity, will be one-tenth as competent as the human brain.

The transistor, like the vacuum tube, was first conceived in the communication industry. Its origin and development by the Bell

Telephone Laboratories is well known. It is expected to have important applications in the telephone system.[14] In the local telephone system, the transistor could amplify small signals at high efficiency with long life and reliability and be supplied with the necessary small amount of power over the line. Another important application of transistors is expected to be a part of the "brain" of the new telephone national toll dialing system.

References

1. J. M. Early, "P-N-I-P and N-P-I-N Junction Transistor Triodes," *Bell System Tech. J.*, Vol. XXXIII, No. 3, May 1954, pp. 517–533.
2. W. E. Bradley, "The Surface-Barrier Transistor, Part I—Principles of the Surface-Barrier Transistor," *Proc. IRE*, Vol. XLI, No. 12, Dec. 1953, pp. 1702–1706.
3. F. L. Hunter and B. N. Slade, "High-Frequency Operation of P-Type Point-Contact Transistors," *RCA Review*, Vol. XV, No. 1, March 1954, pp. 121–134.
4. C. W. Mueller and J. I. Pankove, "A P-N-P Triode Alloy-Junction Transistor for Radio-Frequency Amplification," *RCA Review*, Vol. XIV, No. 4, Dec. 1953, pp. 586–598.
5. *Data Sheet, Types 903, 904, 904A, 905, X-15 Silicon Grown Junction Transistors*, Aug. 1954, Texas Instruments, Incorporated, Dallas, Texas.
6. J. S. Schaffner, "Transistor Applications," *General Electric Review*, Vol. LVII, No. 2, March 1954, pp. 50–54.
7. Thomas Roddam, "Transistors, 5-Applications in Trigger Circuits," *Wireless World*, Vol. LIX, No. 6, June 1953, pp. 256–260.
8. V. K. Zworykin, "Possibilities of Electronic Control of Automobiles," *Electrical Engineering*, Vol. LXXII, No. 9, Sept. 1953, pp. 849–850.
9. "Development Progress Report—Electronics," *Aviation Age*, Vol. XXII, No. 1, July 1954, pp. 140–146.
10. J. A. Becker, "Transistors," *Electrical Engineering*, Vol. LXIX, Jan. 1950, pp. 58–64.

11. E. F. W. Alexanderson, "Control Applications of the Transistor," *Proc. IRE,* Vol. XL, No. 11, Nov. 1952, pp. 1508–1511.

12. R. L. Bright, "Transistor Possibilities, Automatic Production," *Electrical Manufacturing,* Vol. LIII, No. 6, June 1954, pp. 116–117. Copyright 1954 by the Gage Publishing Co.

13. Louis N. Ridenour, "A Revolution in Electronics," *Scientific American,* Vol. CLXXXV, No. 2, Aug. 1951, pp. 13–17.

14. J. W. McRae, "Transistors in Our Civilian Economy," *Proc. IRE,* Vol. XL, No. 11, Nov. 1952, pp. 1285–1286.

Chapter 2

FUNDAMENTAL DEFINITIONS AND CONCEPTS

1. *Conductors, insulators, and semiconductors*

A transistor is an active semiconductor device with three or more electrodes. By active we mean that the transistor is capable of current gain, voltage amplification, and power gain. A transistor is an electron device in which electronic conduction takes place within a semiconductor.

A semiconductor is an electronic conductor, with resistivity in the range between metals and insulators, in which the electrical charge carrier concentration increases with increasing temperature over some temperature range. The resistivity of semiconductors is of the order of 10^0 ohm-cm, compared with 10^{-6} ohm-cm for metals, and 10^6 ohm-cm for insulators. The resistivities of semiconductors and insulators decrease rapidly with rising temperatures, while those of metals increase relatively slowly. Unlike metals and insulators, the resistivity of semiconductors depends upon the direction of current flow. The direction of easiest current flow or lowest resistivity is called the forward direction; the direction of restricted current flow or highest resistivity is known as the reverse or back direction. The resistivity of a dry rectifier, consisting of a metal in contact with a semiconductor, may change by a factor of 1000 as the polarity of the applied potential is reversed.

Semiconductors, such as the elements germanium and silicon, possess two types of current carriers, namely, negative electrons and positive holes. A hole is a mobile vacancy in the electronic valence structure of a semiconductor which acts like a positive electronic charge with a positive mass.

2. *P-N junctions*

A P-N junction is the name given to the boundary between P-type and N-type regions occurring in the same crystal. A P-type region is one in which conduction takes place principally because of the movement of positive charges or holes, whereas an N-type region is one where conduction is due mainly to the movement of negative charges or electrons. A P-N junction acts as a rectifier.[1] The operation is illustrated in Fig. 2.1, where only the charges taking part in conduction

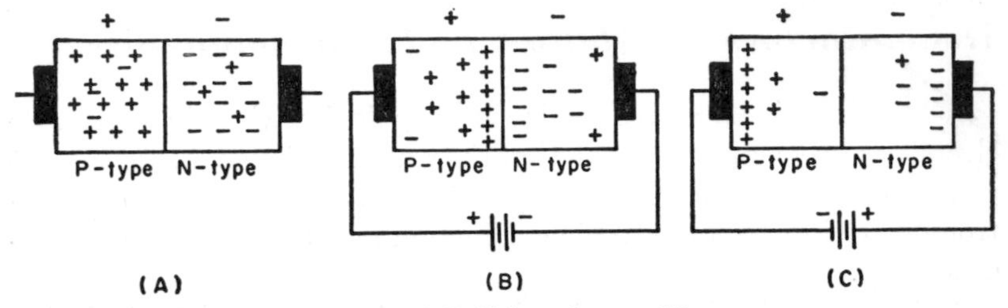

Fig. 2.1. A P-N junction rectifier.

are shown. The junction with the charges in a state of thermal equilibrium is shown in (A). In (B) a battery biases the junction in the forward direction. Since the P-region is made positive and the N-region negative, holes move from left to right and electrons from right to left. They move toward each other and recombine. Hence, there are an abundant number of current carriers flowing across the

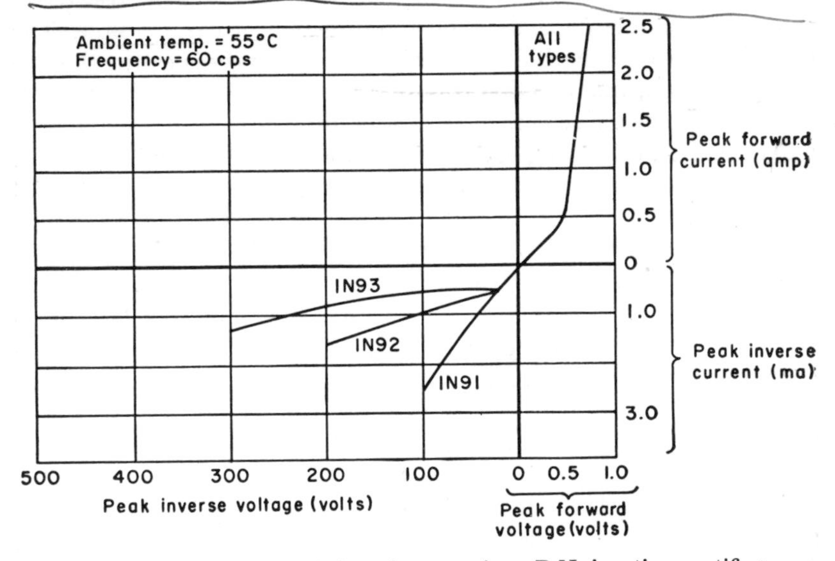

Fig. 2.2. *E-I* characteristics of germanium P-N junction rectifiers. *Courtesy of General Electric.*

junction, and the forward resistance is low. Only a small forward voltage is necessary to keep the current flowing. The battery polarity is reversed for (C). This makes the P-region negative and the N-region positive, so that holes and electrons move away from each other. This leaves the junction with few current carriers, and the back resistance becomes large. There is only a small back current consisting of electron-hole pairs formed by thermal agitation in the junction, but this current increases rapidly with temperature.

P-N junctions can be manufactured by diffusing donor and acceptor impurities into germanium.[2] A donor impurity is an element such as antimony which may induce electronic conduction in a semiconductor. An acceptor impurity is an element such as gallium which may induce hole conduction in the crystal.

P-N junctions can be manufactured by diffusing donor and acceptor impurities into germanium.[2] Figure 2.2 shows the characteristics of such rectifiers. Similar units will withstand inverse potentials exceeding 700 v, with less than 2 ma leakage current. No permanent damage results when these units are repeatedly broken down by high inverse voltages. These rectifiers have peak forward current densities of hundreds of amperes per square centimeter, and efficiencies greater than 99 per cent. For comparison, tubes have per cent efficiencies in the 80's, and selenium rectifiers in the 70's.

3. *P-N junction transistors*[3,4]

An N-P-N junction transistor has the structure shown in Fig. 2.3. A thin layer of P-type germanium is formed in the middle of a bar of single-crystal germanium. The three resulting regions are known,

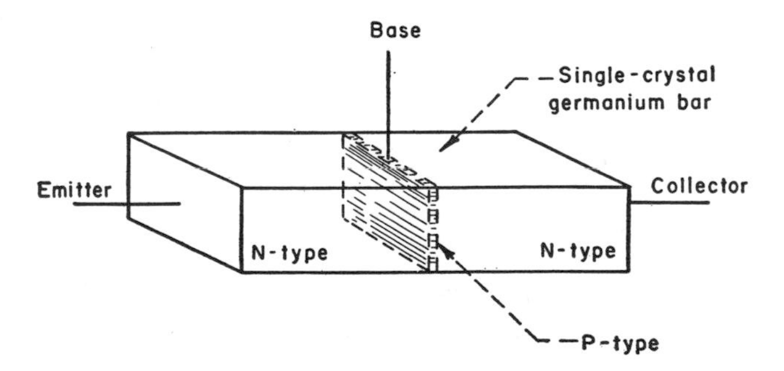

Fig. 2.3. Structure of N-P-N junction transistor.

respectively, as the emitter, base, and collector; they are provided with nonrectifying contacts.

Figure 2.4 illustrates the schematic diagram of such a junction transistor. If the collector junction is biased in the reverse direction by making the collector positive to the base, only a small residual back current of holes and electrons will diffuse across the collector barrier. Since the reverse impedance of such a bulk barrier is large, this reverse current will be small, and relatively independent of the collector potential. Also, if the emitter junction is biased in the forward direction, by making the emitter a few tenths of a volt negative to the

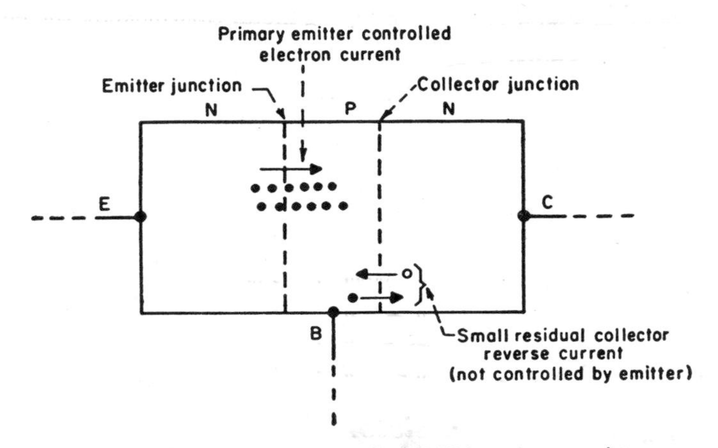

Fig. 2.4. Schematic diagram of N-P-N junction transistor.

base, a comparatively large forward current of electrons will flow from the N-type emitter region across the lower emitter barrier into the base region. If the base region is made thin enough, the above electrons will not combine with the holes of the P-type base region, and nearly all the injected emitter electrons can flow over to the collector junction. Here they are swept through the collector barrier field, and become the controlled part of the collector current. The collector current is normally less than the emitter current in such simple bulk structures. The ratio of the change in collector current to the change in emitter current for a constant collector voltage is known as "alpha," the current gain. Accordingly, junction transistors have an alpha of less than unity. However, large voltage amplification may be achieved, since electrons are injected through a low input impedance and collected through a high output impedance. A good power gain per stage may be realized for the same reason.

P-N-P junction transistors have also been developed. The operation of these is similar to that of N-P-N transistors, except that the bias potentials are reversed in polarity.

4. *Point-contact transistors*

The mechanical structure of a typical cartridge-type, point-contact transistor[5] is shown in Fig. 2.5. The physical operation of the device[4] is illustrated in Fig. 2.6. Two rectifying metal catwhiskers, the emit-

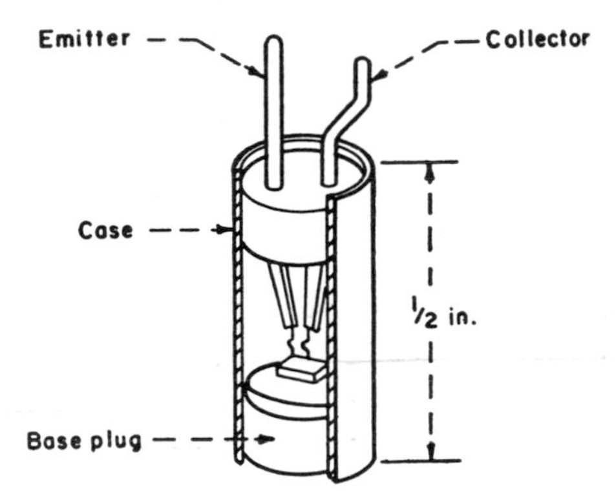

Fig. 2.5. Structure of cartridge-type, point-contact transistor.

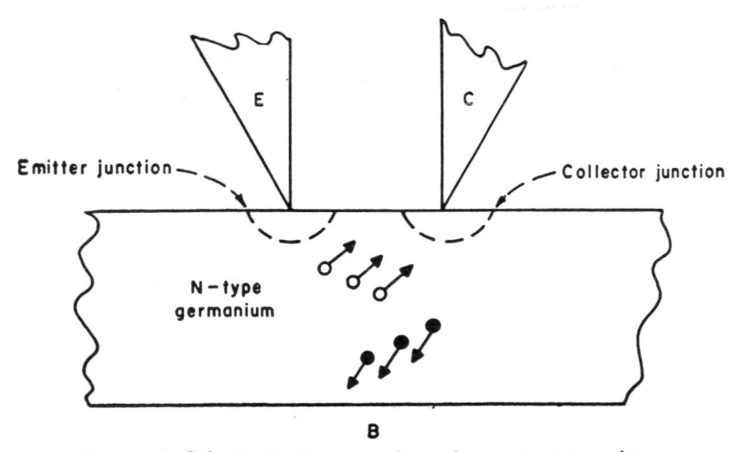

Fig. 2.6. Schematic diagram of a point-contact transistor.

ter E and the collector C, press down upon the surface of a small die of N-type germanium. A third electrode, the base, makes a large-area ohmic contact with the bottom of the germanium die. Small P-type regions under each catwhisker point form P-N junctions (indicated by the dotted lines) with the N-type bulk material, and these give the emitter and collector their rectifying properties. When the collector is biased in the reverse direction with a fairly large negative voltage, causing the collector barrier to present a relatively high impedance, only a few electrons (shown by the small black circles) flow from the collector to the base, constituting a small amount of reverse current. Now if the emitter is biased in the forward direction by making it positive by a few tenths of a volt with respect to the base, the emitter will inject a current of holes (represented by the small open circles) into the N-type material. The field set up by the original collector electron current sweeps these holes along to the collector, giving a controlled increase to the collector current. By lowering the potential barrier for electrons flowing from the collector to the base, due to the positive charges of the above holes, several electrons may flow in the collector circuit for every hole which enters the collector barrier region. Hence, in point-contact transistors, alpha is normally larger than 1; values of about 2 are typical. Since the emitter current is injected into a low impedance, while the collector current flows through a high impedance, voltage amplification is also obtained.

References

1. John A. Doremus, "Point-Contact and Junction Transistors," *Radio-Electronic Engineering Section, Radio and Television News*, April 1952, pp. 14–16.

2. John S. Saby, "Recent Developments in Transistors and Related Devices," *Tele-Tech and Electronic Industries*, Vol. X, Dec. 1951, pp. 32–34.

3. R. L. Wallace, Jr. and W. J. Pietenpol, "Some Circuit Properties and applications of N-P-N Transistors," *Proc. IRE*, Vol. XXXIX, No. 7, July 1951, pp. 753–767.

4. J. A. Morton, "Present Status of Transistor Development," *Bell System Tech. J.*, Vol. XXXI, No. 3, May 1952, pp. 411–442.

5. Herbert J. Reich, "Transistors and Transistor Circuits," *Electrical Manufacturing*, Part I, Vol. L, No. 5, Nov. 1952, pp. 106–112; Part II, Vol. L, No. 6, Dec. 1952, pp. 102–105. Copyright 1952 by the Gage Publishing Co.

Chapter 3

POINT-CONTACT TRANSISTORS

1. *Introduction*

As previously stated, a point-contact transistor normally consists of two catwhiskers, known as the emitter and collector, which make point contacts with a die of N-type germanium in ohmic contact with a block of metal called the base.

The emitter, when biased positively with reference to the base, as shown in Fig. 3.1, mainly emits holes. The emitter collects few electrons. Neither the material of the emitter nor the exact position of this electrode seems to be critical. It has a low dynamic resistance when biased in the forward direction.

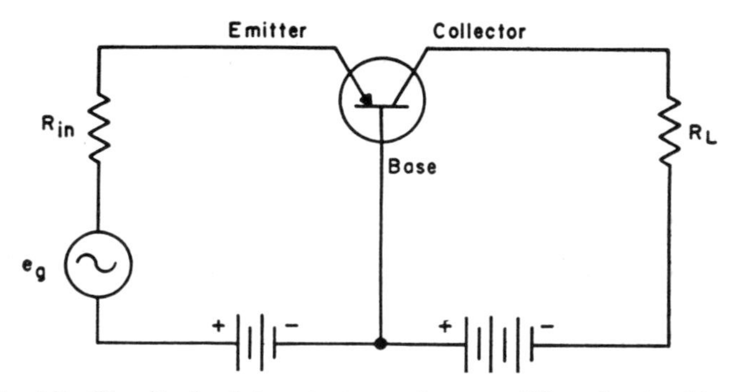

Fig. 3.1. Circuit of point-contact transistor amplifier, showing biasing batteries.

The collector, when biased negatively with respect to the base, collects the holes from the emitter and emits several electrons for each hole. The collector has a comparatively high dynamic resistance when biased in the reverse direction. Both the material of the collector and the position of this contact greatly affect the collector action. Although a number of impurity alloys give good transistor action, pure germanium does not.

Assuming that we have placed the emitter and collector catwhiskers in contact with the germanium base and have supplied suitable biases, we find that the transistor action is small. Now we must form the collector. We can do this by passing a comparatively large current through the collector for an instant.

After forming, the point-contact transistor has a current amplification factor, alpha, of about 2, and a lower collector dynamic resistance. This current amplification occurs even with only a few tenths of a volt of negative collector bias. Alpha normally decreases when the emitter and collector are separated by more than a few mils.

2. *Characteristic curves*

The transistor is a current-operated device. Therefore we can draw a set of transistor collector characteristics somewhat like a family of vacuum tube plate characteristics, except that now we plot collector voltages as a function of collector current for constant emitter cur-

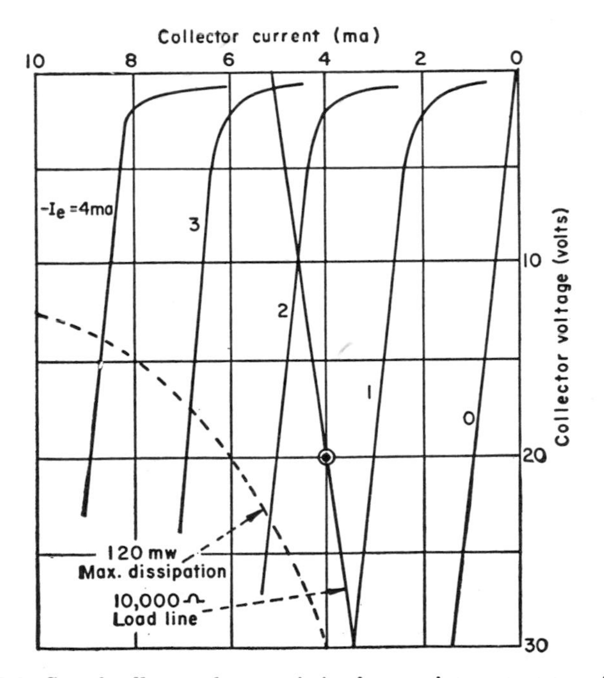

Fig. 3.2. Set of collector characteristics for a point-contact transistor.

rents. Figure 3.2 shows such a graph.[1] If one turns the page upside down, this set of curves looks much like those of a triode vacuum tube. The curves are fairly evenly spaced.

3. *Relative magnitudes of currents in point-contact transistors*[2]

The relative magnitudes of the currents in a point-contact transistor are illustrated in Fig. 3.3. The emitter injects holes into the N-type germanium, and these holes appear in the barrier region of the

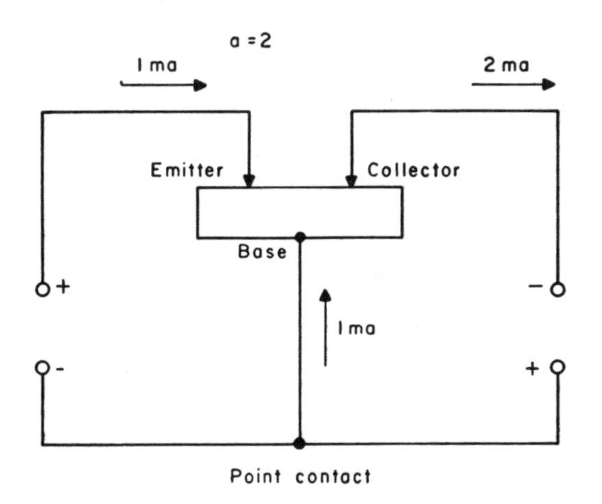

Fig. 3.3. Relative magnitudes of currents in point-contact transistor.

inverse biased rectifier. There is a physical multiplying effect, which results in more current being collected than was originally emitted, twice as much for a typical unit (alpha = 2).

4. *Control of frequency response and stability*

In designing point-contact transistors the frequency response and stability are determined mainly by controlling the point-contact spacing and the germanium resistivity.[3] Stability, or freedom from a tendency to oscillate, is especially important in amplifiers where the impedances of the emitter and collector circuits are very small in the frequency range for which the transistor is designed to operate.

Figure 3.4 is an alternating current equivalent circuit of a point-contact transistor amplifier. The equivalent T-network of the transistor itself is enclosed by dashed lines. The quantities r_e, r_b, and r_c are the emitter, base, and collector resistances respectively. The parameter r_m is the transfer resistance, which represents the effect of the emitter current on the collector circuit. An internal generator whose voltage is the product of the emitter current i_e and r_m is shown in series with the collector lead. This is the active part of the circuit and corresponds to the familiar μe_g of vacuum tube circuit theory.

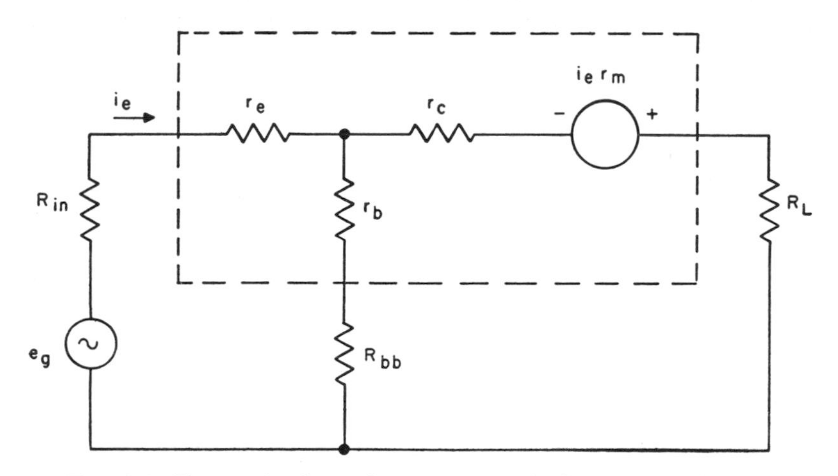

Fig. 3.4. T-network alternating-current equivalent circuit of point-contact transistor amplifier.

It has been shown that a decrease in the point-spacings increases the equivalent base resistance r_b, the resistance of that part of the equivalent circuit of the transistor which is common to both the input and output circuits. Since the point-contact transistor has a current amplification factor of about 2, this results in positive feedback from output to input, causing regeneration. A large equivalent base resistance may increase this positive feedback to the point where the transistor breaks into oscillation, destroying its usefulness as an amplifier.

In Fig. 3.4, e_g represents the open-circuit voltage of the signal source having an internal resistance of R_{in}, the element R_{bb} might be an external resistor to supply bias for the emitter, and R_L is the load resistance. It can be shown that the transistor will not oscillate in such a circuit provided that the conditions stated in the following expression are fullfilled:

$$\frac{R_e}{R_b} + \frac{R_e}{R_c} + 1 > \frac{r_m}{R_c} \tag{1}$$

where $R_e = r_e +$ external emitter source resistance R_{in}, $R_b = r_b +$ external base resistance R_{bb}, and $R_c = r_c +$ external collector load resistance R_L. The above expression says that the circuit can be stable if the emitter and collector total resistances are large enough or if r_m is not too large. In other words, resistance in the base lead tends toward instability or oscillation if r_m is large; resistance in emitter or collector leads tends toward stability.

When the transistor is considered by itself with no external resistance or impedance connected in series with any of its three terminals, expression (1) becomes

$$\frac{r_e}{r_b} + \frac{r_e}{r_c} + 1 > \frac{r_m}{r_c} \tag{2}$$

The quotient r_m/r_c closely approximates the current amplification factor, alpha, of the transistor. A large equivalent base resistance r_b may cause the sum of the left hand terms of the above expression to

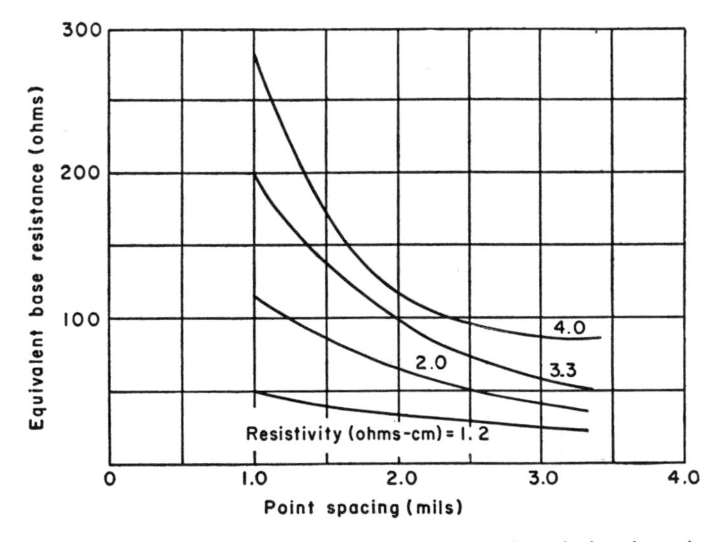

Fig. 3.5. Effect on equivalent base resistance of variation in point spacing and germanium resistivity.

become less than r_m/r_c. Hence the transistor may become unstable and oscillate, except when alpha is unity or less. The alpha of most point-contact transistors is 2 or larger.

The equivalent base resistance can be kept low for small point spacings by reducing the germanium resistivity. Figure 3.5 shows how the equivalent base resistance varies with the point-contact spacing for several germanium samples with resistivities of from 1.2 ohm-cm to 4.0 ohm-cm. For the larger resistivities the equivalent base resistance rises rapidly for spacings less than 2.0 mils. For the germanium samples with resistivities of 2 ohm-cm or less, the equivalent base resistance is more nearly linear with the point spacing. Moreover, the equivalent base resistance is much lower at the small resistivities for a given point spacing.

Shockley[4] has shown that the transit time of the hole carriers which travel from the emitter to the collector may be given by the equation

$$\tau = \frac{S^3\sigma}{\mu I_e} \tag{3}$$

where τ is the transit time in seconds, μ is the mobility or average drift velocity of the holes in centimeters squared per volt-second, I_e is the emitter current in amperes, σ is the germanium conductivity in

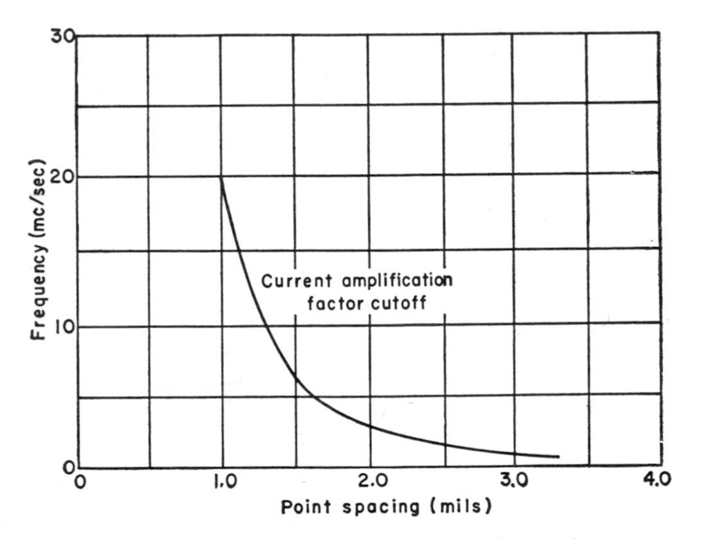

Fig. 3.6. Frequency response versus point spacing.

reciprocal ohm-centimeters, and S the spacing in centimeters between the point contacts. The frequency response is approximately inversely proportional to the transit time. Hence the frequency response should vary inversely with the cube of the point spacing, provided that the other factors remain constant.

The above equation for the transit time would seem to indicate that the frequency response will increase as the germanium resistivity becomes larger. Actual measurements,[3] however, have shown that the frequency response was little affected when the resistivity was increased from 1.2 to 4.0 ohm-cm. Figure 3.6 is a plot of frequency cutoff (3 db down in current amplification factor) versus point spacing for samples with germanium resistivities of from 1.2 to 4.0 ohm-cm. The curve shows that the high-frequency response increases rapidly for point spacings less than 2 mils. Actually, the curve closely follows the theoretical cube relationship of frequency cutoff with point spacing.

Normally, an equivalent base resistance of 100 ohms or less will provide transistor stability. To obtain these low resistivities and also have good frequency response, it becomes necessary to employ low-resistivity germanium with smaller contact spacings. As Fig. 3.5 shows, for a germanium resistivity of 3.3 ohm-cm and a point-contact spacing of 2.0 mils, a transistor would have an equivalent base resistance of 100 ohms. Figure 3.6 indicates that such a transistor would have a frequency cutoff of approximately 3.3 mc/sec. If the germanium resistivity is 2.0 ohm-cm, a spacing of 1.3 mils will result in an equivalent base resistance of 100 ohms, and the frequency cutoff will be about 11.0 mc/sec. However, for a germanium resistivity of 1.2 ohm-cm and a 1 mil spacing, the equivalent base resistance becomes 50 ohms, and the frequency cutoff would occur at approximately 20 mc/sec. Hence, by a suitable choice of the germanium resistivity and the point spacing, higher frequency responses may be achieved without sacrificing stability.

By the above methods stable transistors have been produced with frequency cutoffs as high as 30 mc/sec, low-frequency power gains of 20 db, and equivalent base resistances of 100 ohms and lower. Figure 3.7 gives a typical frequency reponse curve for such a transistor. These design methods have also produced transistors which could operate at frequencies much higher than 30 mc/sec. Many of these oscillate at frequencies greater than 100 mc/sec with a few oscillating above 200 mc/sec, and one reaching 300 mc/sec.

Valdes[5] has derived an expression for the equivalent base resistance, which is within 1 per cent of the true solution at $s/w = 1$ and even

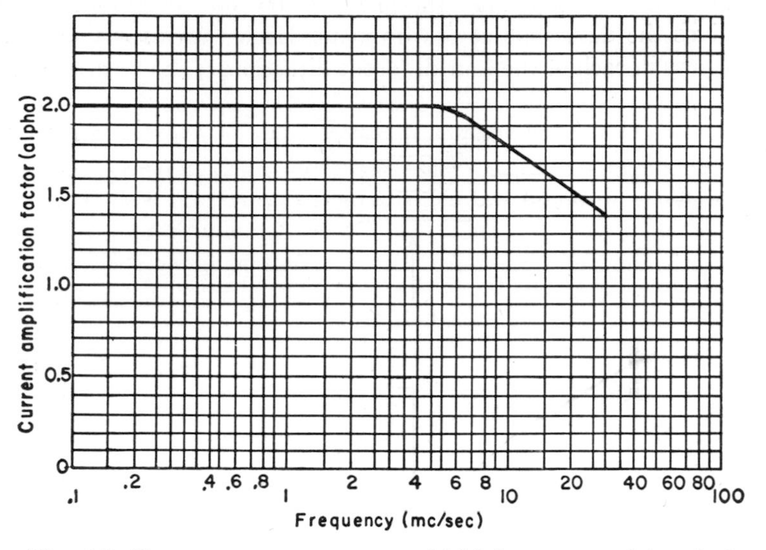

Fig. 3.7. Frequency response curve of high-frequency point-contact transistor.

more exact at smaller values of s/w. Therefore, for all practical cases at s/w less than 1.0,

$$r_b = \frac{p}{2\pi s}\left[1 - 0.693\,\frac{s}{w} + 0.113\left(\frac{s}{w}\right)^3\right] \tag{4}$$

where r_b = equivalent base resistance in ohms
p = resistivity of the germanium in ohm-centimeters
s = electrode spacing in centimeters
w = thickness of the germanium slice in centimeters.

5. *Mechanical stability**

When a point-contact transistor is completely embedded in a good thermosetting resin, the device demonstrates high resistance to shock and centrifugal force. The operating emitter and collector voltages

* The material in this section has been taken from B. N. Slade, "A Method of Improving the Electrical and Mechanical Stability of Point-Contact Transistors," *RCA Review*, Vol. XII, No. 4, Dec. 1951, pp. 651–659.

and currents, and the power gains of four transistors were measured, one at a time, in an amplifier before and after receiving impacts causing acceleration 1000 times the acceleration due to gravity. Figure 3.8 gives the directions of the impacts. Each transistor was struck five blows in each of the four different directions. The measurements

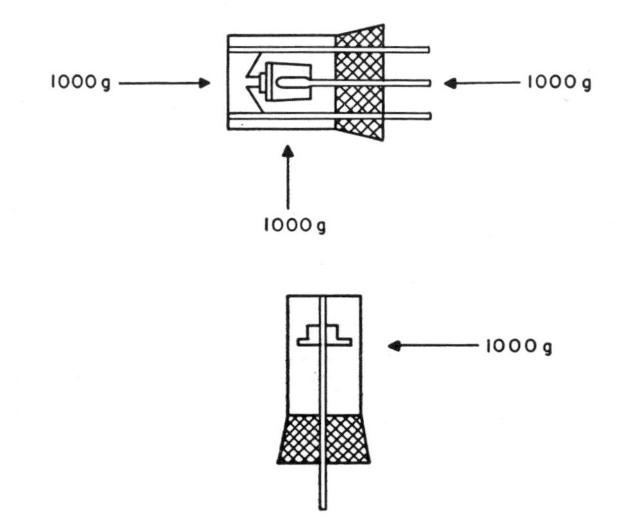

Fig. 3.8. Magnitude and directions of impacts applied to embedded point-contact transistors.

showed that the impact test had practically no effect on the transistor characteristics. The largest change in the power gain of any transistor was only 0.4 db.

Four transistors were also tested in a centrifuge. Figure 3.9 indicates the magnitudes and directions of the centrifugal accelerations

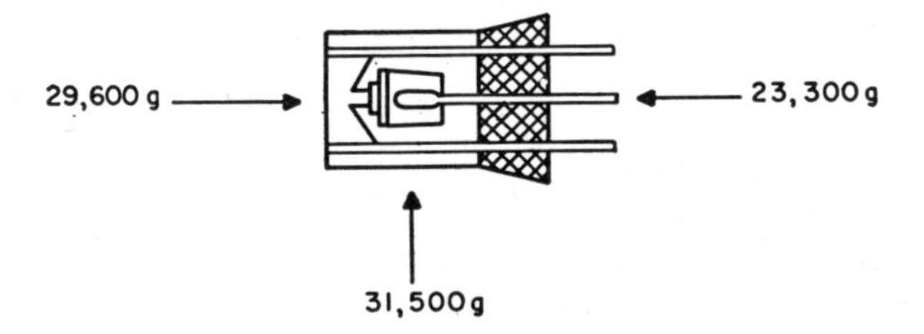

Fig. 3.9. Magnitudes and directions of centrifugal accelerations applied to embedded point-contact transistors.

applied to the transistors. The same kinds of measurements as before demonstrated that the test caused practically no change in operating characteristics or gain. Only one transistor showed any change in power gain, recording a decrease of only 0.4 db. When the transistors were visually inspected after the impact and centrifuge tests, no evidence of any physical damage was found.

6. *Transistor reliability studies*[6]

Tests on early transistors at Bell Telephone Laboratories showed quite excellent life and led to extrapolated values of average life which were remarkably high, such as 70,000 hours. These transistors were encapsulated with waxlike materials. The tests simulated an early telephone application, and were made under ordinary laboratory conditions. It is now known that shelf tests under high temperatures and humidity conditions would have shown much shorter life.

When early transistors were exposed to the pitiless gaze of various circuit users, a number of ailments were found which can be tabulated in a sort of transistor "toxicology."

First, a very gradual drift occurs in the characteristics with time. Particularly affected are the reverse currents of the collectors, both in point-contact and junction transistors. This disease was the factor which limited the life to 70,000 hours in the original life tests; since it ordinarily takes a long time to become appreciable, it is known as the "slow death."

Second, there is a gradual development with time of what appears to be a leakage path between the collector and emitter. Not very noticeable in most point-contact transistors, this disease is more virulent in junction transistors, particularly grown types which normally have very high resistance levels; it shows up as a variable floating potential on the emitter when the current is cut off. Since the ailment concerns emitter current cutoff conditions, it is called "sleeping sickness."

Third, in some point-contact transistors the current multiplication factor alpha may become markedly reduced, particularly at low voltages. Though normally rare, this occurrence has at times reached an incident as high as 25 per cent for some types. Since this disease may occur quickly without previous warning, it goes by the name "sudden death."

Fourth, sometimes loss of alpha has occurred prior to receipt of the transistor by the customer. Such units are declared "dead on arrival."

The "slow death" is explained in terms of ions resident on the germanium surface. A number of different kinds of ions can change the surface conditions of the semiconductor; in particular, water vapor is a common contaminant which can cause considerable changes. The effect of shelf-aging five bead-type M1689 point-contact transistors, prior to design changes, in 97 per cent humidity, is shown in Fig. 3.10. The collector current $I_c(0, -40)$ drawn at zero emitter current and

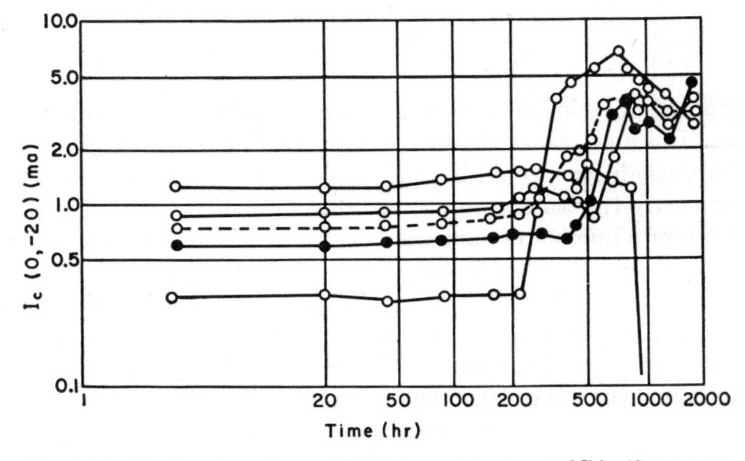

Fig. 3.10. Shelf-aging of bead M1689 transistors at 25°C in 97 per cent humidity, prior to design changes.

-40 v collector voltage, under these high humidity conditions shows a sharp change, usually an increase, rather suddenly after about 400 hours.

The malady, "sleeping sickness," is illustrated in Fig. 3.11. A normal biasing potential is applied to the collector of the transistor, and the "floating" potential appearing at the open-circuited emitter is measured with a high-impedance voltmeter. This floating potential should have the value $-(kT/q) \ln (1 - \alpha)$, where k is Boltzmann's constant, T is the Kelvin temperature, q is the charge on an electron, and α is the current amplification factor of the transistor. This is about 0.05 v for normal units at 25°C. However, if the unit has "sleeping sickness," the emitter floating potential may drift to much higher values, approaching the collector potential in severe cases. The unit acts as if a surface leakage resistance were developing, connecting the emitter and collector regions by a conducting channel across the surface of the base layer. Such a channel may be induced in several ways, a common one being exposure to high humidity.

Figure 3.11 also shows the results of tests on two groups of grown N-P-N junction transistors. The top curve shows the behavior of M1752 units encased in a wax-plastic assembly, whereas the lower

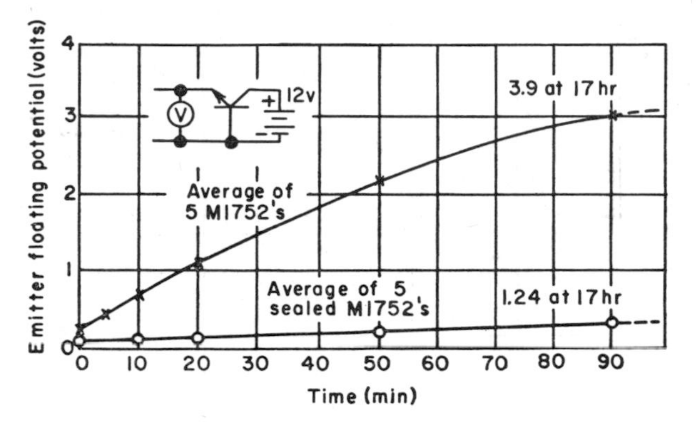

Fig. 3.11. Improvement of emitter floating potential, by sealing N-P-N grown junction transistors.

curve is for similar units sealed in a glass-metal container. We can see that the sealed units are improved, but not entirely free of the problem. Besides sealing, it appears necessary also to take more stringent precautions against sealing up water or other ions inside the units when they are made. At present the difficulty is most severe for grown junction units because the leakage path across the base layer is very short. More recent tests indicate that it may be possible by proper cleaning and surface treatments to eliminate "sleeping sickness" even for the most severe accelerated tests.

In alloy junction transistors having longer leakage paths, and in point-contact transistors having lower impedance levels, it is possible that for many purposes adequate protection against "sleeping sickness" may be obtainable with proper plastic encapsulation without resort to glass-metal seals.

The electrical condition known as "sudden death" is described in

Fig. 3.12, in which the dashed curves depict the collector characteristics of a normal M1689 bead point-contact transistor. The solid lines are the characteristics of a particular unit after "sudden death" has occurred. It is seen that the current amplification factor alpha, corresponding to the spacing between curves, is substantially less than before, particularly at low voltages. Note that a particularly sensitive measure of this effect is a large increase in the parameter $V_c(1, -2)$,

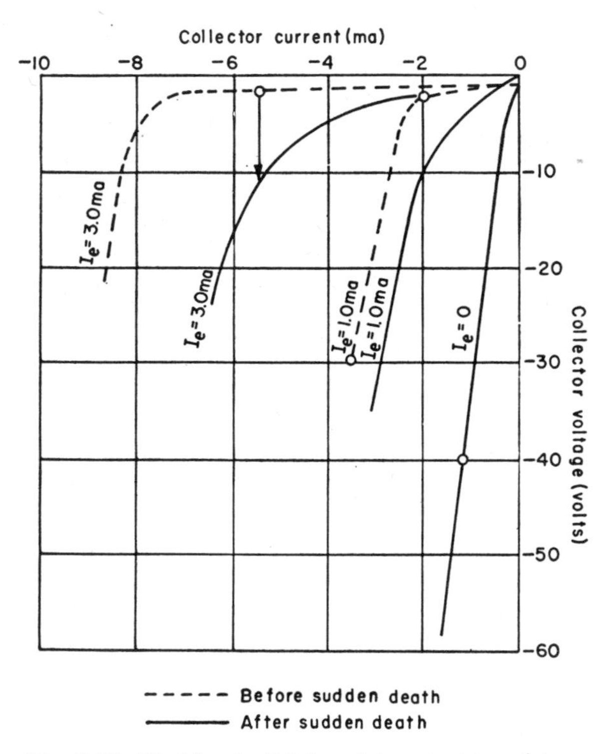

Fig. 3.12. "Sudden death" in point-contact transistors.

the collector voltage at currents of 1 ma in the emitter and 2 ma in the collector. It is both curious and significant that "sudden death" often produces practically no change in the collector diode characteristic line ($I_e = 0$); the change is only in alpha, the transfer characteristic between emitter and collector diodes.

By experiments in a manipulator it has been found that the symptoms of "sudden death" can be induced by a surprisingly small mechanical change in the angle of the collector point of a lightly formed transistor. Most probably this same effect occurs in the transistor because of slight warping of the plastic supporting insulator resulting from moisture absorption. Design changes which have been introduced appear to have cured this trouble, especially if factory aging tests weed out the failures in the first few hours.

In other life tests simulating the application of transistors to amplifiers, the changes in the collector resistance r_c and the current

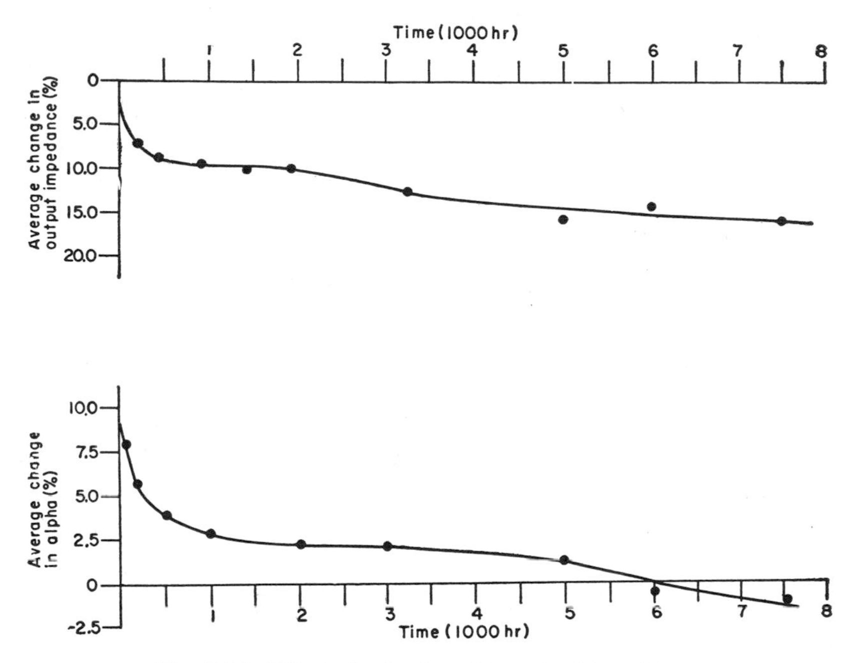

Fig. 3.13. Effect of aging in point-contact transistors.

amplification factor alpha with time have been measured.[7] As shown in Fig. 3.13, point-contact transistors similar to Type M1729 demonstrate a slow decrease in both the collector resistance and alpha. This figure gives average data for a number of units life tested up to about 7500 hours. After an initial change of approximately 5 per cent in the first few score hours, there is a slow drift which lasts at least a few thousand hours. The effect of the above changes in an amplifier would be a gradual loss of gain. To interpret the above results on a quantitative basis, it should be noted that for a matched grounded-base circuit with negligible feedback, the power gain equals $\alpha^2 r_c/4r_e$. Hence, to lose a decibel of gain from a circuit which was originally matched would require a reduction of either 11 per cent in alpha or 20 per cent in r_c. The changes in α and r_c are additive.

7. *The P-type germanium point-contact transistor*

Everything which has previously been said about point-contact transistors in this chapter has referred to the usual variety made of N-type germanium. However, it is also possible to make point-contact transistors out of P-type germanium.[8] Figure 3.14 shows the operation of the P-germanium transistor. A large part of the emitter current consists of electrons, which are injected into the germanium, and are attracted to the positively biased collector. Voltage gain and current gain are possible as in the N-type transistor.

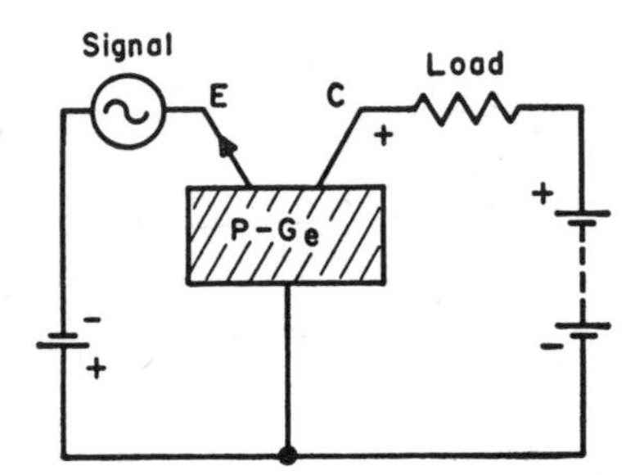

Fig. 3.14. Schematic showing operation of P-germanium transistor.

An electrical forming treatment greatly increases the ability of the emitter to inject electrons into the P-germanium. If it is desired to use either point electrode as the emitter, both points may be pulsed.

Figure 3.15 represents the T network equivalent circuit for describing the a-c small signal performance of the P-germanium transistor at low frequencies. The impedance associated with the emitter contact is r_e, which is normally small because the emitter junction is biased in the forward direction. The collector impedance r_c is relatively large because the collector junction is biased in the reverse direction. The base resistance r_b is common to

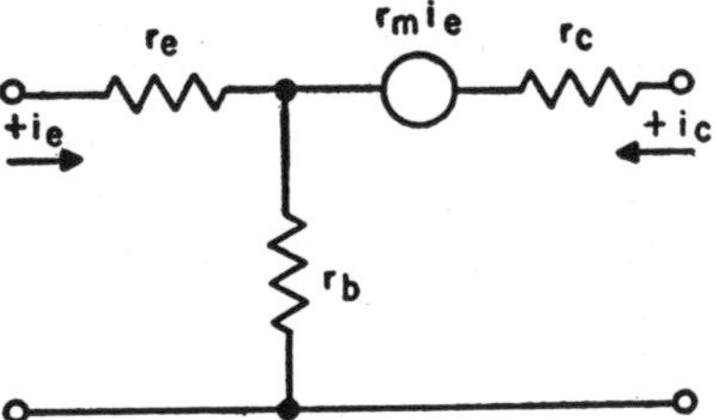

Fig. 3.15. Equivalent circuit representation of the P-germanium transistor.

both emitter and collector currents, and constitutes a positive feedback. The transfer impedance r_m represents the active properties of the network. This equivalent circuit is for the grounded-base connection.

For a typical P-germanium transistor, Fig. 3.16 shows the above impedances versus the emitter currents with the collector current held constant at +2.0 ma. The approximate values of these impedances for emitter currents greater than a few tenths of a milliampere are as follows:

$$r_e \sim 200 \text{ ohms}, \qquad r_c \sim 12{,}500 \text{ ohms}$$

$$r_b \sim 100 \text{ ohms}, \qquad r_m \sim 22{,}500 \text{ ohms}$$

The ratio r_m/r_c is approximately equal to alpha, the current amplification factor, which is about 1.5 to 2.

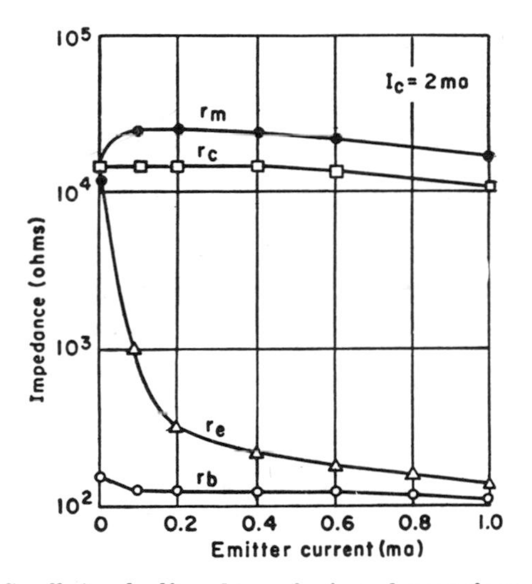

Fig. 3.16. Small-signal self- and transfer-impedances of a representative P-germanium transistor.

Like N-germanium, the gain of the P-germanium transistor decreases in the megacycle frequency range. It appears that the P-germanium transistor will operate at higher frequencies. Cutoff frequencies above 15 mc/sec are common. (By definition the cutoff frequency is that at which alpha is down 3 db.) The P-germanium transistor is superior in frequency response mainly because the mobility of electrons in germanium exceeds that of holes by a factor of about 1.5. Since the emitted carriers in the P-germanium transistor are electrons, and since it is dispersion in transit times of emitter carriers which limits the operating frequency, the observed superiority of the P-germanium transistor is to be expected.

The P-germanium transistor demonstrates a peculiarity which occurs when the germanium possesses an especially high resistivity. Then the forward current-voltage characteristic of the emitter has a negative resistance region of the voltage maximum type, the peak

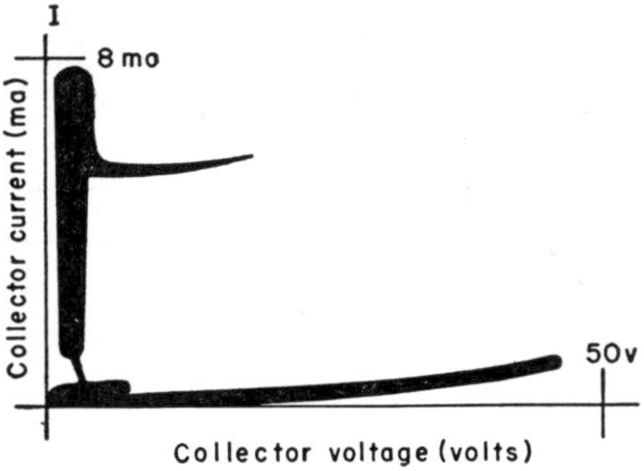

Fig. 3.17. Oscillograph pattern showing "snap" effect in P-germanium transistor.

voltage being several tenths of a volt. When the series resistance in the emitter circuit is low, and the emitter bias exceeds the above peak voltage, the emitter current suddenly increases, causing a corresponding change in the collector circuit. This action is known as the snap effect and is visible in Fig. 3.17, which is the oscilloscope pattern of the current-voltage characteristic of the collector junction traced out at a frequency of 60 cycles per second. The nearly horizontal portion of the trace represents the reverse current through the collector for an emitter bias which is just below the voltage maximum. At the extreme tip of the characteristic a small amount of positive feedback due to increase in collector current has caused the emitter bias barely to exceed the voltage maximum. As a result the collector trace snaps suddenly to the high-current position as indicated by the vertical trace. The return trace remains in the low-resistance position until the current falls to a small value, whereupon the characteristic again snaps back to the high-resistance position.

The above negative resistance in the forward current-voltage characteristic of the emitter is a diode effect which can occur in a single point-contact to P-germanium. This should not be confused with a similar effect which can be produced in an ordinary transistor by placing positive feedback resistance in the common base lead.

From a limited number of measurements, the noise factor of P-germanium transistors appears to be about the same as that of N-germanium transistors.

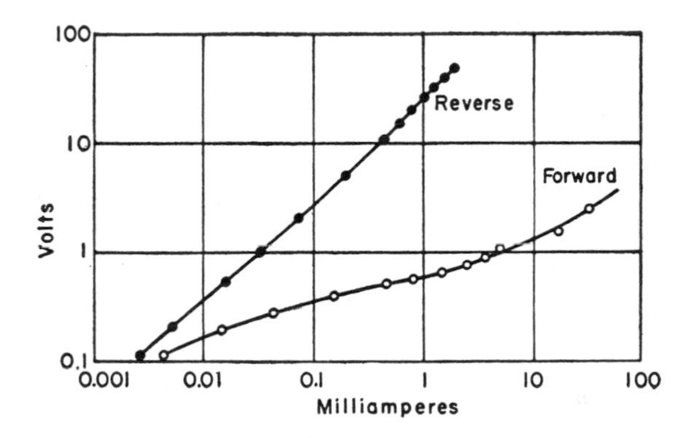

Fig. 3.18. Current-voltage characteristic of collector junction in a typical P-germanium transistor.

Figure 3.18 shows the current-voltage characteristics of the collector junction at zero emitter current for a typical P-germanium transistor. In common with the N-germanium transistor, the reverse impedance is lower than the highest which can be obtained, because too high a reverse impedance prevents the best collector performance.

In general, the properties of P-germanium and N-germanium transistors are similar, although the P-germanium transistor appears to be superior in frequency response and inferior in alpha to the N-germanium transistor. A P-germanium point-contact transistor is reported to have oscillated at 425 megacycles, the highest frequency known for transistor operation to date.

References

1. Thomas Roddam, "Transistors—1. Introductory Survey of Recent Developments," *Wireless World*, Vol. LIX, No. 2, Feb. 1953, pp. 70–73.

2. John S. Saby, "Recent Developments in Transistors and Related Devices," *Tele-Tech and Electronic Industries*, Vol. X, Dec. 1951, pp. 32–34.

3. B. N. Slade, "The Control of Frequency Response and Stability of Point-Contact Transistors," *Proc. IRE*, Vol. XL, No. 11, Nov. 1952, pp. 1382–1384.

4. *Electrons and Holes in Semiconductors*, W. Shockley, Bell Telephone Laboratories, Inc. Copyright 1950, D. Van Nostrand Company, Inc., p. 107.

5. L. B. Valdes, "Effect of Electrode Spacing on the Equivalent Base Resistance of Point-Contact Transistors," *Proc. IRE*, Vol. XL, No. 11, Nov. 1952, pp. 1429–1434.

6. R. M. Ryder and W. R. Sittner, "Transistor Reliability Studies," *Convention Record IRE*, 1953, Part 6, pp. 9–14.

7. "Aging and Temperature Response of Point-Contact Transistors," by R. M. Ryder, Bell Telephone Laboratories, Inc., New York, 1951, pp. 123–126.

8. W. G. Pfann and J. H. Scaff, "The P-Germanium Transistor," *Proc. IRE*, Vol. XXXVIII, No. 10, Oct. 1950, pp. 1151–1154.

Chapter 4

JUNCTION TRANSISTORS

1. *Introduction*

The junction transistor[1] consists of two P-N junctions in a single crystal of germanium. A P-N-P transistor with operating biases is shown schematically in Fig. 4.1. The left-hand junction is biased in the forward direction and is known as the emitter junction or simply the emitter. The right-hand junction is biased in the reverse direction and is called the collector. The region between the two junctions is known as the base. External ohmic contacts are made to all three of these regions.

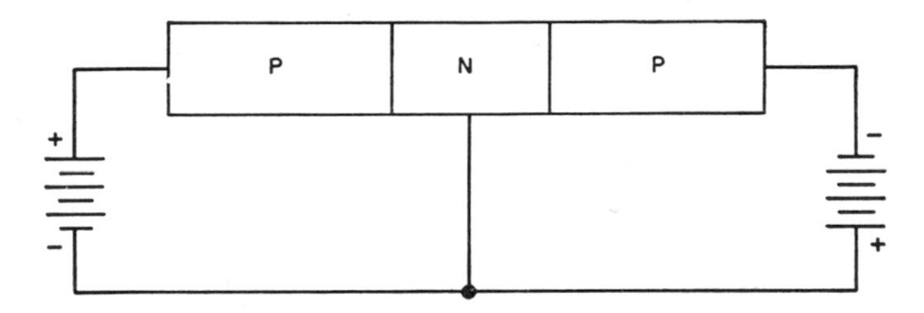

Fig. 4.1. Schematic of P-N-P junction transistor with operating biases.

Since the collector junction is biased in the reverse direction, the collector current is simply the saturation current, which depends upon the density of the minority carriers in the vicinity of the junction. Hence a change in the hole density in the base can vary the collector current. The hole current at the emitter junction controls this hole density, provided that the width of the base is small compared with the diffusion length, which is the average distance holes will travel in the N-region before recombining with electrons. A signal voltage applied between the emitter and the base changes the height of the barrier at the emitter junction, modulating the hole flow at the emitter. In other words, holes which are injected into the base at the emitter diffuse across the base region to the collector, and add to the collector current.

If the current gain between the collector and the emitter, α_{ce}, is defined as the ratio of a change in collector current to a change in emitter current with the collector voltage held constant, α_{ce} is always less than 1. Hence in this mode of operation (the grounded-base circuit) there is no current gain. However, because the impedance of the collector junction is normally much larger than that of the emitter junction, both voltage gain and power gain may be obtained. Moreover, there is a method of operating the junction transistor (the grounded-emitter circuit) in which large current gains can be achieved. This will be discussed later.

Junction transistors are produced commercially by two methods. The original method of the Bell Telephone Laboratories changes the impurity content of the molten germanium during the time that a single crystal is being grown from the melt. If the original melt contains P-type impurities, the first section of the crystal grown from the melt will be P-type. After a suitable region of P-type crystal is grown, a pellet of N-type material is dropped into the melt. The concentration of N-type impurity in this pellet must be high enough to neutralize completely the P-type impurity. As long as this condition prevails, the growing crystal will be N-type. After the right length of N-type region is grown, a pellet containing P-type impurities is dropped in the melt to give a P-type melt, from which a second P-type region is grown on the crystal. After such a crystal is grown it is cut into a large number of small sections. Ohmic contacts are made to each region. Since the base region of transistors grown in this way is only 1 mil thick, it is quite difficult to make contact to the base. However, this can be accomplished. After proper surface treatment, the transistor is encased in plastic or in a hermetically sealed can.

A second way of making junction transistors is the alloy method employed by Radio Corporation of America. Two indium dots of correct size are placed on the opposite sides of a small wafer of N-type germanium. After proper heating the indium will alloy with the germanium to form two P-type regions for the emitter and collector junctions. In this method it is no problem to make connections to the base, since it consists of the original germanium wafer.

2. *Outstanding properties of junction transistors*[2]

Junction transistors have a comparatively low noise figure. This measures between 10 and 20 db at 1000 cps.

They are completely free from short-circuit instability. Regardless of the circuit configuration, the input and output impedances are always positive. The circuit designer may choose the grounded-base, the grounded-emitter, or the grounded-collector circuit to obtain the input and output impedances which he requires.

High power gains of from 40 to 50 db per stage may be achieved.

Class A amplifiers can be operated at efficiencies as high as 49 per cent (in comparison with the maximum theoretical 50 per cent). Correspondingly high efficiencies can be realized for class B and class C operation.

A junction transistor may be constructed as a hard plastic bead as small as $\frac{3}{16}$ in. in diameter. Three pigtail connections are securely fastened mechanically and electrically to the germanium inside the bead to form a rugged device.

These units are relatively free from microphonic noise at audio frequencies, as indicated by vibration tests.

The small power consumption of these transistors is quite remarkable. For example, one audio oscillator required only 0.1 v at 6 μa, or 0.6 μw of power. Contrast this with the million or more microwatts which an ordinary radio receiver tube needs to heat its cathode.

The frequency response of ordinary junction transistors is limited by the collector capacitance to a few kilocycles at full gain. However, a useful amount of gain with a frequency response flat up to at least 1 mc/sec may be obtained by a suitable impedance mismatch.

3. *Static characteristics*[2]

Figure 4.2 shows the symbol for an N-P-N transistor along with the convention of signs for currents and voltages. Positive currents flow into the emitter and collector, and positive voltages are as indicated in the figure.

The static characteristics of a typical N-P-N junction transistor are given in Fig. 4.3. The upper family of curves shows that V_c is positive over the operating range. Hence the collector bias is positive with respect to the base, a suitable bias voltage being from about 0.1 v to 35 v. These collector curves are for constant negative emitter currents. Thus the emitter must be biased negatively with respect to the base. The collector current for any constant emitter current curve is almost as large as the emitter current. Since these two currents have opposite signs, most of the current flowing out of the emitter flows into the collector, making the base current very small. This particular transistor may have collector currents from about 20 μa to 5 ma.

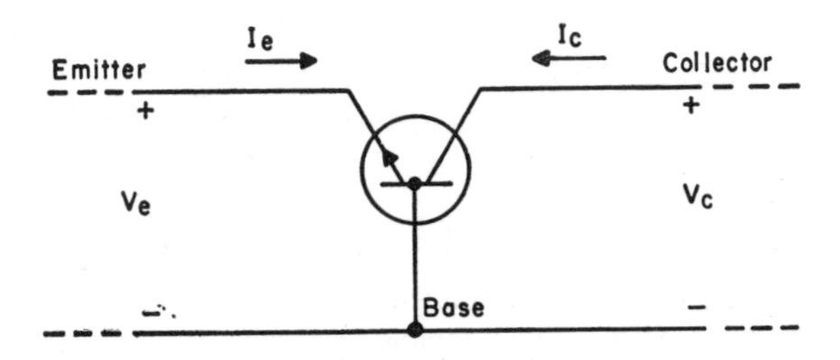

Fig. 4.2. Symbol for N-P-N junction transistor, with convention of signs for currents and voltages.

The required power output determines the collector current and voltage. For class A operation the signal power output cannot be larger than one-half the power supplied by the battery, because of the theoretical limit of 50 per cent for the collector circuit efficiency. For example, the class A power output cannot exceed 20 mw, when the collector operating point is 20 v at 2 ma.

The lower curves of Fig. 4.3 indicate the bias voltage required for the emitter. The family of voltage curves covers only small emitter voltages close to zero, and the operating range is only a few tenths of a volt. Therefore, for a constant collector voltage, small changes in emitter voltage will cause fairly large changes in collector current, or with constant collector current small changes in emitter voltage will give comparatively enormous changes in collector voltage. Thus this transistor could act as a direct voltage amplifier between a low-impedance source and a high-impedance load, increasing the voltage about 10,000 times.

Since the collector circuit is so sensitive to the emitter voltage, a-c amplifiers should have a constant current source for the emitter bias supply. A battery with a large resistance in series will meet this requirement. Since the emitter needs only a few tenths of a volt for its bias, the designer can calculate the emitter current by dividing the battery voltage by the series resistance.

The large signal continuous-wave operation of the transistor may

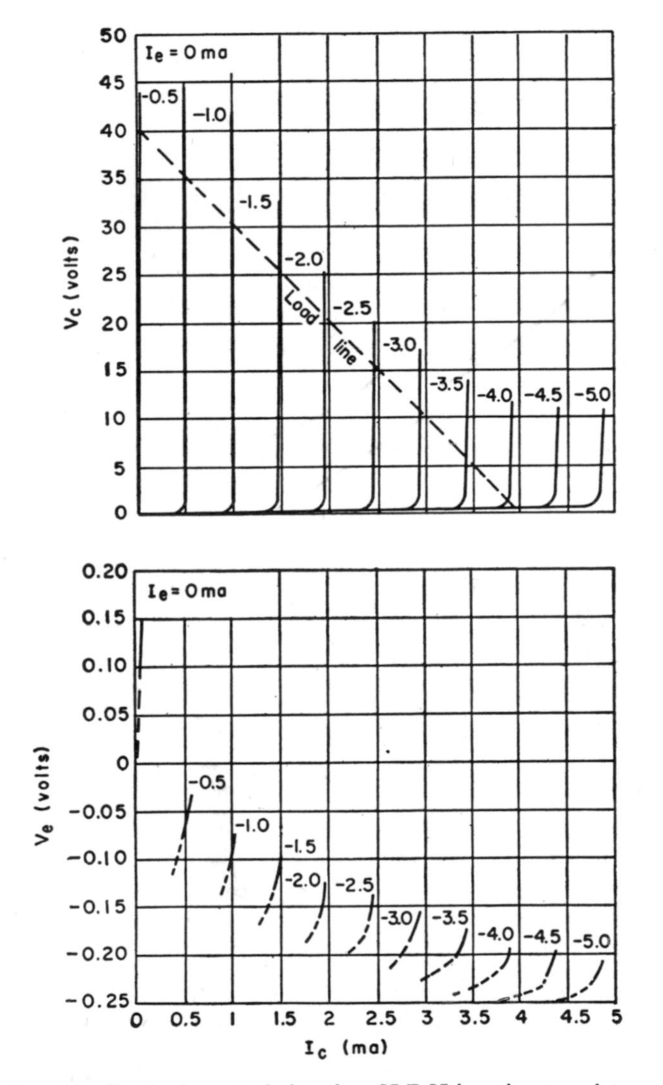

Fig. 4.3. Static characteristics of an N-P-N junction transistor.

be predicted from the static characteristics. A resistive load line is shown with the upper curves of Fig. 4.3. The instantaneous operating point moves up and down along this straight line, which represents the a-c load resistance of 10,000 ohms. Assume that the collector is biased at 20 v and 2 ma, or a 40 mw power consumption. The output signal can vary almost down to zero collector volts and nearly up to zero collector current without distortion, because the collector characteristics are nearly linear and uniformly spaced over a wide range of voltage and current values. The lower limit is due to the curvature of the collector characteristics for values of V_c lower than about 0.1 *v*. The upper limit is caused by the failure of the collector current to fall to zero when I_e becomes zero. This transistor has about 50 μa for the lower limit of collector current. This current flowing through 10,000 ohms results in a voltage drop of 0.5 v. The limits for the instantaneous collector voltage are therefore 0.1 v and 39.5 v. The permissible positive swing is thus 19.5 v above the 20 v bias value, and the allowable negative swing is 19.9 v. These excursions may be equalized at 19.7 v by reducing the bias voltage to 19.8 v without changing the load line. The power output is then 19.45 mw, for a collector circuit efficiency of 48.5 per cent out of a possible 50 per cent.

These calculations of efficiency have assumed that a sinusoidal current was applied to the emitter. However, as will be shown shortly, the emitter resistance changes with the emitter current. This makes it necessary to drive the emitter from a high-impedance source, if high efficiency is to be achieved with low distortion.

4. *Operation with small power consumption*[2]

The same transistor whose characteristics were shown in Fig. 4.3 may also be applied to small signal amplification. Then useful gain may be realized with much lower voltages and currents than those of the previous example. This is shown in Fig. 4.4, which is a graph limited to a maximum collector voltage of only 2 v and to a maximum collector current of only 200 μa. The upper plot indicates that the collector characteristics are still linear and uniformly spaced in this micropower region. Small-signal operation may be obtained with a collector voltage only slightly greater than 0.1 v and a collector current slightly over 10 μa. Hence only a few microwatts of power can

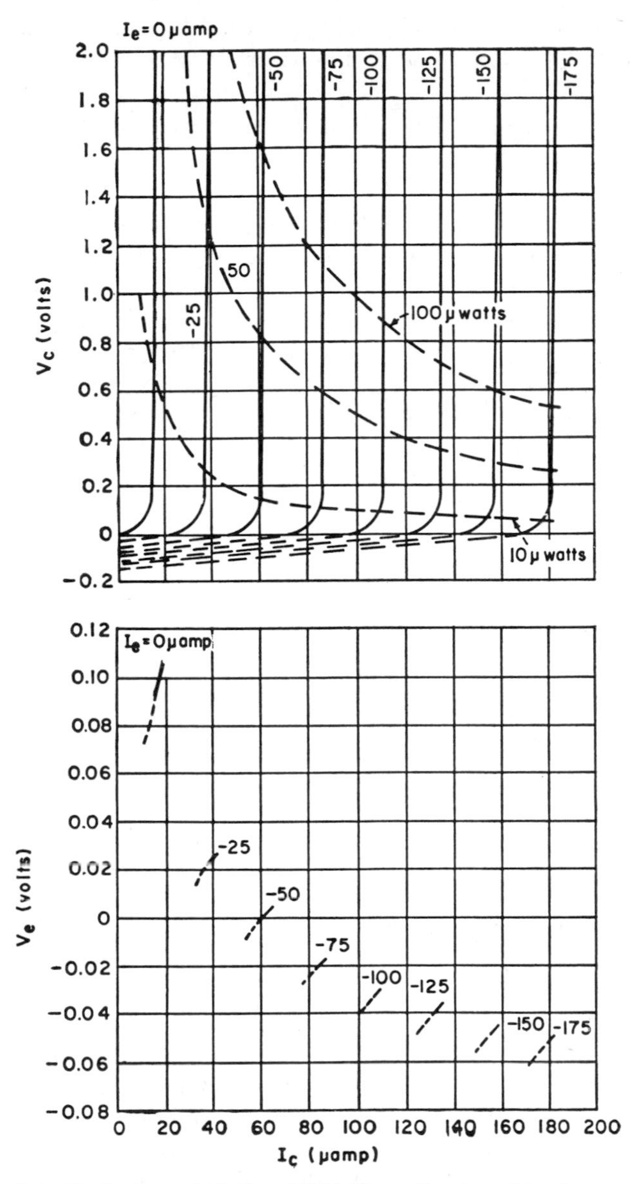

Fig. 4.4. Static characteristics of N-P-N junction transistor for very low applied voltages and currents.

bias the collector into an operating region. The figure includes curves for power supplies of 10, 50, and 100 μw.

5. *Variation of transistor properties with operating point*[2]

A convenient equivalent circuit for analyzing the small signal properties of a transistor at low frequencies is represented in Fig. 4.5.

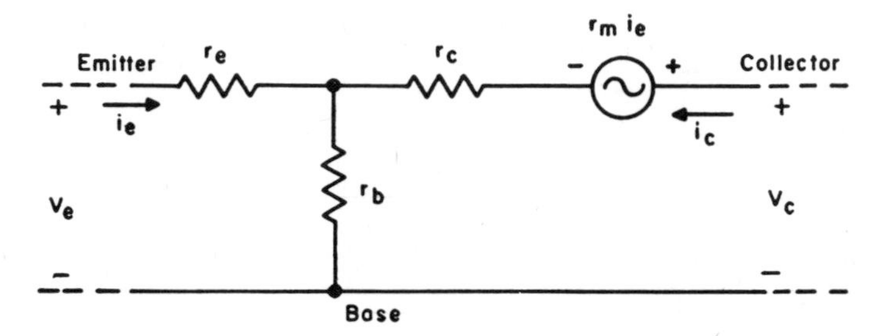

Fig. 4.5. Low-frequency equivalent circuit of a transistor.

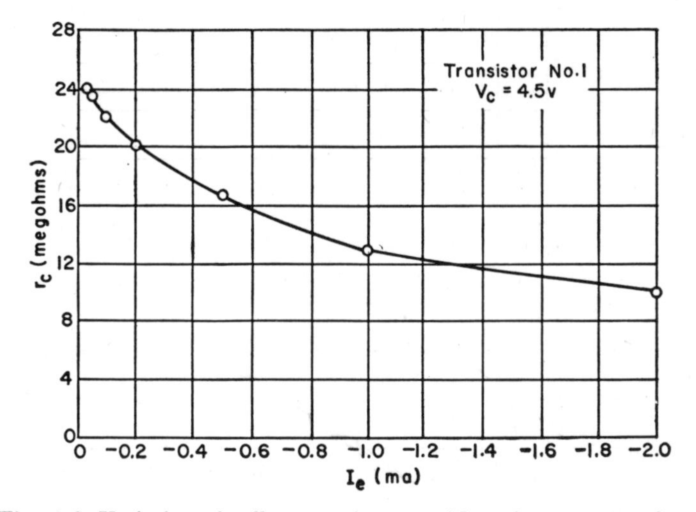

Fig. 4.6. Variation of collector resistance with emitter current, for a constant collector voltage.

The resistance r_e is known as the emitter resistance, r_b as the base resistance, and r_c as the collector resistance. The active part of the circuit is the internal generator $r_m i_e$, which is similar to the well-known μe_g for vacuum tubes.

For point-contact transistors these four r's can be found directly from the static characteristics. However, for N-P-N junction transistors it would be difficult to obtain satisfactory accuracy from

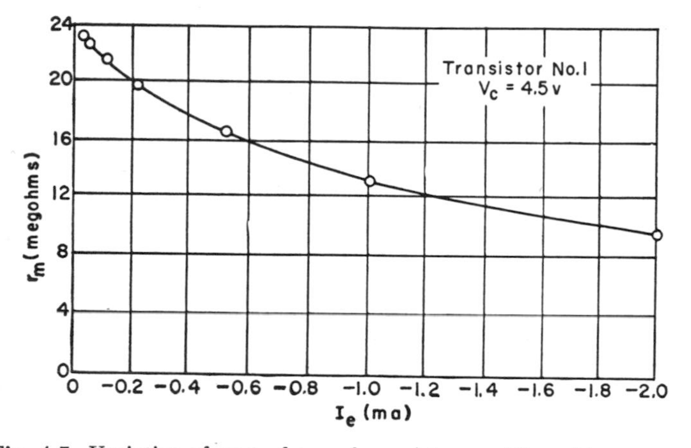

Fig. 4.7. Variation of mutual transfer resistance with emitter current, for a constant collector voltage.

static characteristics like those of Fig. 4.3 and 4.4 because of the magnitudes of these quantities. Therefore a-c methods have been used to measure the 4-pole r's. These methods are outlined in Chapter 6.

Such measurements indicate that all these r's are roughly independent of the collector voltage as long as it exceeds a few tenths of a volt, and no appreciable heating of the transistor results from collector power dissipation.

It should be enlightening to see how these quantities vary with emitter current for a constant moderate value of collector voltage. Figure 4.6 gives the variation of r_c, and Fig. 4.7 indicates the change in the mutual transfer resistance r_m. These parameters decrease as I_e increases, and are nearly equal. Laboratory samples have had values as high as 60 megohms.

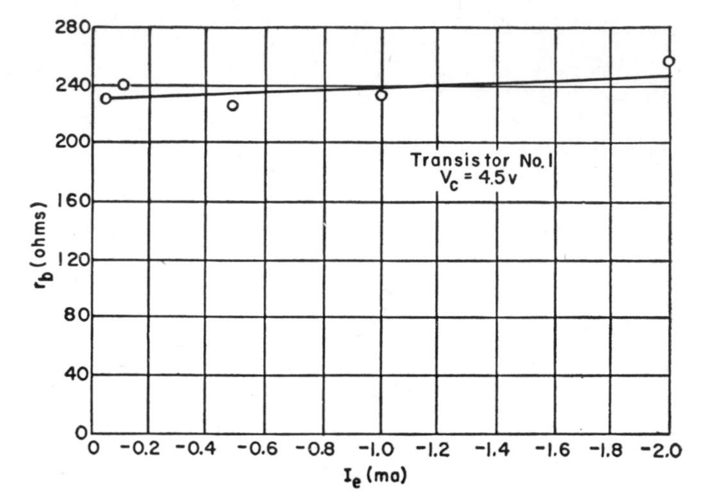

Fig. 4.8. Variation of base resistance with emitter current, for a constant collector voltage.

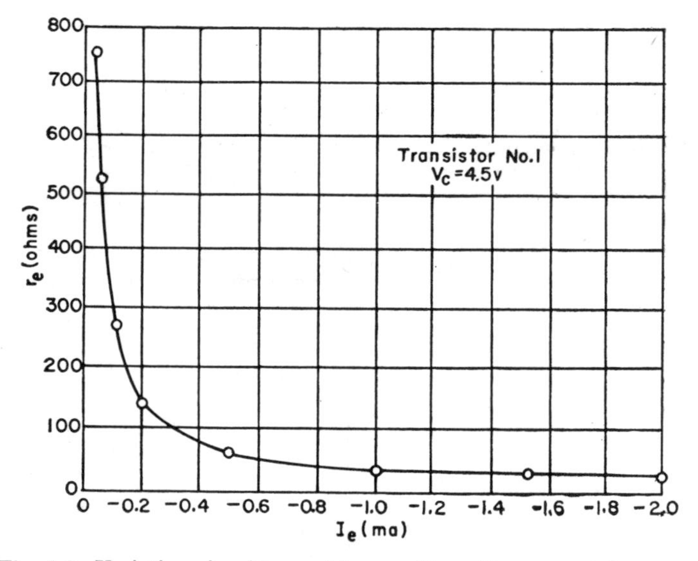

Fig. 4.9. Variation of emitter resistance with emitter current, for a constant collector voltage.

Figure 4.8 shows that r_b is independent of I_e, and has a value of about 240 ohms in this transistor.

Figure 4.9 demonstrates that r_e is inversely proportional to the emitter current, varying from about 500 ohms at 50 μa down to approximately 5 ohms at 5 ma. This is in perfect agreement with the theoretical relation shown by Shockley,[3]

$$r_e = \frac{kT}{qI_e} \tag{1}$$

where k is Boltzmann's constant, T is the Kelvin temperature, q is the charge of an electron, and I_e is the emitter current. For a temperature of about 80°F, this expression becomes

$$r_e = \frac{25.9}{I_e} \tag{2}$$

where I_e is in milliamperes.

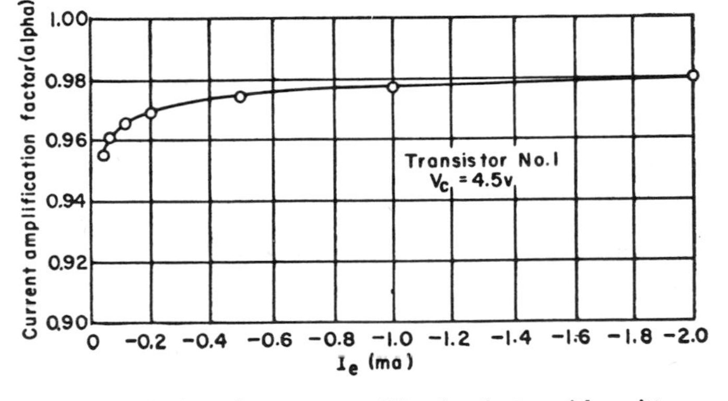

Fig. 4.10. Variation of current amplification factor with emitter current, for a constant collector voltage.

The current amplification factor α_{ce} may also be defined by the equation

$$\alpha_{ce} = \frac{r_m + r_b}{r_c + r_b} \tag{3}$$

This is approximately equal to r_m/r_c, because both r_m and r_c are large in comparison with r_b. Figure 4.10 shows that alpha increases slightly with increasing emitter current, and is approximately 0.98 for this transistor. For these junction transistors, 0.9965 is the largest value of alpha so far produced.

6. *Frequency response*[2]

Shockley has shown that there are several theoretical physical reasons for a high-frequency cutoff in the response of N-P-N junction transistors. First, in transistor action electrons are injected into the P-layer at the emitter junction, travel across this thin layer, and arrive at the collector junction. These electrons do this mainly by diffusion, and require a small finite time for the trip. If all electrons took exactly the same time, the output signal would be delayed with respect to the input, but the frequency response would not be affected. However, a dispersion in the transit time occurs; the electrons representing a particular portion of the input signal wave do not all arrive together at the collector. When this difference in the time of arrival constitutes an appreciable part of a cycle, some of the electrons tend to neutralize the effects of others so that the frequency response starts to fall off. When the signal frequency continues to increase, the dispersion becomes greater and the frequency response declines still further.

The effect on the equivalent circuit of this dispersion in transit time is that, above a certain frequency, r_m (and therefore alpha) starts to decrease with increase in frequency. Thus we may say that the transistor has an alpha cutoff, designated $f_{c\alpha}$. Shockley has shown that $f_{c\alpha}$ varies inversely with the square of the P layer thickness and hence increases rapidly as the thickness of the P layer is decreased. Currently available N-P-N junction transistors have an $f_{c\alpha}$ of between 5 and 20 mc/sec.

Second, at sufficiently high frequencies, the emitter junction no longer acts as a pure resistance but has a capacitive component. The effect on the equivalent circuit is that r_e is shunted by a capacitance. This effect on the frequency response can be minimized by keeping the emitter source impedance low. However, for the emitter junction, r_b is always in series with the source impedance. At a frequency roughly the same as $f_{c\alpha}$, this capacitive reactance becomes appreciable compared with the emitter resistance. The emitter cutoff frequency f_{ce} will be about the same as $f_{c\alpha}$ if r_b is large, and will increase as r_b is decreased.

Third, the frequency response is limited by the capacitance of the collector junction. A parallel-plate capacitor is formed by the N-type germanium on one side of the junction acting as one plate, and the P-type germanium on the other side constituting the other plate. This capacitance may be appreciable because the transition from N- to P-type germanium may take place in only a few thousandths

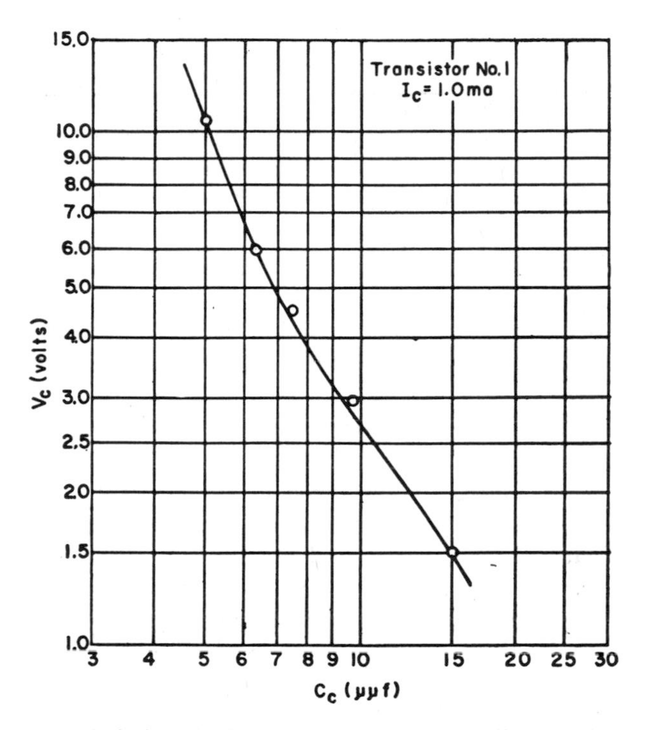

Fig. 4.11. Variation of collector capacitance with collector voltage, for a constant collector current.

of an inch, so that the plates of the capacitor are close to each other. Collector capacitance also varies with the collector voltage, decreasing as this voltage increases. Theory indicates that this capacitance should be inversely proportional to the cube root of V_c.

Figure 4.11 gives the variation of measured values of C_c with collector voltage. The agreement of these data with theory is not close.

For V_c equal to 4.5 v, the capacitance is about 7 $\mu\mu$f. As Fig. 4.12 indicates, the effect on the equivalent circuit is to place this capacitance in parallel with series combination of r_c and the generator $r_m i_e$.

The variation of C_c with collector voltage is important in battery-operated radio receivers where the intermediate-frequency amplifiers are neutralized to prevent oscillation. When the battery voltage decreases sufficiently, the set oscillates due to C_c increasing.

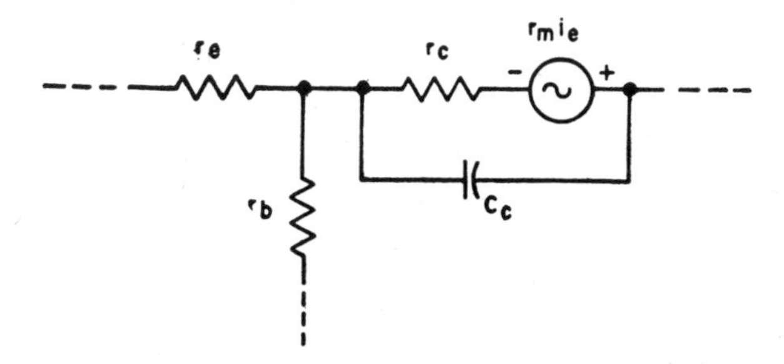

Fig. 4.12. Equivalent circuit for a transistor, including collector capacitance.

7. *Life data on N-P-N junction transistors*[4]

The results of life tests on 35 developmental M1752 N-P-N junction transistors are shown in Fig. 4.13. After slightly more than 5000 hours of operation, no failures had occurred on the life rack. The parameters α, r_c, and the saturation current I_{co} varied in the direction of poor performance, while r_b improved by decreasing.

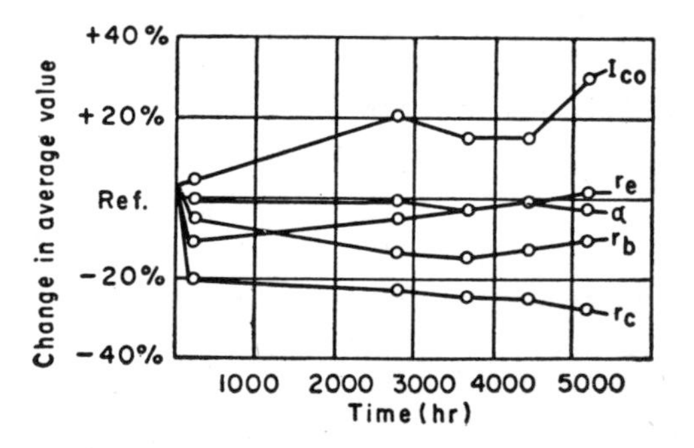

Fig. 4.13. Life data for N-P-N junction transistors.

8. *The P-N-P junction transistor produced by the alloy method* [5]

The N-P-N junction transistors previously described were made by the grown junction method. This section will describe the properties of P-N-P junction transistors produced by the alloy method.

Figure 4.14 shows the collector characteristics for constant emitter currents of 0 to 3 ma in 10 equal steps. For a good junction transistor

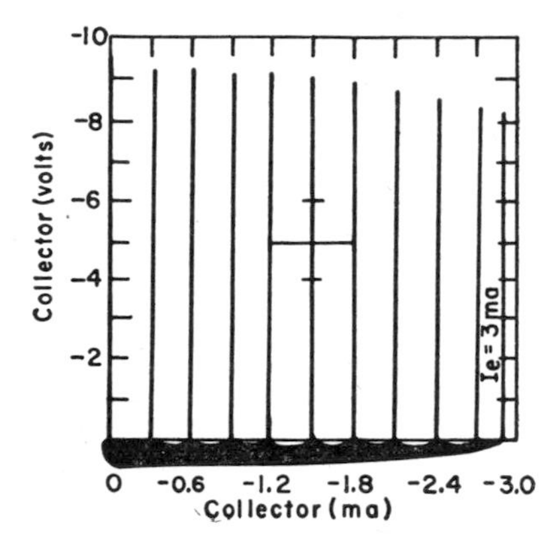

Fig. 4.14. Collector characteristics with constant emitter current, for typical P-N-P junction transistor.

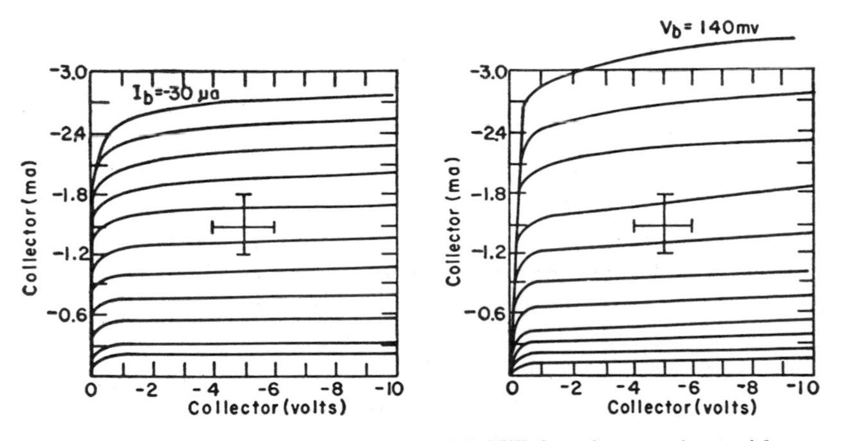

Fig. 4.15. Collector characteristics of P-N-P junction transistor with base-input connection.

the collector current is almost equal to the emitter current, and the slope of the curves is small. Hence the static characteristics of Fig. 4.15 are preferred. The rounded knee in the output characteristics of the latter figure results from a better inspection which these characteristics provide. These figures were traced out on an oscilloscope and photographed with an automatic curve tracer. However, the small-signal properties must be measured directly if they are to be determined accurately. Equipment for performing both of the above kinds of measurements is described in Chapter 6.

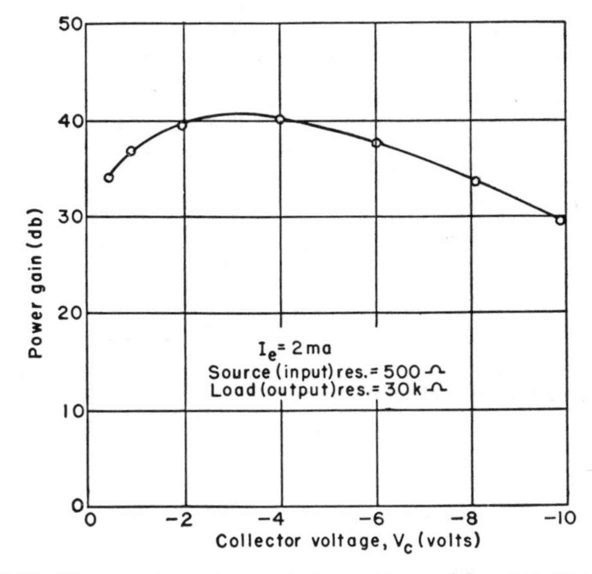

Fig. 4.16. Power gain versus collector voltage with constant emitter current, for a typical P-N-P junction transistor.

The base-input (grounded-emitter) circuit is desirable for many applications. This connection gives a high power gain, and simplifies the interstage coupling problem since the output impedance more nearly matches the input impedance. Therefore this circuit was employed to measure the data shown in Fig. 4.16 for the variation of the power gain with the collector voltage for a constant emitter current. The values of I_e = 2.0 ma, source resistance = 500 ohms, and load resistance = 30,000 ohms were chosen because they are nearly optimum for this transistor. The curve shows a broad maximum for a collector voltage of about −4 v.

The collector-to-base current gain may be defined as the negative of the ratio of a change in collector current to a change in base current

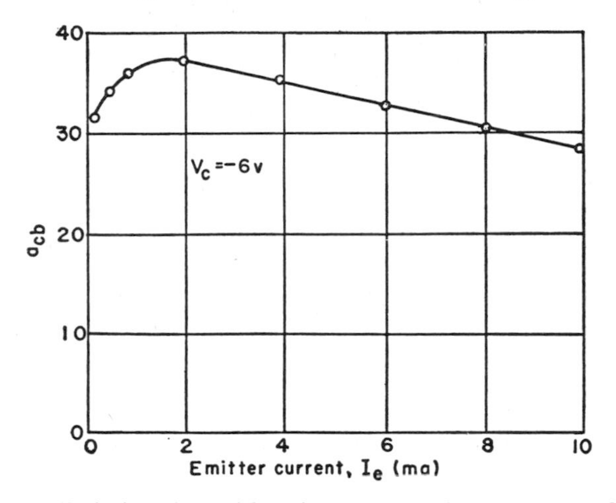

Fig. 4.17. Variation of α_{cb} with emitter current, for a constant collector voltage in a typical P-N-P junction transistor.

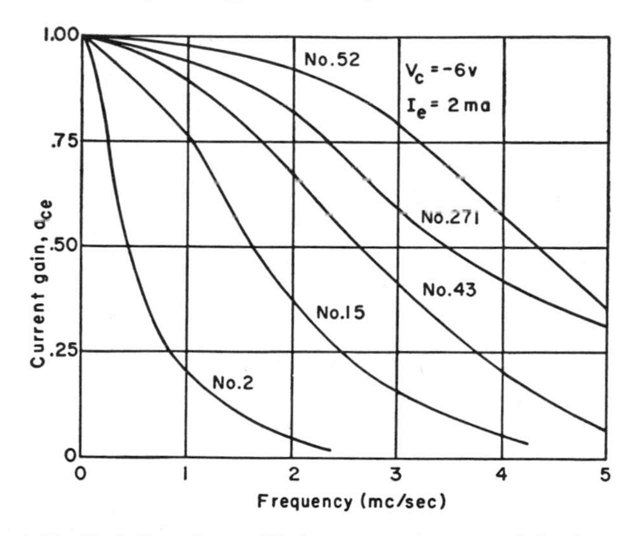

Fig. 4.18. Variation of α_{ce} with frequency, for several developmental P-N-P junction transistors.

with the collector voltage held constant. The word negative is included in this definition to signify that the collector current is 180° out of phase with the base current. Figure 4.17 represents the variation of α_{cb} with emitter current for a constant collector voltage of -6.0 v with respect to the base. The collector-to-base current gain exhibits a broad maximum for emitter currents from 1 to 3 ma.

The collector-to-emitter current gain limits the high-frequency performance as previously explained. The variation of α_{ce} with frequency for a constant emitter current and a constant collector voltage is shown in Fig. 4.18. These curves indicate the spread obtained when no attempt was made to control this parameter. Nevertheless some units demonstrate a usable α_{ce} at 4 mc/sec, and selected units have given useful amplification over the standard broadcast band.

9. *Vacuum tube analogy*[6]

The junction transistor can be related directly to the vacuum tube. The emitter is analogous to the cathode, the base to the grid, and the collector to the plate.

The collector characteristics of a junction transistor are similar to those of a pentode vacuum tube, in that the collector current saturates with the collector voltage. In other words, the collector current is independent of the collector voltage, or the collector voltage does not appreciably influence the emitter.

Figure 4.19 shows the collector characteristics of a P-N-P junction

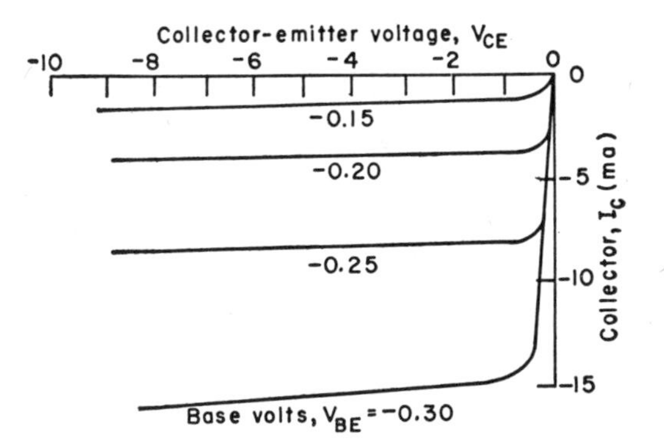

Fig. 4.19. Collector characteristics for P-N-P junction transistor, for constant base voltages.

transistor plotted with the base-to-emitter voltage as the constant parameter to emphasize the tube analogy. Also like vacuum tube practice, the voltages in Fig. 4.19 are measured with respect to the emitter, so that V_{ce} differs slightly from V_{cb}.

Figure 4.20 gives the input characteristics corresponding to the output characteristics of Fig. 4.19. Figure 4.21 presents the transfer characteristics, which are similar to those for a vacuum tube if the difference in carrier polarity is taken into account. It is evident that

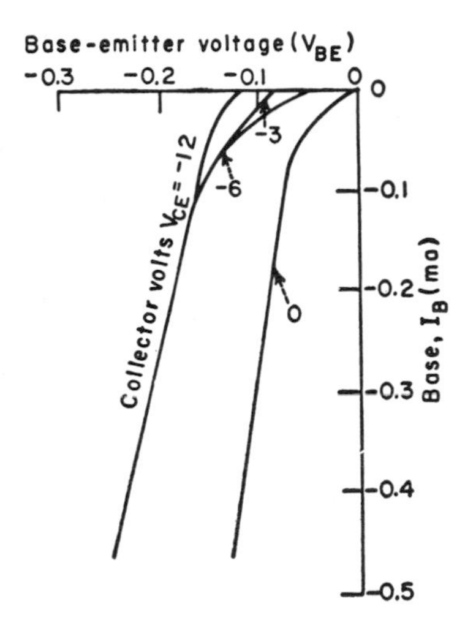

Fig. 4.20. Base characteristics of P-N-P junction transistor, for constant collector voltages.

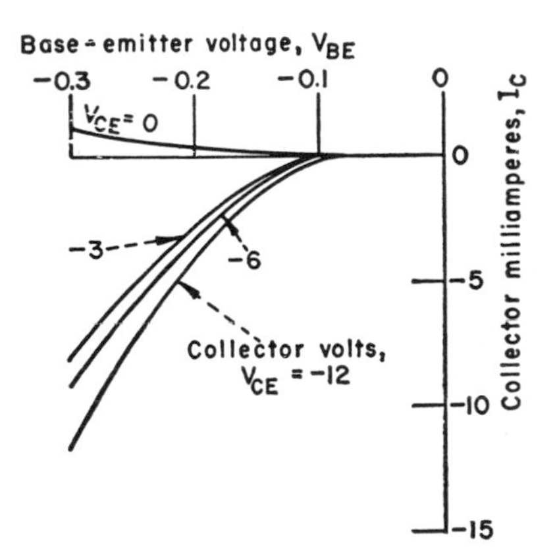

Fig. 4.21. Transfer characteristics for P-N-P junction transistor, for constant collector voltages.

the transfer characteristics of the transistor are nonlinear. As with a vacuum tube, if linear operation of a transistor is desired, degeneration is required.

Figure 4.22 shows the transistor transconductance versus the base-emitter voltage with the collector-emitter voltage constant. The g_m characteristic is roughly exponential and except for magnitude is somewhat like that of a vacuum tube. Since the collector current is about equal to the emitter current, the transconductance is approximately the same as the emitter conductance, $1/r_e$, which Shockley[3] has shown to be eI_e/kT, where e is the absolute charge of an electron, I_e is the emitter current, k is Boltzmann's constant, and T is the absolute operating temperature of the transistor. Therefore the ratio of the transconductance to the emitter current, $g_m/I_e = e/kT = 38.6$. Although this ratio of 38.6 is theoretical, measured values do not differ appreciably from it when the emitter current is small. The theoretical ratio for vacuum tubes is 11.6, but measured values seldom exceed 2. Hence this important constant is 20 times larger for junction transistors than for vacuum tubes.

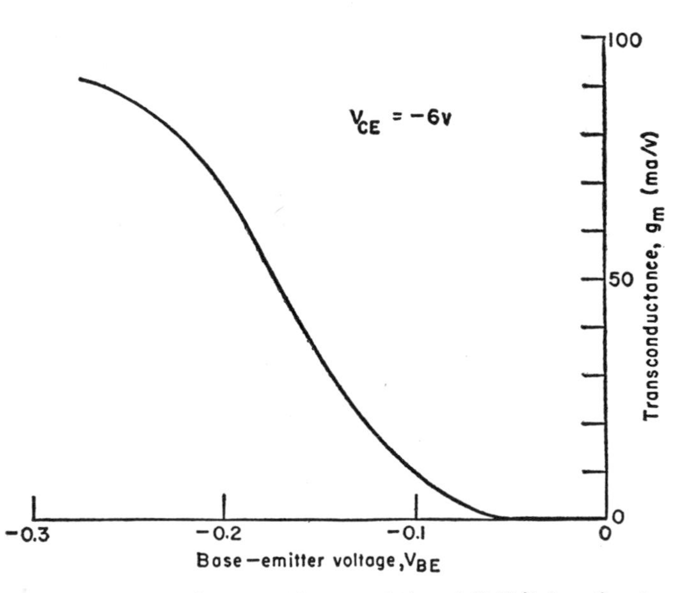

Fig. 4.22. Transconductance characteristics of P-N-P junction transistor.

10. *A P-N-P alloy junction transistor for radio frequency amplification*[7]

The power gain of alloy junction transistors decreases with an increase in frequency. Previously, the main reason for this has been the effect of the resistance-capacitance low-pass filter in the base-emitter input circuit. The germanium resistance between the external base connection and the active junction region, and the emitter-to-base diffusion capacitance cause this effect. This capacitance may be unusually large because of the comparatively slow diffusion of charge carriers into the base region which must be charged up and discharged with minority carriers. In fact, this capacitance is roughly 0.01 μf in the TA-153 junction transistor which was described in Section 8 of this chapter.

In the new transistor, a cross-sectional view of which is shown in Fig. 4.23, resistance and capacitance have been decreased by employing a thick wafer of low-resistance germanium, and locating the active junctions on a thin section formed by drilling a well into the wafer. The separation between the junctions is about 0.0005 in. The figure is drawn approximately to scale. Beyond the immediate vicinity of

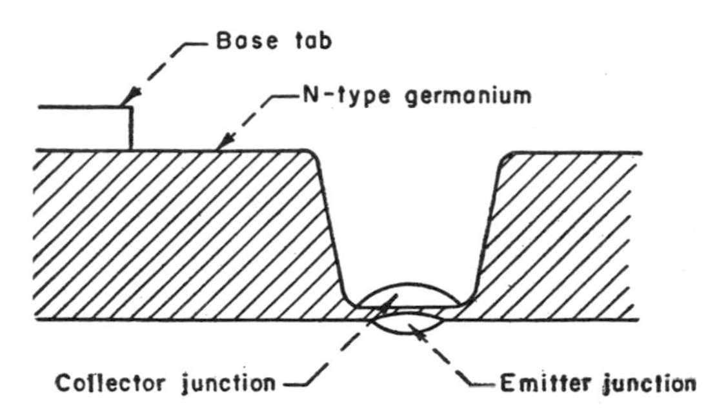

Fig. 4.23. Cross-sectional view of P-N-P alloy-junction transistor, for r-f amplification. *Courtesy of RCA.*

the junctions, the thickness of the wafer is made larger to decrease the series base lead resistance. Low surface recombination is likewise obtained, since the junctions are surrounded with only germanium.

The collector-to-base capacitance must be kept small. The alloy type transistor normally has the abrupt or Shottky type junctions. Shockley[8] has developed formulas for the capacitance of such an abrupt junction, which lead to the following equation.

$$C = 0.071d^2 \frac{1}{\sqrt{p_b V_c}} \quad \mu\mu\text{f} \tag{4}$$

where d = diameter of the junction in mils, V_c = collector voltage, and p_b = resistivity of the base material in ohm-centimeters. Hence the diameter of the collector is the dominant factor and should be made small. The parameter α_{ce}, the collector-to-emitter current amplification factor, should not be decreased in the process. If the area of the emitter is limited to two-thirds or less than that of the collector, α_{ce} will remain large.

When the area of the emitter is decreased, the ratio of emitter circumference to area increases, and surface recombination becomes greater. Therefore etching must be done carefully. Likewise, it is more difficult to align the emitter and collector as their areas are decreased. An engineering compromise fixed the emitter diameter at 0.010 in. and the collector diameter at 0.015 in. The junctions were formed with germanium-indium alloy disks, resulting in nearly planar junctions, which prevented limitation due to transit-time dispersion.

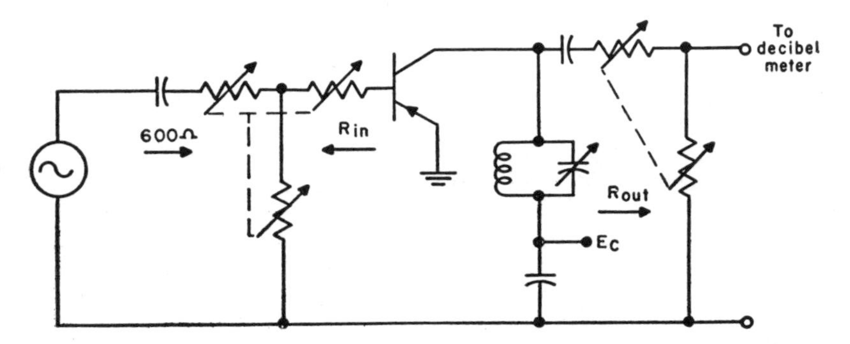

Fig. 4.24. Simplified diagram of circuit for measurement of gain versus frequency. *Courtesy of RCA.*

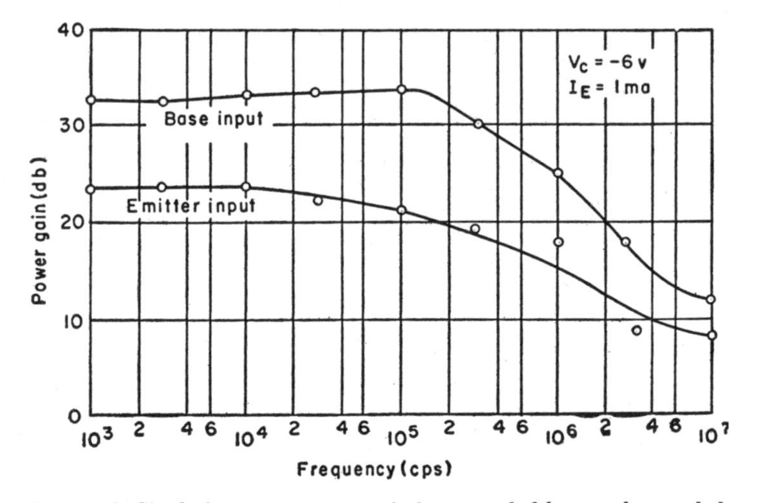

Fig. 4.25. Single-frequency power gain for grounded-base and grounded-emitter circuits. *Courtesy of RCA.*

It is interesting to compare the low-frequency parameters of the grounded-base T-network equivalent circuit with those of the TA-153 transistor. The high-frequency transistor has slightly poorer r_c and α_{ce} because these parameters were compromised to obtain better high-frequency response.

The variation of the single-frequency power gain with frequency is an important property of a high-frequency transistor. A simplified circuit of the test equipment for measuring the power gain is shown in Fig. 4.24. Only the resistive component is matched at the input, but the capacitance and resistance are adjusted for a conjugate match at the output. The feedback is not neutralized. Figure 4.25 presents the gain versus frequency for both the grounded-emitter and the grounded-base configurations of a transistor. In a neutralized, conjugate-matched circuit a gain of 39 db was achieved at 455 kc. At 10 megacycles, 12 db was obtained without neutralization. These high-frequency transistors have oscillated in a simple oscillator circuit at frequencies up to 75 megacycles.

11. *An N-P-N alloy junction transistor*[9]

This section discusses an N-P-N alloy junction transistor which is the counterpart to the P-N-P junction transistor previously described in Section 8 of this chapter. A fundamental difference between these two types is that the active charge carriers in the P-N-P transistors are positive holes, but those of the N-P-N transistor are negative electrons. The two types may be combined advantageously in complementary symmetry circuits to eliminate components and fulfill unusual requirements, because the power sources which operate these devices are of opposite polarity. The N-P-N transistor may have a better high-frequency response than its P-N-P counterpart because the mobility of electrons is more than twice that of holes.

In making this N-P-N junction transistor, a binary lead-antimony is fused into the opposite faces of a thin wafer of P-type single-crystal germanium. Relatively large electrodes may be employed with less danger of producing differential expansion strains since this is a ductile alloy. More planar junctions and better control of junction spacing are obtained from the more uniform penetration by the binary alloy.

These N-P-N alloy junction transistors were intended for small-signal, low-power applications at low frequencies. The grounded-emitter circuit is emphasized because it has been used extensively in equipment, and the similarity between the junction transistor and the vacuum tube aids in the understanding and design of the circuitry.

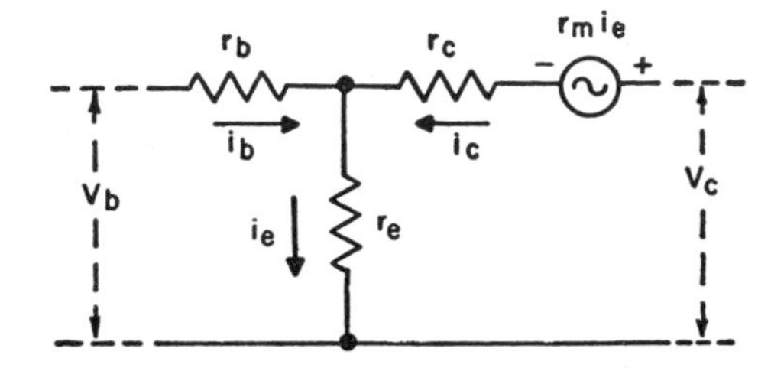

Fig. 4.26. T-network equivalent circuit of N-P-N junction transistor in grounded-emitter circuit.

Figure 4.26 gives the small-signal, T-network equivalent circuit suitable for low frequencies. The N-P-N alloy junction transistors may have the following ranges of resistances when operated at 2 ma emitter current:

r_b = 100 ohms to 2500 ohms
r_e = 2 ohms to 20 ohms
r_c = 100,000 ohms to 10 megohms
r_m = 100,000 ohms to 10 megohms

The base resistance r_b largely depends on the germanium resistivity and can be decreased with low resistivity germanium. The collector resistance r_c determines the quality of the collector junction, and is greatly affected by the etching process. The forward characteristics of the emitter junction to some extent determine the emitter resistance r_e. Finally, the transfer resistance r_m is approximately equal to the product of r_c and the current gain, alpha, and hence is always smaller than r_c in these junction transistors.

A set of four static characteristic curve families for a typical unit is shown in Figs. 4.27, 4.28, 4.29, and 4.30. Unlike the vacuum tube, the transistor requires all these curves to give an adequate picture of its behavior. It is not sufficient to present only the output characteristics with constant input potentials, because the transistor has a finite input impedance.

One of the best ways of describing transistor characteristics con-

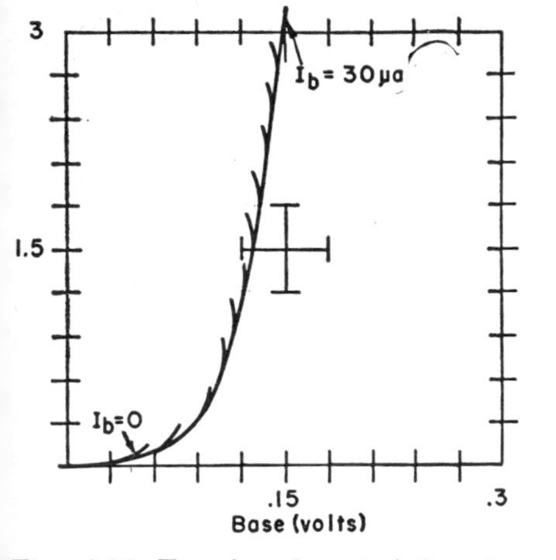

Fig. 4.27. Transfer characteristics of a typical low-power N-P-N alloy transistor (base current I_b in ten equal steps from 0 to 30 μa).

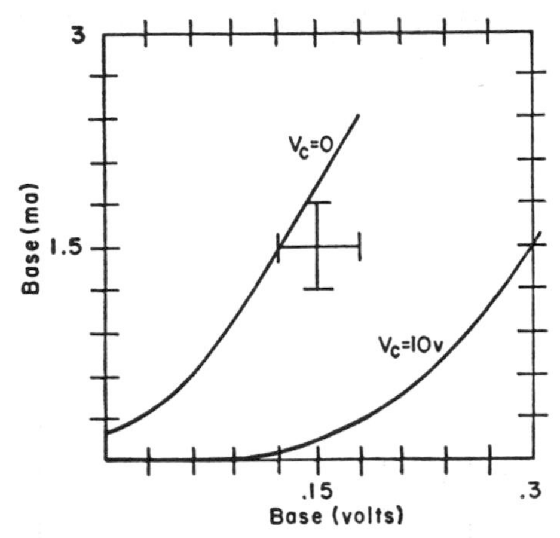

Fig. 4.28. Input characteristics of a typical low-power N-P-N alloy junction transistor (collector potential V_c equals 0 to 10 v).

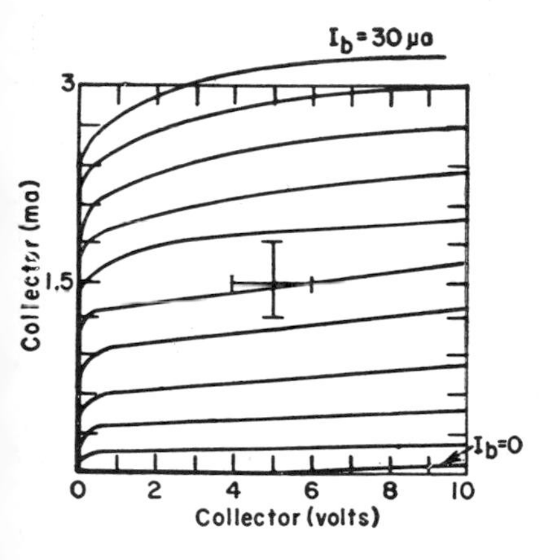

Fig. 4.29. Output characteristics of a typical low-power N-P-N alloy junction transistor (base current I_b in ten equal steps from 0 to 30 μa).

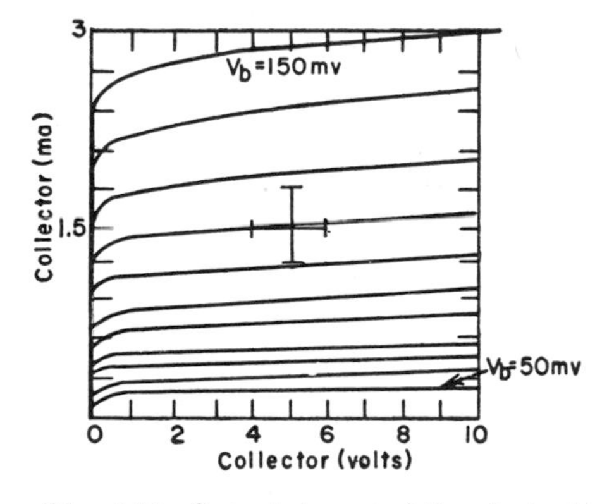

Fig. 4.30. Output characteristics of a typical low-power N-P-N alloy junction transistor (base potentials in ten equal steps from 50 to 150 mv).

sists in measuring such important factors as power gain, current gain, etc., under typical bias and impedance conditions and at different frequencies. Some of the important parameters of a typical transistor are given in Figs. 4.31, 4.32, 4.33, and 4.34. These data were obtained from the same unit except for the frequency response data. Figure 4.31 shows that the current gain is essentially constant for emitter currents of from 2 to 10 ma, corresponding to a current density of several amperes per square centimeter. Likewise, Fig. 4.32 indicates that the power gain has a negligible variation with collector

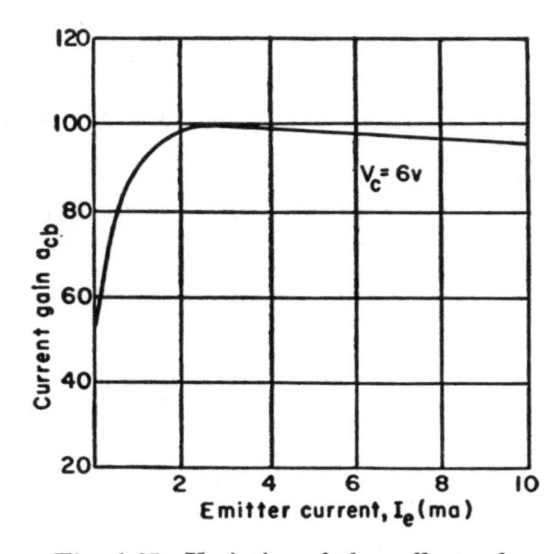

Fig. 4.31. Variation of the collector-base current gain, α_{cb}, with emitter current, for a typical N-P-N transistor.

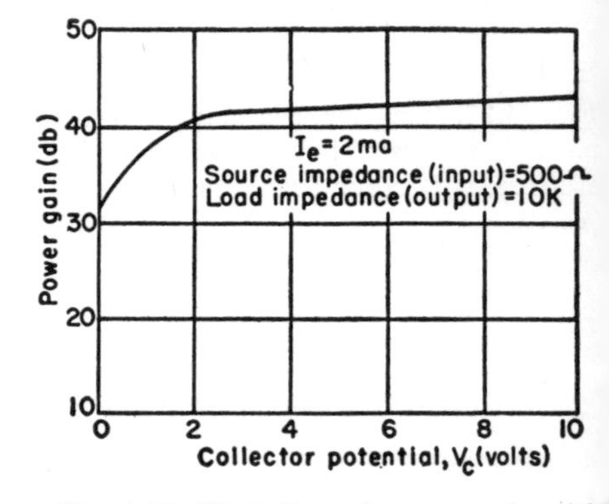

Fig. 4.32. Variation of power gain with collector potential, for a typical N-P-N alloy junction transistor.

potentials of between 2 and 10 v. The source impedance of 500 ohms and the load impedance of 10,000 ohms were chosen as the average matching impedances for maximum power gain at an emitter current I_e of 2 ma and a collector potential V_c of 6 v. Although the choice of the operating currents and potentials is arbitrary, they lie within the most probable application range.

Even though these transistors were intended only for audio-frequency applications, the high-frequency performance is of interest. Figure 4.33 shows the variation of the current amplification factor with frequency for a group of 100 N-P-N alloy junction transistors. It will be noticed that the spread is large at the high-frequency end. The cutoff frequencies occur between 1.2 and 4 mc/sec. Figure 4.34

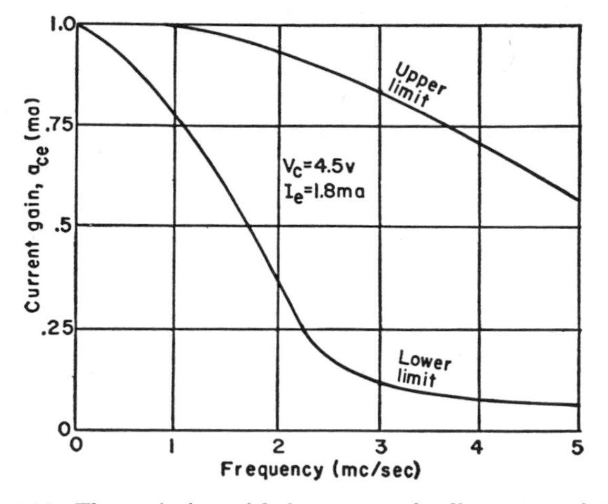

Fig. 4.33. The variation with frequency of collector-to-emitter current gain, α_{ce}, for a lot of 100 N-P-N alloy junction transistors; all units fall between the two curves shown.

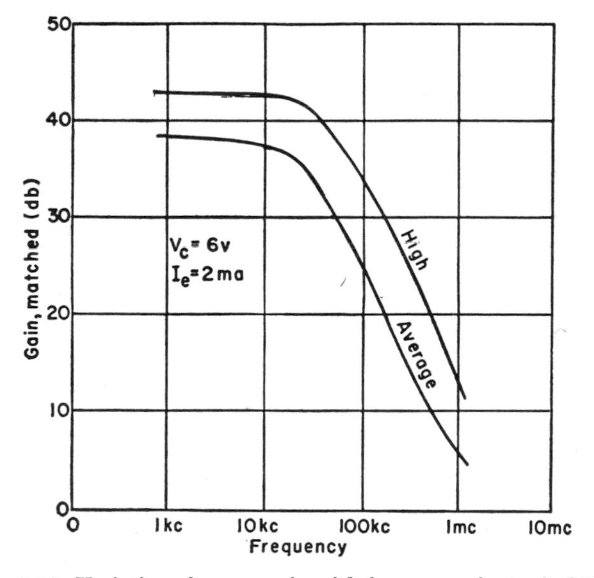

Fig. 4.34. Variation of power gain with frequency, for typical N-P-N alloy junction transistors. A resistive input and conjugate-matched output were used.

illustrates the power gain versus frequency for a typical transistor with a resistive input and a conjugate-matched output. Higher gains presumably would have resulted if a conjugate match also had been made for the input. Useful gains were obtained at 455 kc/sec, and selected units gave good amplification in the standard broadcast band (500 to 1500 kc).

References

1. *Electrons and Holes in Semiconductors,* W. Shockley, Bell Telephone Laboratories, Inc. Copyright 1950, D. Van Nostrand Company, Inc.
2. R. L. Wallace, Jr. and W. J. Pietenpol, "Some Circuit Properties and Applications of N-P-N Transistors," *Proc. IRE,* Vol. XXXIX, No. 7, July 1951, pp. 753–767.
3. W. Shockley, M. Sparks, and G. K. Teal, "P-N Junction Transistors," *Physical Review,* Vol. LXXXIII, No. 1, July 1951, p. 151.
4. K. D. Smith, "Properties of Junction Transistors," *Tele-Tech and Electronic Industries,* Vol. XII, No. 1, Jan. 1953, pp. 76–77.
5. R. R. Law, C. W. Mueller, J. I. Pankove, and L. D. Armstrong, "A Developmental Germanium P-N-P Junction Transistor," *Proc. IRE,* Vol. XL, No. 11, Nov. 1952, pp. 1352–1357.
6. L. J. Giacoletto, "Junction Transistor Equivalent Circuits and Vacuum-Tube Analogy," *Proc. IRE,* Vol. XL, No. 11, Nov. 1952, pp. 1490–1493.
7. C. W. Mueller and J. I. Pankove, "A P-N-P Triode Alloy Junction Transistor for Radio-Frequency Amplification," *RCA Review,* Vol. XIV, No. 4, Dec. 1953, pp. 586–598.
8. W. Shockley, "The Theory of P-N Junctions in Semi-conductors and P-N Junction Transistors," *Bell System Tech. J.,* Vol. XXVIII, July 1949, pp. 435–489.
9. Dietrich A. Jenny, "A Germanium N-P-N Alloy Junction Transistor," *Proc. IRE,* Vol. LIX, No. 12, Dec. 1953, pp. 1728–1734.

Chapter 5

POWER TRANSISTORS

Point-Contact Transistors

1. *Power output and distortion*[1]

The problem of obtaining good "undistorted" power output from a transistor at low frequencies may well be considered with the aid of the static characteristics. Although this is a slightly nonlinear problem, the curves of Fig. 5.1 may illustrate it. This plot shows the family of collector characteristics of a Type A transistor. Essentially linear operation is obtained in that region of the graph where the curves are equally spaced, have constant slopes, and fall within the allowable power dissipation of the device.

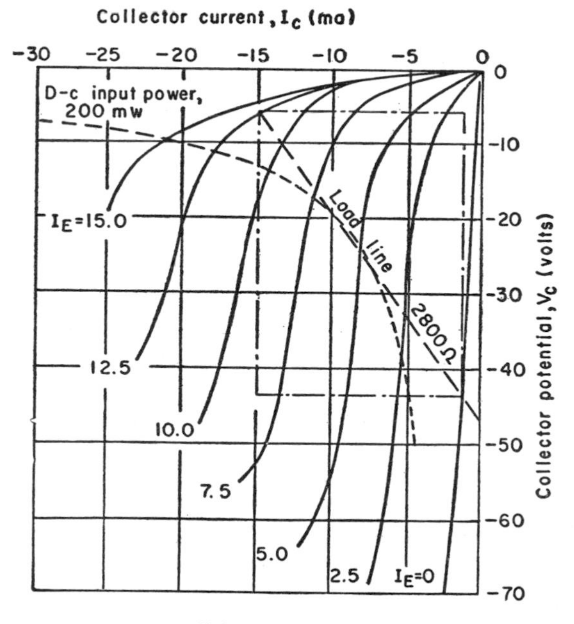

Fig. 5.1. Collector power-output plot.

When a Type A transistor is driven harder and harder to obtain more power output, four types of overload distortion, similar to those of vacuum tubes, may be discovered. First, like grid cutoff in a vacuum tube, the emitter may be driven negative into the cutoff region such that the collector current does not follow the changes in the emitter potential. Second, as with positive grid distortion, the emitter may be driven positive into an emitter overload section where the variation of the emitter impedance with the emitter voltage causes nonlinear distortion. This, however, is a minor effect for both vacuum tubes and transistors, and in actual practice may be helpful. Third, similar to plate "bottoming" in a vacuum tube, one may drive the collector down to such a low potential that it can no longer pass the current necessary to follow the applied emitter current changes. Fourth, like inadequate cathode emission in a vacuum tube, one may drive the collector up to high currents where heating effects cause nonlinear voltage response, resulting in collector overload.

In view of the above, it is necessary to select an operating point and load impedance to avoid these nonlinear effects over as large a region as possible, if good power output is to be obtained. As illustrated in Fig. 5.1, the product of ΔV and ΔI should be as large as possible. Considered as a problem in geometry, we desire to construct the largest possible rectangle with the load line as a diagonal, falling within the "linear" region of operation. The proper load impedance is given by the slope of this load line; the collector supply voltage for resistance coupling is determined by its intercept with the Y axis; and the maximum values of the collector current and voltage are represented by the sides of the rectangle. The quiescent or small-signal operating point is located approximately at the center of the rectangle.

As in class A vacuum tube amplifiers, power efficiencies of from 20 to 35 per cent with a few per cent harmonic distortion may be achieved for optimum conditions of load impedance and operating point. Lower load impedances and higher currents are normally required by the optimum conditions for power output than are recommended for good low-level gain for the Type A transistor. Typical values are:

load impedance = 5000 ohms
collector current = -8 ma at -35 v bias
emitter current = 3 ma
power output = 60 mw (with less than 10% distortion)

If the power transistor is short-circuit unstable, it may tend to oscillate when the optimum load impedance is low. Stability may be achieved by adding resistance to the emitter circuit; a higher generator impedance may stabilize the transistor, and probably will decrease the gain. A high-power point-contact transistor may have a low or even a negative input impedance.

The power-handling ability of the point-contact transistor is severely limited by heating at the contact itself, which must be of small area and high thermal resistance. If the allowable collector dissipation is increased, the transistor can deliver a higher power output. Cooling fins mounted on a copper base soldered directly to the thin wafer of germanium have aided the removal of heat generated in the collector point region. The allowable dissipation was increased from 200 to 600 mw. Power outputs of about 200 mw were achieved at a collector efficiency of 33 per cent.

A point-contact transistor may also be liquid cooled in a manner similar to that described for junction transistors later in this chapter.

Junction Transistors

2. *Introduction*

For power amplifier application the junction transistor has a fundamental advantage over the point-contact transistor in that the heat source is not concentrated in the vicinity of a small collector point, but is distributed over the area of the collector junction. In the N-P-N junction transistor, the currents pass over two interfaces between the N and P types of germanium, which may be of substantial area. As a result, power levels of at least 3 w may be handled in units specially built for power service. Moreover, there appears to be no fundamental bar to handling power levels equal to that of any receiver power tube. As a result a broadcast-band receiver with normal sensitivity and power output can now be built completely without vacuum tubes.

3. *A three watt N-P-N power junction transistor*[2]

The important role which heat dissipation by radiation plays in low and medium power vacuum tubes cannot be duplicated in germanium transistors. The available temperature difference between the transistor and its surroundings is low, since the maximum temperature of the semiconductor must not exceed about 70°C. Therefore the power radiated per square centimeter of area will be low.

The outlook for conduction cooling is more promising. The thermal conductivity of germanium is about 0.125 in the temperature range of interest, or approximately the same as the thermal conductivity of

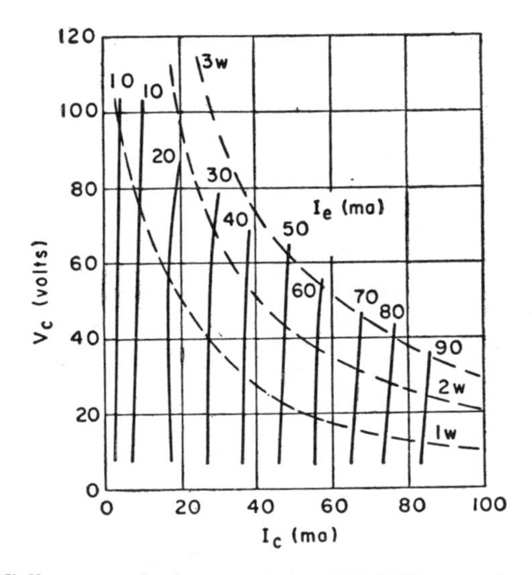

Fig. 5.2. Collector static characteristics of N-P-N power junction transistor.

brass. Assuming that all the power dissipated in the transistor appears as heat at the collector junction and is conducted to a heat sink at one end of the transistor, the temperature rise at the junction would be given by the equation

$$\Delta T = 0.24Wl/\sigma A = 1.92Wl/A \tag{1}$$

where W = power dissipated in watts

l = length of germanium between junction and heat sink

σ = thermal conductivity of germanium = 0.125 cal/°C at 55°C

A = area of germanium bar.

In practice it is impossible to hold the heat sink at ambient temperature, and the thermal impedances external to the transistor must be taken into account. Thermal impedance must be reduced by all possible means, if the total temperature rise is to be kept small.

An N-P-N junction transistor has been designed for a power dissipation of about 3 w. Figure 5.2 shows typical collector static characteristics. This unit mounts directly in contact with a metal chassis or other thermal sink. The class A power output is 1 w for a collector potential of 60 to 80 v at an efficiency of 33 per cent. At this power level the distortion is about 8 per cent, and the power gain is 26 db. The input and output distortion may be reduced by making the generator impedance low.

4. *One hundred watt P-N-P power junction transistor*[3]

A fused impurity contact transistor, made by fusing a small acceptor impurity contact to each side of an N-type germanium wafer as shown in Fig. 5.3, is capable of delivering a few watts of output power.

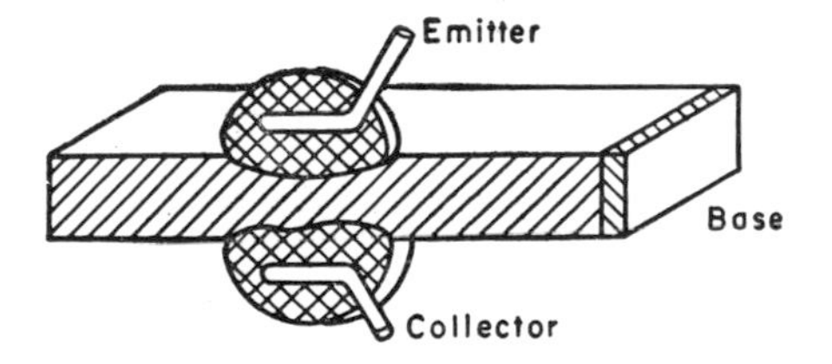

Fig. 5.3. Fused impurity contact transistor.

However, this type of transistor is limited in that a substantial rise in power output cannot be obtained simply by increasing the areas of the emitter and collector contacts. All three electrodes must be placed close together, and each must have a large area of contact with the germanium for satisfactory high-power operation. Figure 5.4 illustrates an electrode arrangement for a P-N-P transistor which meets these requirements. The emitter and collector electrodes consist of intermeshing grid structures fused to one side of an N-type germanium wafer. The base electrode on the opposite side functions as an electron source and as a heat remover.

In operation, the emitter and base inject holes and electrons, respectively. The collector, biased in the reverse direction, acts as a perfect sink for holes, and competes with the recombination process for the holes injected by the emitter. The collector must pick up a large fraction of the injected holes for efficient transistor action. If surface and volume recombination is to be kept at a minimum, the electrodes should be closely spaced and should not be high-recombination-rate contacts. The best performance requires that the wafer thickness be slightly less than the emitter-collector spacing. A sufficient flow of holes from emitter to collector are provided by these proportions without the excessive volume of recombination which a thick wafer of germanium would have produced.

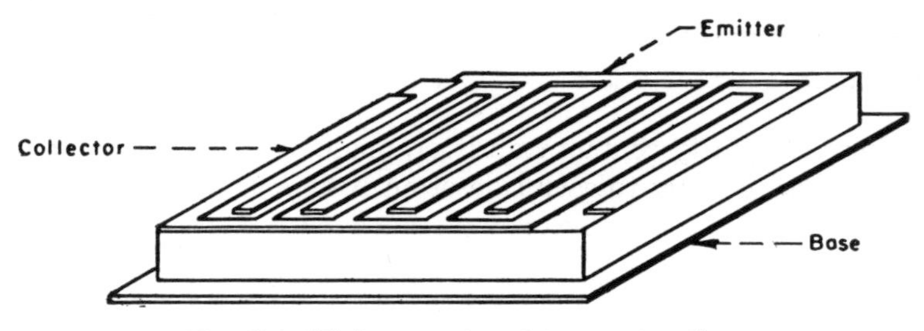

Fig. 5.4. High-power transistor construction.

The current gain of the transistor, defined as the ratio of the collector current to the emitter current, may be shown to have the form

$$\alpha = 2/(1 + \cosh d/L) \tag{2}$$

where d is the emitter-collector spacing, and L is the high-level diffusion length, or average distance to which holes diffuse between generation and recombination.

If a reasonable current gain is to be obtained for high-power operation, the electrode spacings should be no greater than the high-level diffusion length, which is observed to be roughly half a millimeter. Due to spreading effects which were not taken into account in the derivation, the gain will be somewhat lower in actual practice than that given by the above formula.

Figure 5.5 shows the collector characteristics of a power transistor having electrode spacings of $\frac{1}{2}$ mm and a total area of 1 sq cm. As is typical for junction transistors, the collector current is almost independent of the collector voltage. Because of the decrease in lifetime with the injection level, the current gain falls from 0.6 at low level to about 0.3 in the region of high-current operation. The power output of this transistor is about 100 watts for class C operation and somewhat less under class A conditions because of the increased collector dissipation.

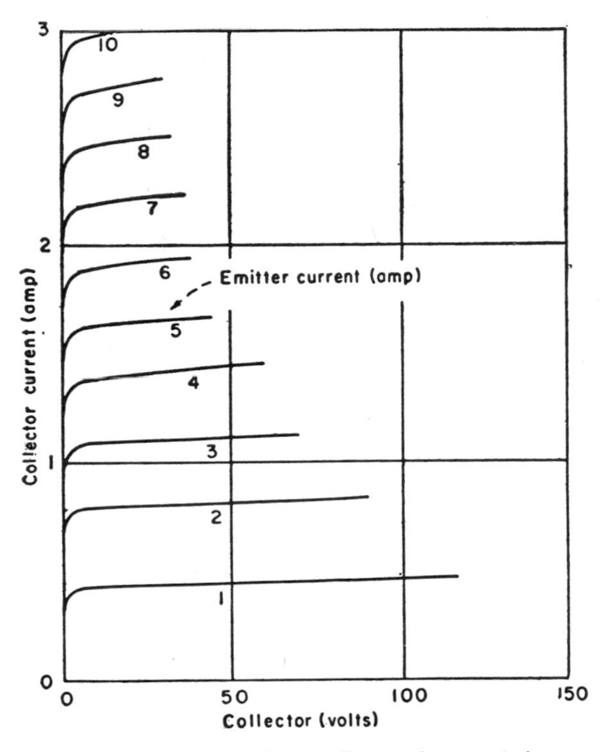

Fig. 5.5. Power transistor collector characteristics.

Changes in the collector circuit have little effect upon the current-voltage characteristics of the emitter. Since the emitter has a low impedance which varies considerably with the emitter current, it is extremely difficult to achieve all the available power gain, which is normally between 10 and 20 db for full-power output.

The above power transistor is in an early stage of development. When techniques are developed for applying closely spaced electrode contacts to the germanium, considerable improvement in current gain and frequency response may be expected. The time required for injected carriers to diffuse through the germanium limits present units, with ½ mm electrode spacings, to audio frequency applications.

5. *Fused impurity P-N-P power junction transistors*[4]

Fused impurity P-N-P junction transistors may be employed at high-dissipation levels provided that allowance is made for the high-temperature effects, because in some instances these transistors can operate safely in circuits with collector voltages exceeding 150 v. Power design must minimize the temperature difference between the active region of the transistor and the ambient medium, otherwise the transistor will be handicapped by unnecessarily high junction temperature. This difficulty may sometimes be encountered with transistors encased in a plastic material.

Thermal instability may occur even though alpha remains less than unity. If I_{co} increases, the dissipation also may increase, causing a temperature rise with a further increase of I_{co}, and lead to thermal runaway. Hence one must allow some safety margin. However, the safe dissipation may be increased, provided that one employs suitable current stabilization circuitry. Such circuits are given in Chapter 10.

Grounded-emitter amplification above 120°C and operation at comparatively high dissipation levels are possible with P-N-P fused-junction transistors, since alpha remains essentially constant with temperature variation. Such transistors having an active junction area of about 1 mm^2 have been operated at more than 8 w with forced cooling. In an ambient temperature of 25°C within properly designed cases, these transistors have operated continuously at more than 3 w dissipation with good gain. Even in plastic imbedments, dissipations of several hundred milliwatts are possible.

Proper circuit design will permit high-power operation with good efficiency. Examples of this may be found in Chapter 12.

6. *Alloyed power junction transistors*[5]

Transistors made from germanium cannot operate at excessive temperatures, either ambient or caused by internal heat generation.

Germanium, like all semiconductors, has this inherent property, because thermal energy creates electron-hole pairs. Power transistors generate heat, and temperature effects constitute one of the chief limitations in their design.

Low-power alloyed-junction N-P-N and P-N-P transistors suffer permanent deterioration when the ambient temperatures are increased much above 110°C. Electrical characteristics also cause limitations in the same temperature range.

These junction transistors operated for short intervals at temperatures up to approximately 110°C with satisfactory power gain and current gain. However, as the temperature rose, changes in characteristics became more and more evident. The increased reverse or back current to the collector due to the thermal generation of carriers at the higher temperatures was the most obvious and most important of these changes.

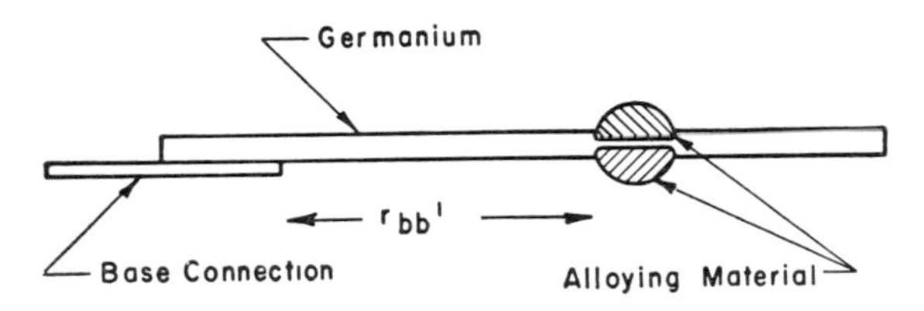

Fig. 5.6. Sectional view of alloyed junction transistor.

The effect of this collector current is best considered in connection with the structure of an alloyed-junction transistor as shown in Fig. 5.6. The construction consists of a slab of germanium, with two alloyed junctions on opposite sides, and a base connection to the germanium somewhat removed from the junction. The resistance $r_{bb'}$ of the germanium between the junctions and the base connection is several hundred ohms in typical transistors.

The base contributes that part of the collector current which does not come from the emitter. The reverse current due to thermal generation constitutes a major part of this current at high temperatures. The base current flows through the germanium resistance $r_{bb'}$, causing a voltage drop which appears across the emitter junction, and affects the emitter current. This voltage increases the emitter current. The heat generated within the transistor may cause it to "run away" and destroy itself. The effect is somewhat comparable to grid emission in vacuum tubes. The N-P-N units exhibited larger reverse currents due to thermal generation at an internal temperature of 100°C than the counterpart P-N-P transistors. The direct current added to the collector circuit by thermal generation is normally small compared with the average collector current in most power applications. However, unless special circuit arrangements are made, the transistor element should be maintained at a temperature well below 100°C, because of the above effect on the emitter-base control bias.

The operation of a power transistor is affected by the base lead resistance in two ways. The first effect, that on the emitter bias, has already been described. Figure 5.7 illustrates the second result. The output current generator is proportional only to that part of the input

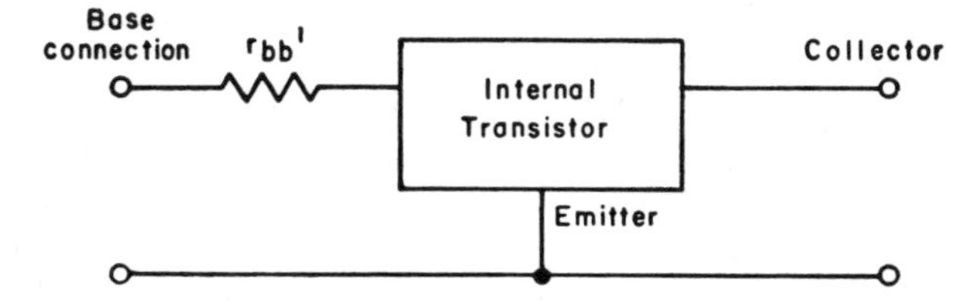

Fig. 5.7. An equivalent circuit of a junction transistor for the grounded-emitter connection.

voltage that is developed across the internal elements of the transistor. A higher driving power must be applied at the input of the transistor for a given output, since $r_{bb'}$ acts like an attenuator. In effect, the power gain is decreased.

The base lead resistance may be lowered by increasing the thickness of the germanium wafer, by decreasing the resistivity of the germanium, or by by-passing some of the wafer resistance by plating the wafer with a low resistivity metallic layer. However, in practice the amount of alloying penetration that can be obtained controls the germanium thickness. An increasing percentage of poor junctions results when the germanium resistivity is reduced. Also with decreasing germanium resistivity the maximum collector voltage falls off rapidly, and the current gain generally becomes lower. Plating can reduce $r_{bb'}$ by 50 per cent. All these factors are taken into account for the most effective reduction of the base lead resistance for the given operating conditions in designing practical transistors. Depending on the resistivity of the germanium, typical values of $r_{bb'}$ range from 50 to 250 ohms for these power transistors.

Large emitter current densities cause the collector-to-emitter current-gain factor α_{ce}, or the related collector-to-base current gain factor α_{cb} to decrease. Variations in the current-gain factor should be reduced to a minimum over the operating range of currents, if the transistors are to handle large signals. This requires that large junctions be employed to reduce the current density.

The early general-purpose low-power alloyed-junction transistors exhibited an alpha fall-off with increasing emitter current which was much less for N-P-N than for P-N-P units for the same junction areas. However, the P-N-P type has been improved by modifying the firing schedule. Equivalent and satisfactory fall-off characteristics for the two types have been obtained by a combination of larger emitter areas and the modified firing schedule for the power P-N-P transistor.

The resistivity of the germanium, the firing schedules, and the type of unit determine the maximum collector voltage. The P-N-P alloy units withstand higher voltages than the N-P-N transistors made from similar resistivity germanium. The maximum voltage increases with the resistivity of the base germanium. However, the base lead resistance $r_{bb'}$ also rises with germanium resistivity. Therefore a proper balance must be found to give the desired operating characteristics.

To increase the power dissipation, the elements of the transistor must be cooled to prevent the effects of increased operating temperature. Unless special circuits are provided to control the biases, the the temperature of the transistor wafer should not exceed 80°C. The heat dissipation of the transistors may be increased by immersion in a cooling liquid, by soldering a cooling fin to the wafer, and by soldering a cooling fin to the collector contact. Figure 5.8 shows a liquid-cooled unit and one with a cylindrical cooling fin attached to the collector. In the liquid-cooled unit the transistor is immersed in a cooling liquid contained in a metal shell. Liquid convection transfers the heat generated in the transistor to the metal shell. The liquid coolant should meet the following requirements: first, low viscosity to allow rapid circulation; second, high heat capacity for efficient heat transfer; third, a boiling point well above the operating temperature; and fourth, excellent electric insulation properties, since the liquid is in direct contact with the junction surfaces. The above requirements are met by benzene, toluene, and zylene. Because of its low viscosity and relatively high boiling point, toluene has proved the most successful. During mounting, the junctions suffer little deterioration, although the liquid-cooled unit is not rugged mechanically and the liquid is inflammable. As a result, power units, which require very low collector reverse saturation current, have employed this mounting.

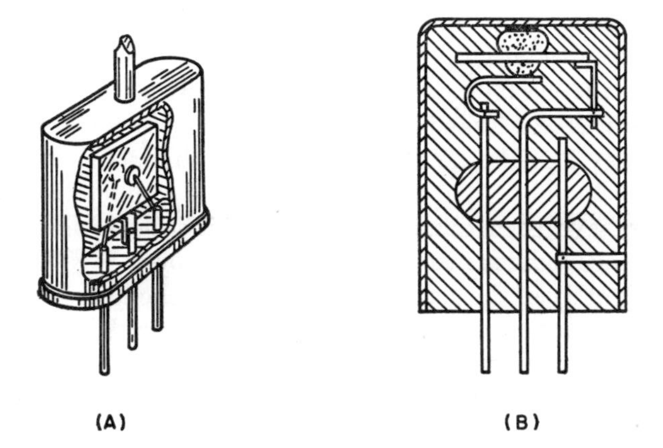

Fig. 5.8. Assembly details of (A) liquid-cooled and (B) metallic-conduction-cooled power transistors.

The other cooling methods employ metallic conduction paths to transfer the heat. Although these methods are rugged and contain no inflammable liquid, they are more difficult to apply than liquid cooling. Metallic conduction transfers the heat to a large metal fin or enclosure, which may be attached directly to the germanium wafer. However, since the collector junction generates most of the heat, it is advantageous to attach the cooling metal directly to the collector. Figure 5.8(B) shows a successful design, consisting of a copper cup to the inside of which the collector of the transistor is attached by a solder, which is initially a liquid. The liquid solder, a saturated solution of indium in mercury, forms a good electric and thermal contact between the collector and the bottom of the metal cup. The cup is then filled with a molding resin to protect the unit mechanically. Later operation of the device at higher operating temperature diffuses enough of the impurity material into the liquid solder to form finally a solid metallic bond.

These laboratory type power transistors can dissipate about 1 w. With additional forced-air or water cooling, they have been operated experimentally up to 3 w. A given dissipation may be obtained with high voltage and low current or vice versa. However, junction transistors, unlike vacuum tubes, operate unusually well with low voltages and low output impedances, so that relatively high currents are usually preferred.

Units that will meet various application requirements may be obtained by varying the processing parameters. Thus low resistivity germanium is employed for power units that will operate at high currents and low voltages, for example, 6 v applications. On the

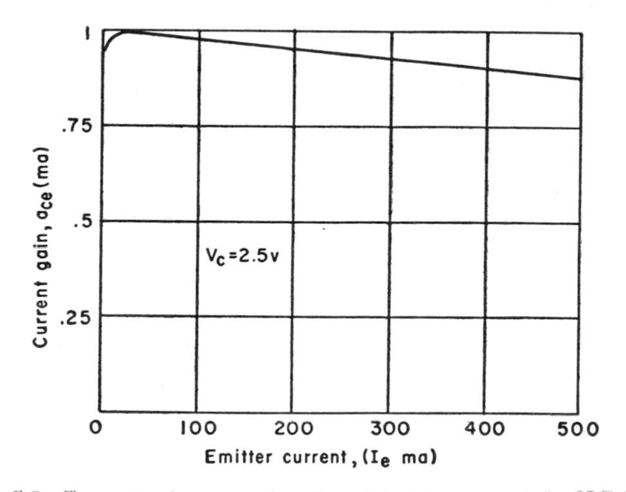

Fig. 5.9. Current gain α_{ce} as a function of emitter current, for N-P-N or P-N-P power transistors.

other hand, some special transistors required higher resistivity N-type germanium. These units were required to withstand 100 v on the collector with less than 1 ma cutoff current, and to have collector-to-emitter current gain factor greater than 0.90 with 100 ma emitter current. The current gain factor α_{ce} versus the emitter current for both N-P-N and P-N-P power transistors is given in Fig. 5.9.

Figures 5.10 and 5.11 show small-signal power-gain curves taken with nearly matched impedances as a function of power dissipation, with varying collector potential and emitter current, respectively. The grounded-emitter circuit was employed.

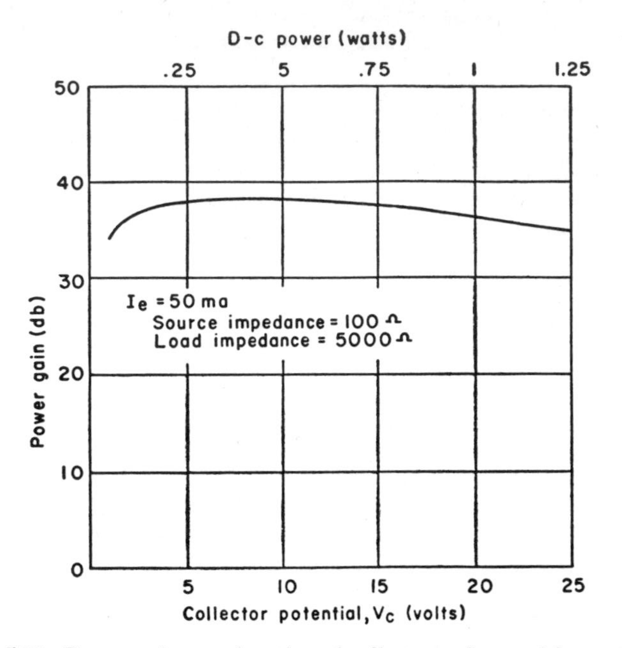

Fig. 5.10. Power gain as a function of collector voltage with constant emitter current, for N-P-N or P-N-P power transistors.

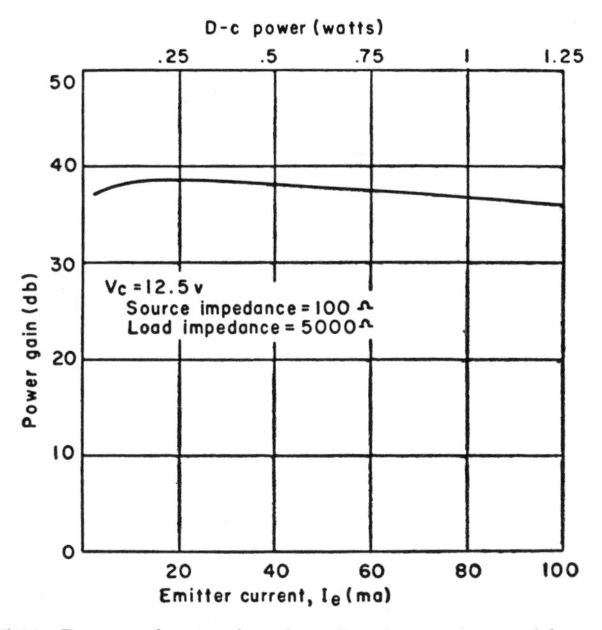

Fig. 5.11. Power gain as a function of emitter current with constant collector voltage, for N-P-N or P-N-P power transistors.

TABLE 1. CLASS A AUDIO AMPLIFIER PERFORMANCE OF POWER TRANSISTORS

Unit	Collector, volts	Collector, milliamperes	Load resistance, ohms	Signal input power, milliwatts	Output power, milliwatts	Power gain, db	Efficiency, per cent
P-N-P	7.2	130	100	0.94	340	26	36
P-N-P	17	65	400	0.30	430	32	39
P-N-P	28	35	800	0.37	560	32	56
N-P-N	10.5	100	100	0.45	480	30	46
N-P-N	22	40	400	0.20	420	33	48

Table 1 presents the behavior of these power transistors as class A audio amplifiers with loads giving reasonable audio outputs. The data are indicative of the performance obtained with the grounded-emitter connection, a constant-current d-c emitter supply, and about 1 w d-c input to the collector. The input was increased until the distortion rose to 10 per cent in each instance. It may be noted that the efficiency exceeded 50 per cent, because the distortion was allowed to become 10 per cent.

7. *Power transistors for audio output circuits*[6]

Class A Output Stage. In the design of an output stage the power supply direct voltage is usually specified. Assume that this is 12 v. Normally, the supply direct voltage is limited to approximately one-half of the collector breakdown voltage.

The d-c amplification factor α_{CB} may be defined as

$$\alpha_{CB} = -\frac{I_C}{I_B} \tag{3}$$

Figure 5.12 shows the variation of the d-c amplification factor with the collector current. For relatively large collector currents, it is apparent that α_{CB} falls off approximately hyperbolically. This decrease of the current amplification factor becomes important in power transistor operation.

The maximum power dissipation for the metallic conduction cup transistor, illustrated in Fig. 5.8(B), was found to be 1.28 w for a 50°C temperature rise above 25°C ambient temperature. Hence for a 12 v power supply the static collector current may be 100 ma. Maximum power output therefore requires an output resistance of 120 ohms. The load line in Fig. 5.13, which shows the output load character-

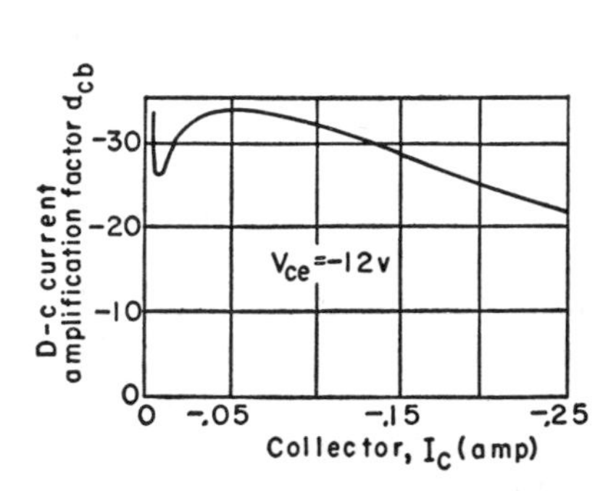

Fig. 5.12. Variation of d-c amplification factor with collector current.

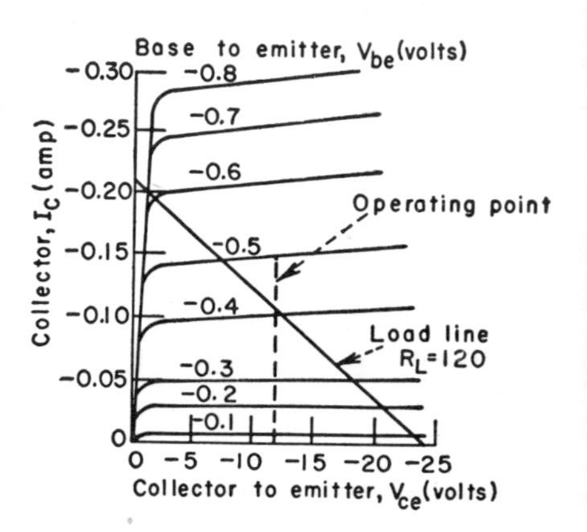

Fig. 5.13. Output load characteristics of power transistor.

istics, represents this resistance. The maximum a-c power output may be calculated approximately as

$$\frac{1}{2} \cdot \frac{12^2}{120} = 0.6 \quad \text{w}$$

The transfer characteristics given in Fig. 5.14 supply additional details of the output stage. A difference in operating temperature causes the apparent current discrepancy between Fig. 5.13 and Fig. 5.14. Referring to the transfer curve (solid curve marked $R_G = 0$) of Fig. 5.14 it will be seen that the -100 ma operating point requires a base-to-emitter bias voltage of -0.48 v. The peak driving voltage is $0.76 - 0.48 = 0.28$ v. Since the input resistance consists largely of $r_{BB'}$, the a-c input power may be calculated approximately as

$$\frac{1}{2} \cdot \frac{0.28^2}{75} = 5.2 \times 10^{-4} \quad \text{w}$$

The power gain therefore is

$$\frac{0.6}{5.2 \times 10^{-4}} = 1150 \quad \text{or} \quad 30.6 \quad \text{db}$$

Since these calculations do not take into account distortion and other factors, they are only approximate. Output distortion can be computed with the aid of the transfer characteristics as is well known. For the static current of -100 ma and a peak input voltage of 0.28 v, the peak fundamental and the first three harmonics in the output current are $I_1 = 95$ ma, $I_2 = 4.75$ ma, $I_3 = 0.5$ ma, and $I_4 = 0.4$ ma. The static current changes from -100 ma to -104 ma. The opera-

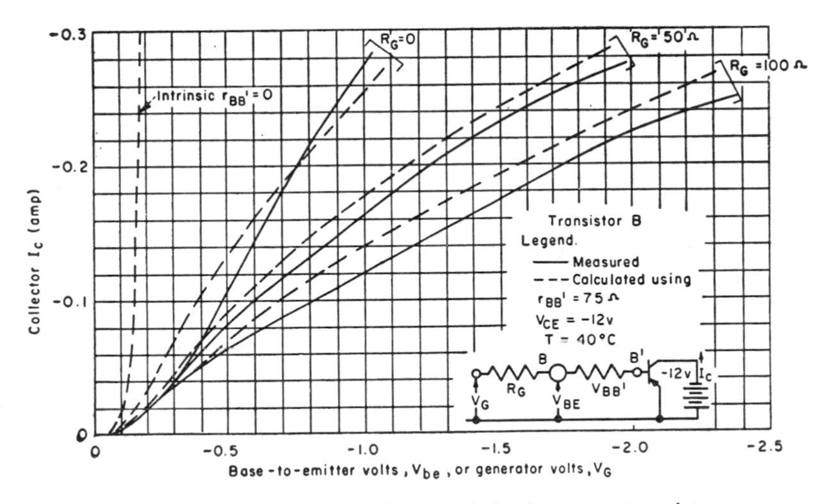

Fig. 5.14. Static transfer characteristics for power transistor.

tion of the output stage may be calculated more exactly with the above data as follows:

fundamental power output	= 0.54 w
d-c power input	= 1.25 w
efficiency	= 43 per cent
total distortion	= 5.1 per cent
power gain	= 30 db.

A signal source of zero internal resistance, $R_G = 0$, was assumed in the preceding calculations. Normally this is not true. Since the grid draws no current, a finite source resistance does not matter for a vacuum tube. When a vacuum tube is driven into grid current conduction, the situation is similar to that of the transistor. An increase in distortion and an increase in the driving voltage required for full output occur in both cases. As shown in the circuit of Fig. 5.15, the frequency response of the transistor will decrease. Therefore one should keep the driving source resistance as small as possible.

The following method can determine the circuit operation including the finite source resistance. Thévenin's theorem states that the source may be considered a voltage generator with a voltage V_G in series with an internal resistance $R_{G'}$. In the transistor circuit R_G is

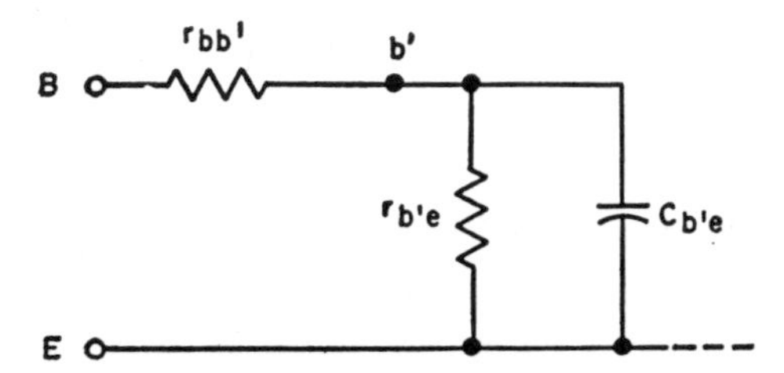

Fig. 5.15. Equivalent input circuit for small-signal operation.

in series with $r_{BB'}$ and the two resistances may be lumped together and considered as part of the transistor. A transistor with a larger effective $r_{BB'}$ results, driven from a generator of zero internal resistance. The transfer characteristics for the new transistor can be constructed. Two transfer characteristics for R_G = 50 ohms and 100 ohms are given in Fig. 5.14. The generator voltage becomes the base-to-emit-

TABLE 2. OPERATING CHARACTERISTICS OF CLASS A OUTPUT STAGE

	$R_G = 0$	R_G = 100 ohms
Peak input voltage	0.28 v	0.60 v
A-c input power	0.52 mw	1.03 mw
Dynamic collector direct current	−104 ma	−96 ma
Fundamental collector current	95 ma	71 ma
Second harmonic collector current	4.75 ma	4 ma
Third harmonic collector current	0.5 ma	1 ma
Fourth harmonic collector current	0.4 ma	0.5 ma
Total distortion	5.1%	5.9%
Fundamental power output	0.54 w	0.30 w
D-c power input	1.25 w	1.15 w
Efficiency	43%	26%
Power gain	30 db	25 db

ter voltage which includes the voltage drop across R_G. This figure also shows the measured transfer characteristics.

A detailed calculation of the circuit with a finite source resistance, $R_G = 100$ ohms, has been made, and the results are given in Table 2. The data computed previously for $R_G = 0$ are included for comparison. In both instances the supply direct voltage is -12 v, and the quiescent collector current is -100 ma. These results demonstrate that an increased source resistance causes the output power, efficiency, and power gain to decrease, and the input voltage and distortion to increase.

One must give careful attention to the biasing of the output stage to obtain satisfactory operation over a range of temperatures. Figure 5.16 shows how the operating point changes with variations in temperatures. For constant-voltage bias, as the temperature increases the quiescent electric current will increase. The increase in heat dissipation which results may cause the maximum power rating of the transistor to be exceeded. An increase in distortion will probably result from the change in the operating point with increased temperature for constant-current bias. Although more difficult and expensive to achieve, constant-current bias seems to be the only safe alternative for stability. An absolute constant-current bias is not possible under practical conditions; an intermediate bias condition like that shown in Fig. 5.16 is normally obtained.

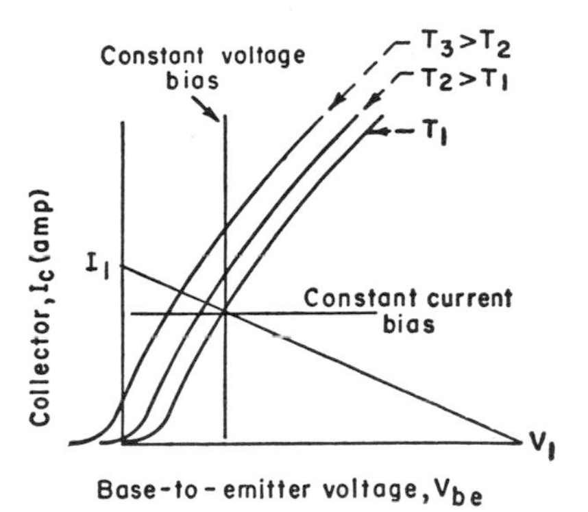

Fig. 5.16. Effect on bias of changes in temperature.

Figure 5.17(A) gives a circuit for obtaining an intermediate bias. This bias arrangement may be designed as follows. First, R_1 is selected such that all the emitter current flows through it, and that the voltage drop across R_1 directly reduces the maximum output voltage. Then an equivalent internal resistance $R_{11} = V_1/I_1$ is determined as the desired intermediate bias line as indicated in Fig. 5.16. This must equal the equivalent internal resistance of the bias circuit, or

$$R_{11} = \frac{R_1 R_2}{R_1 + R_2} \tag{4}$$

This equation determines R_2. Since V_1 is the open-circuit voltage of the bias circuit, V_2 can be calculated from

$$V_2 = \frac{R_1 + R_2}{R_1} V_1 \tag{5}$$

This design is for no voltage drop between the base and ground such as when the transistor is driven by a transformer. When the base return is completed by a resistor, the base current will cause a voltage

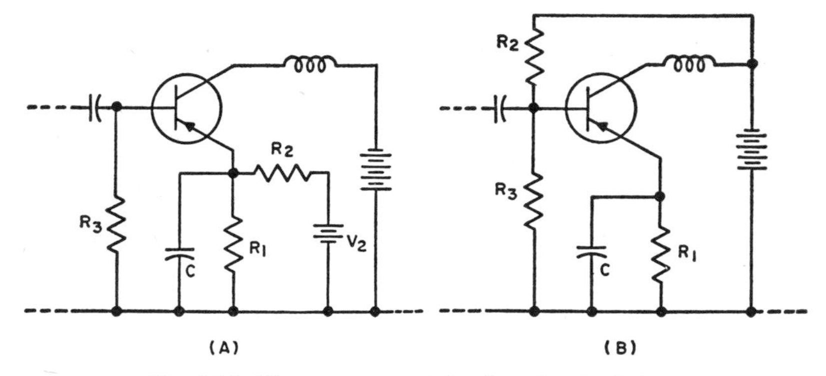

Fig. 5.17. Bias arrangement for class-A output stage.

bias $I_B R_3$, which the bias circuit must also provide. Capacitor C may be chosen to give the desired by-pass characteristics, or may be omitted to produce negative feedback and reduce distortion. The calculations for the above output stage are as follows. The emitter current will be about 100 ma. Assuming that an output voltage loss of 1 v may be tolerated, $R_1 = 10$ ohms. Then $V_1 = -1$ v and $I_1 = -200$ ma from the desired intermediate bias line. Then $R_{11} = 5$ ohms, $R_2 = 10$ ohms, and $V_2 = 2$ v. Assume that a 3 v battery is employed for V_2; then the drop across R_3 may be -0.5 v. Figure 5.12 shows that for a collector current of -100 ma, $\alpha_{CB} =$ about -30, from which $I_B = -3.3$ ma. Therefore

$$R_3 = \frac{-0.5}{-3.3 \times 10^{-3}} = 150 \quad \text{ohms} \tag{6}$$

Figure 5.17(B) illustrates a biasing circuit where the collector supply voltage produces the bias. This bias circuit may be designed like the previous one. The design is completed by referring the intermediate bias line of Fig. 5.16 to the base characteristics.

Class B Output Stage. In a manner like that employed for vacuum tubes, one can obtain the composite transfer characteristics for a class

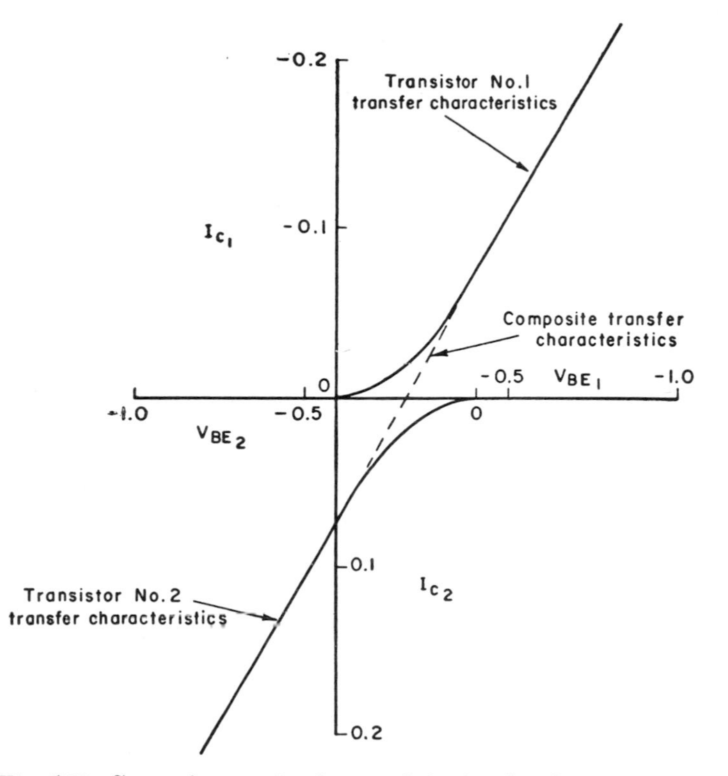

Fig. 5.18. Composite transfer characteristics for class-B output stage.

B output stage. The composite transfer characteristics are given in Fig. 5.18, which was determined from Fig. 5.14. Distortion measurements can determine graphically the correct common base-to-emitter bias for minimum crossover distortion, or an oscilloscope which displays the composite transfer characteristics can provide the proper bias setting. Too small bias results in excessive crossover distortion. Too large a bias voltage causes a larger quiescent collector current, and the amplifier operates class AB.

One can determine the detailed operation of a class B output stage by the method employed for vacuum tubes. The approximate calculations for the same transistors as for the class A output stage are as follows. Assuming the worst possible condition, for a square wave output with an amplitude equal to one-half the supply direct voltage, the collector of each transistor will dissipate power equivalent to

$$\frac{1}{2} \cdot \frac{V_{CS}}{2} \cdot \frac{I_{C\,max}}{2} \tag{7}$$

If the supply direct voltage is -12 v and the permissible power dissipation is 1.2 w, then $I_{C\,max}$ becomes -800 ma. For a sine wave signal

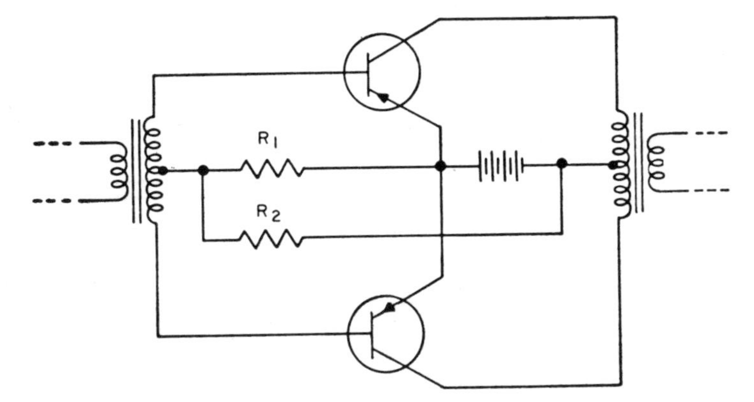

Fig. 5.19. Bias arrangement for class-B output stage.

$I_{C\,max}$ would be approximately -1 amp. Since the calculations are only approximate, the smaller value was chosen. For maximum power output the load resistance becomes 15 ohms for each transistor, or 60 ohms from collector-to-collector. A power output of 4.8 w will be achieved from the two transistors. The input power will be determined largely by the drop-off of the direct current amplification factor. Specific transistor characteristics and circuit configuration will yield more accurate calculations. As in class A output stage the equivalent composite transfer characteristics can include the effect of a finite source resistance.

As shown in the typical circuit of Fig. 5.19, it is easier to bias a class B stage than a class A stage. Figure 5.20 indicates that the required base bias voltage becomes smaller as the temperature increases. For the circuit of Fig. 5.19 the base bias tends to increase as the temperature rises, since the base current normally decreases with a temperature increase. The quiescent collector current will increase because of these two effects. The design of the class B stage must take the above into account, or the maximum rating of the transistor may be exceeded. Stability may be achieved by substituting a temperature-sensitive resistor for R_1 or R_2.

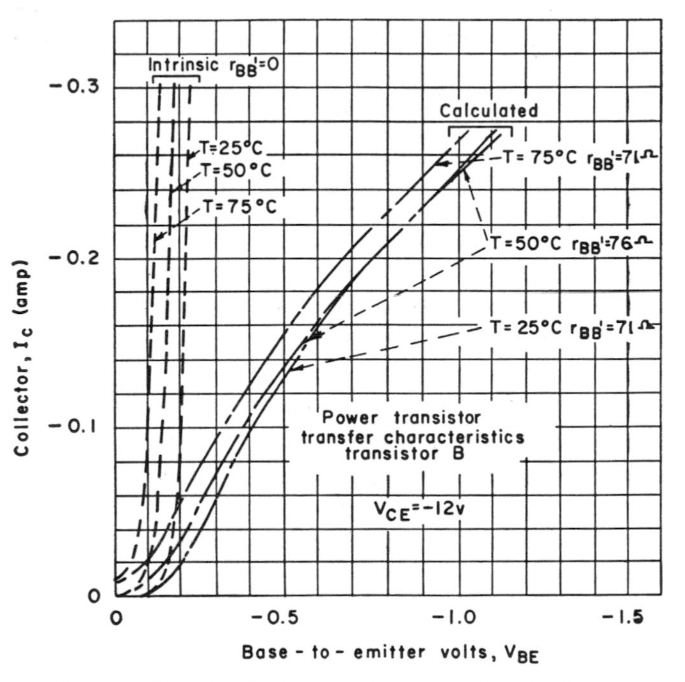

Fig. 5.20. Variation of static transfer characteristics with temperature.

Power transistors may be employed in complementary symmetry circuits, which are discussed in Chapter 12.

8. *Type X-78 P-N-P power junction transistor*[7]

The Type X-78 power junction transistor is reputed to be the first commercially available power junction transistor. It was specifically designed for class B audio circuits requiring 2 w of power output. In the class B circuit shown in Fig. 5.21, a driving power of 200 mw produces an output power of more than 2 w for a power gain of over 10 db at an efficiency higher than 50 per cent. At this power level no heat sink is required. With a heat sink the maximum collector dissipation is 4.5 w for each transistor.

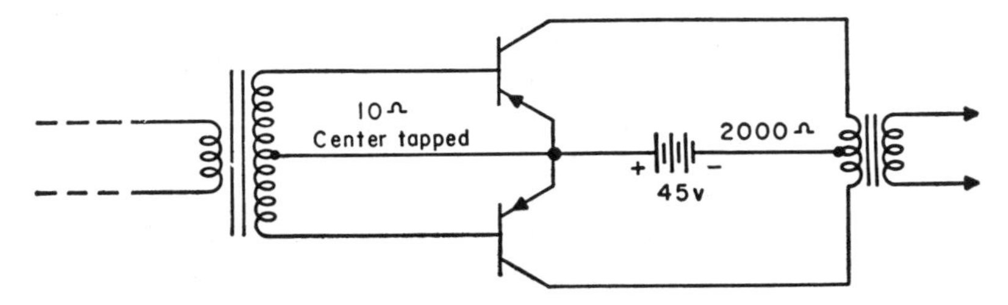

Fig. 5.21. Typical class-B circuit for two Type X-78 P-N-P power junction transistors.

At reduced ratings the X-78 power transistor may be operated as a class A power amplifier with an output of 0.6 w without a heat sink, and 1.0 w with a heat sink.

9. *Type 2N57 P-N-P power junction transistor*[8]

Although it is only $\frac{1}{2}$ in. in diameter and $\frac{5}{16}$ in. thick, the Type 2N57 power transistor has a collector dissipation of 20 w at 70°F. This comparatively large collector dissipation is achieved by providing an 8-32 machine screw to fasten the metal shell of the transistor to a chassis or to cooling fins to act as a heat sink. The collector dissipation depends upon maintaining the base of the transistor shell to the desired temperature limit as shown in Fig. 5.22.

The maximum power output for class A operation is 5 w, for push-pull is 10 w for two transistors, and for d-c switching circuits is 40 w. Under typical operating conditions for class B push-pull with a collector voltage of 28 v the maximum power output is 10 w for a grounded emitter power gain of 12.5 db. For lower power levels the gain is greater.

The maximum collector current is rated at 800 ma. The maximum collector voltage is −60 v for the grounded-base circuit. In the grounded-emitter circuit the collector voltage is limited to −30 v.

This may be exceeded under certain circumstances, such as in class B push-pull operation, in which case the base becomes positive with respect to the emitter during the time the transistor is subjected to its peak voltage. This peak voltage must in no case exceed −60 v.

At I_c equal to 250 ma, r_e is approximately 1 ohm, r_b is about 40 ohms, and r_c is approximately 7000 ohms.

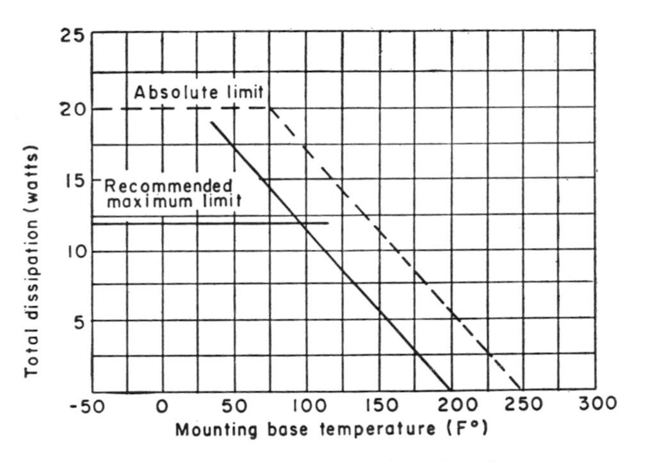

Fig. 5.22. Allowable dissipation as a function of temperature.

References

1. R. M. Ryder and R. J. Kircher, "Some Circuit Aspects of the Transistor," *Bell System Tech. J.*, Vol. XXVIII, July 1949, pp. 367–401.

2. K. D. Smith, "Properties of Junction Transistors," *Tele-Tech and Electronic Industries*, Vol. XII, No. 1, Jan. 1953, pp. 76–77.

3. R. N. Hall, "Power Rectifiers and Transistors," *Proc. IRE*, Vol. XL, No. 11, Nov. 1952, pp. 1512–1518.

4. John S. Saby, "Fused Impurity P-N-P Junction Transistors," *Proc. IRE*, Vol. XL, No. 11, Nov. 1952, pp. 1358–1360.

5. L. D. Armstrong and D. A. Jenny, "Behavior of Germanium Junction Transistors at Elevated Temperatures and Power Transistor Design," *Convention Record IRE*, 1953, Part 6, pp. 22–26.

6. L. J. Giacoletto, "Power Transistors," *1953 Transistor Short Course Proceedings,* Pennsylvania State College, pp. 17–1 to 17–32
7. Transistor Products, Inc., Boston, Mass., *Type X-78 P-N-P Power Junction Transistor, Data Sheet.*
8. Howard T. Mooers, *Recent Development in Power Transistors,* Minneapolis-Honeywell Research Center, Hopkins, Minn.

Chapter 6

MEASUREMENTS OF TRANSISTOR CHARACTERISTICS

1. *Introduction*

A great deal of attention has been paid to equipment for measuring transistor characteristics. The test apparatus varies from elemental setups to quite elaborate racks of equipment. A selection of relatively simple, practical, and inexpensive test devices will be described in this chapter. The first piece of test equipment, the "Transtester," is the only one which is commercially available; the others are suggested as devices which the reader may construct.

2. *Precision measurement of small signal parameters*[1]

If we consider the transistor as a general four terminal network, we can write various relations between the network voltages and the network currents. If we take the currents as the independent variables of the network, we obtain the linear equations,

$$\left.\begin{aligned} v_1 &= r_{11}i_1 + r_{12}i_2 \\ v_2 &= r_{21}i_1 + r_{22}i_2 \end{aligned}\right\} \quad (1)$$

where the lower case v's and i's represent a-c signals and the r's are slopes of the curves we obtain by plotting each d-c voltage versus each d-c current with the other d-c current held constant. These r's are the parameters usually employed to describe the a-c circuit operation of a point-contact transistor.

However, if we take the input current i_1 and the output voltage v_2 of the network as independent variables and the input voltage v_1 and the output current i_2 as dependent variables, we get a different set of linear equations,

$$\left.\begin{aligned} v_1 &= h_{11}i_1 + h_{12}v_2 \\ i_2 &= h_{21}i_1 + h_{22}v_2 \end{aligned}\right\} \quad (2)$$

where the h's are known as the hybrid parameters. The parameter h_{11} is the input impedance in ohms with the output short-circuited, h_{12} is the reverse voltage gain or ratio of v_1 to v_2 with the input open-circuited, h_{21} is the forward current gain or ratio of i_2 to i_1 with the output short-circuited, and h_{22} is the output admittance in mhos with the input open-circuited. These parameters are comparatively easy to measure and are generally considered a better representation of a junction transistor than the r parameters.

The instrument to be described here is known as the "Transtester," is commercially available, and is designed primarily to measure the r parameters of point-contact transistors and the h parameters for junction transistors.

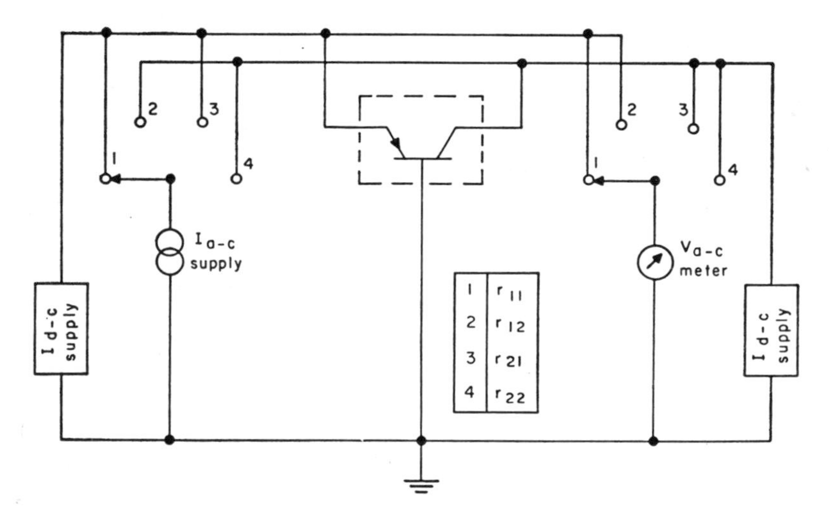

Fig. 6.1. Circuit for measuring r parameters.

As shown in Figs. 6.1 and 6.2 we can measure the previously defined small-signal parameters with an a-c voltmeter (or ammeter) by connecting calibrated a-c current and voltage sources together with appropriate d-c supplies. For instance, if we hold i_2 constant, $r_{11} = v_1/i_1$. The Transtester utilizes a frequency of 270 cps for the a-c measurements as a compromise between frequencies so low that transistor noise (and 60 cps pickup) are troublesome and frequencies where the reactive components of the transistor parameters become appreciable.

The conditions established for the measurement of the various parameters and the values of these parameters which the Transtester indicates are given in Table 3. We can select the parameter to be measured by a single switch which also connects the proper d-c supplies. The range switch controls the magnitude of the input a-c signal and equals 200 μa/R for the a-c current-source and 20 v/R for

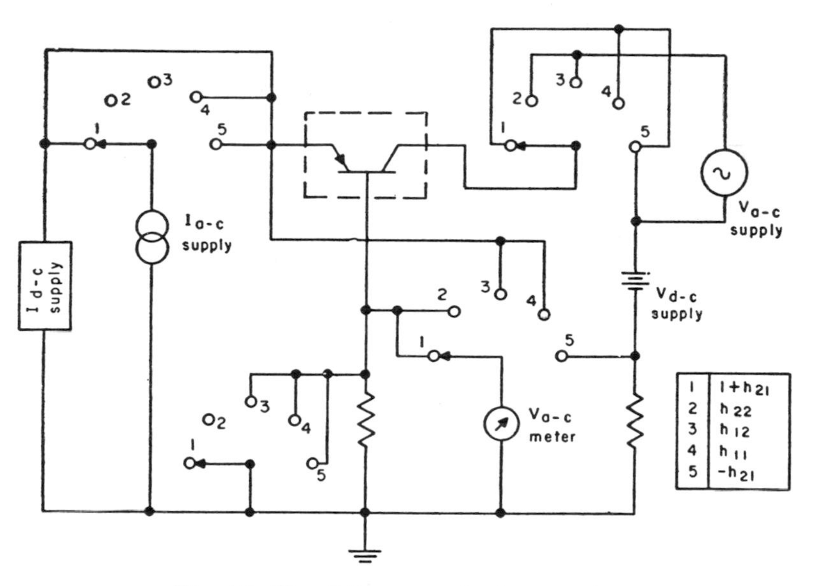

Fig. 6.2. Circuit for measuring h parameters.

the voltage-source. Here R is the setting of the range switch which has positions of 1.0, 2.5, 5.0, 10, 25, 50, 100, 250, 500, and 1000. Normally, we make measurements with R between 100 and 1000 corresponding to signal levels of about 1 μa or 100 mv. The input signal level and the a-c voltmeter sensitivity determine the constant C given in the last column of Table 3. Actually, $C = RM$, where R is defined above and M is the setting of the meter multiplier switch which has values of 0.1, 1.0, and 10. Only the intermediate sensitivity where $M = 1.0$ is required for typical transistors biased in the normal operating range. The 0.1 position gives greater sensitivity when we

TABLE 3. SUMMARY OF PARAMETER MEASUREMENTS BY THE TRANSTESTER

Parameter	Input signal (calibrated)	Condition established	Output signal (read)	Full scale meter reading
r_{11}	i_1	$i_2 = 0$	v_1	C* ohms
r_{12}	i_2	$i_1 = 0$	v_1	C ohms
r_{21}	i_1	$i_2 = 0$	$v_2/100$	$10^2\ C$ ohms
r_{22}	i_2	$i_1 = 0$	$v_2/100$	$10^2\ C$ ohms
h_{11}	i_1	$v_2 = 0$	v_1	C ohms
h_{12}	v_2	$i_1 = 0$	v_1	$10^{-5}\ C$ ohms
$-h_{21}$	i_1	$v_2 = 0$	$10i_2$	$10^{-1}\ C$ ohms
h_{22}	v_2	$i_1 = 0$	$1000i_2$	$10^{-8}\ C$ ohms
$1 + h_{21}$	i_1	$v_2 = 0$	$1000(i_1 + i_2)$	$10^{-3}\ C$ ohms

* The value of the constant C depends on the input signal magnitude and meter sensitivity, both of which may be varied by switches. For the equipment described C may be varied from 10^{-1} to 10^{+4} with three steps per decade.

desire to make measurements at very small input signal levels. We can take readings at higher signal levels by utilizing the meter in its least sensitive position where $M = 10$, if transistor noise produces excessive fluctuations.

The phase sensitive detector employed in the a-c voltmeter is an important feature of the equipment. Since we desire to measure only resistive parameters, we wish to make certain that only those components of the measured voltage or current which are in phase (or 180° out of phase) with the input a-c signal give an indication on the meter. Inaccuracies due to inevitable stray wiring capacities are considerably reduced by a phase detector. Also we can distinguish between negative and positive small-signal parameters.

The signal current and voltage source consists of a Wien bridge oscillator, the frequency of which we can vary 5 per cent from its nominal value of 270 cps by a front panel knob. We normally adjust the output amplitude for about 20 v at 40 ohms impedance level.

Figure 6.3 shows the schematic diagram of the phase detector which consists of an over-driven amplifier and two double diodes. During half of the reference cycle 100 v biases off the diodes and no current flows through the meter. On the other half cycle the diodes conduct strongly. With no signal, the zero adjustment balances the bridge circuit consisting of the four diodes and their resistors. Signals in phase with the oscillator reference voltage unbalance the bridge and cause a meter deflection. Signals 90° out of phase with the oscillator produce equal positive and negative currents during the conducting half cycle and therefore give no net deflection. Likewise, stray 60 cps pickup and random noise cause no average deflection, but excessive spurious voltages make the meter fluctuate about the true reading.

The d-c current-supplies utilize pentodes with large series cathode

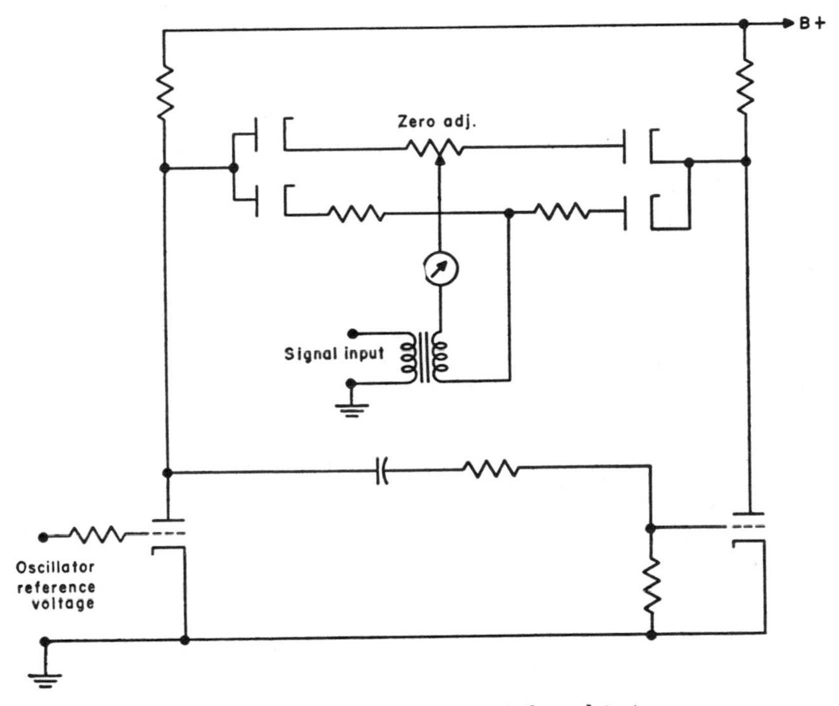

Fig. 6.3. Schematic diagram of phase detector.

resistors to give negative current feedback. These circuits have internal dynamic resistances of about 10 megohms. For a maximum load voltage of approximately 200 v we can adjust the output current of the supply between 0 and 15 ma of either polarity.

To measure transistor *h* parameters the collector terminal in Fig. 6.2 must be returned to either an a-c ground or an a-c generator through a low impedance. In the Transtester we can adjust the voltage from 0 to 100 v of either polarity for a maximum current of 35 ma.

The internal resistance is less than 5 ohms (plus a 10 ohm resistor for measuring a-c current). The injection of oscillator voltage into the feedback loop essentially adds an ideal a-c generator to the supply without increasing the impedance.

Meters indicating the input and output current and voltage continuously monitor the d-c operating point of the transistor under test. The input and output current meters both have seven current ranges (50 μa to 25 ma full scale), whereas the corresponding vacuum tube voltmeters have five ranges (100 mv to 25 v for input voltage and 1 v to 100 v for output voltage).

3. *A practical transistor current-gain meter*[2]

Figure 6.4 shows the circuit of a transistor tester for measuring the current gain of P-N-P junction transistors in a grounded-emitter connection. The current gain is defined as the ratio of output current into a zero impedance load, to input current from an infinite impedance source. The currents referred to are the alternating signal currents, and do not take into account the direct bias currents. Typical values of this current gain range from 10 to 50.

Only the actual circuitry associated with the transistor need be constructed, since this is employed with a standard signal generator and a high impedance voltmeter.

This transistor tester is battery powered with a choice of either a 1.5 v or a 6 v supply.

The tester provides three ways of connecting the transistor. One socket has equal spacings, one socket has the collector position widely spaced, and three binding posts can be utilized when a socket is not convenient.

To test a transistor, connect it in the circuit, a signal generator to the SIG. GEN. terminals, and a high impedance voltmeter to the VOLTMETER terminals. Set the signal generator at a convenient frequency such as 1000 cps, throw switch S_2 to the IN position, and adjust the input to 1 v or some other suitable level. Then throw S_2 to the OUT position, and turn S_1 to position 1 or 3 depending on whether you desire the 1.5 or the 6 v supply. The meter will read the output current directly in milliamperes, since the load resistor is 1000 ohms in either of these positions. The input current is 10 μa for 1 v from the signal generator, and hence the current gain can be determined. The required measuring conditions are fulfilled, since the 100,000 ohm input impedance is practically an infinite impedance compared with the input impedance of the transistor, whereas the 1000 ohm load resistance is negligible compared to the output impedance of the transistor. We can adjust the base bias current by R_6, and there is usually a setting for which the gain is maximum.

We may utilize positions 2, 4, and 5 on S_1 to check the behavior of

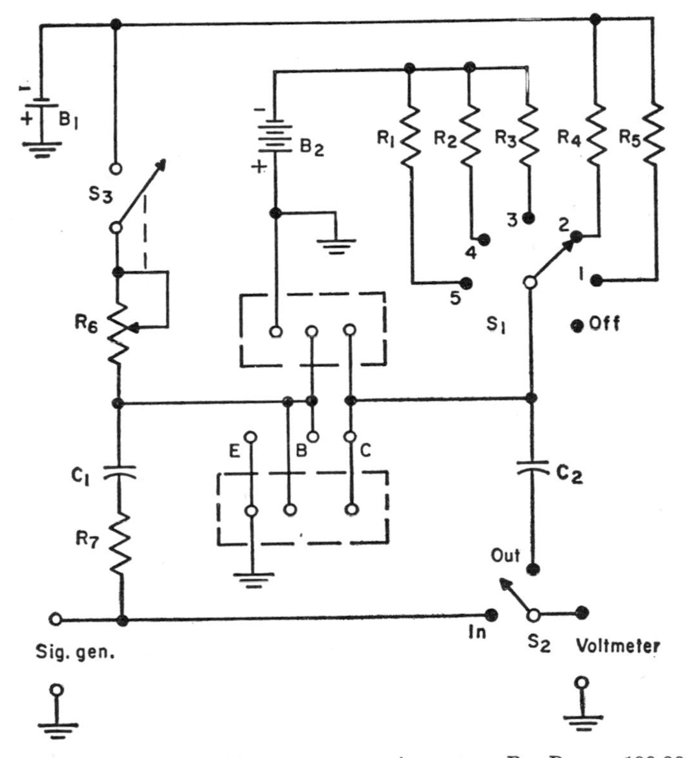

Fig. 6.4. Circuit of transistor current-gain tester. R_1, R_7 are 100,000-ohm $\frac{1}{2}$-w resistors, 5%; R_2, R_4 are 10,000-ohm $\frac{1}{2}$-w resistors, 5%; R_3, R_5 are 1000-ohm $\frac{1}{2}$-w resistors, 5%; R_6 is 500,000-ohm 2-w potentiometer (with switch S_3); C_1, C_2 are 1-μf 100-v capacitors; S_1 is S.P. six-position switch (Centralab 1401); S_2 is S.P.D.T. toggle switch; S_3 is S.P.S.T. switch (on R_6); B_1 is penlight cell, $1\frac{1}{2}$ v; B_2 is four penlight cells in series, 6 v; sockets are 5-pin in-line subminiature (Cinch-Jones 2H5—this type is recommended although different types were originally used. Unused holes can be plugged, if desired, to make these do for either transistors with the RETMA pin arrangement or with equally spaced pins).

the transistor when large load resistors are desirable such as when voltage gain is important. These positions do not measure the current gain directly, because the load resistance is no longer negligible.

Although this circuit is for testing P-N-P transistors, it is only necessary to reverse the polarities of the batteries to check N-P-N transistors. A switch could be included in the circuit for this purpose if desired.

4. *Oscilloscopic display of transistor characteristic curves*[3]

Figure 6.5 gives the circuit of a transistor curve tracer. An accurate characteristic curve may be obtained in less than a minute with this small device. One can obtain a complete family of curves in less than five minutes with suitable additional equipment.

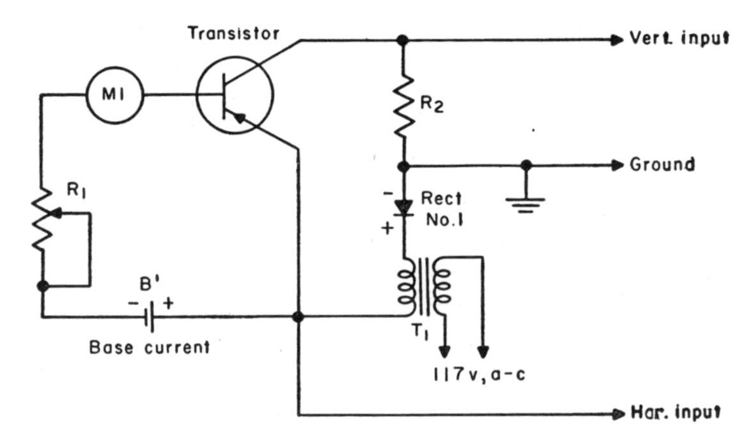

Fig. 6.5. Circuit of transistor curve tracer. R_1 is 50,000-ohm potentiometer; R_2 is 100-ohm $\frac{1}{2}$-w resistor; M_1 is 0–1 ma, or 0–500 μa meters; B_1 is 1.5-v penlight cell; T_1 is 6.3 v at 1-amp filter transformer; Rect_1 is 25-ma selenium rectifier.

The base current for the transistor is supplied by a small penlight cell, and the potentiometer R_1 adjusts the base current to the required value as indicated by the meter M_1. A pulsating direct voltage is applied to the emitter and collector. The secondary of a filament transformer T_1 supplies 6.3 v, which is rectified by a half-wave selenium rectifier, RECT._1, to give pulsating direct voltage. The 100 ohm resistor R_2 is connected in series with the collector to develop a voltage directly proportional to the collector current. However, this resistance is too small to affect the circuit operation otherwise.

The voltage across R_2 is applied to the vertical input terminals of the oscilloscope, producing a vertical deflection proportional to the collector current variations. The pulsating voltage between the collector and emitter of the transistor is applied to the horizontal input terminals of the oscilloscope. This constitutes a horizontal sweep directly proportional to the collector voltage variations.

Figure 6.6 illustrates the waveform of the pulsating voltage applied to the emitter-collector circuit. This waveform may be observed on the oscilloscope by moving the horizontal input lead shown in Fig.

Fig. 6.6. Waveform of pulsating voltage applied to the emitter-collector circuit.

6.5 to the vertical input terminals and employing the regular linear sweep of the scope. However, this built-in sweep is not required to trace transistor characteristic curves, and the horizontal amplifier should be switched to the horizontal input position when testing transistors.

Figures 6.7(A) and 6.7(B) present typical characteristic curves obtained with this equipment. Figure 6.7(A) is for a base current of 100 μa, whereas Fig. 6.7(B) was made with a base current of 20 μa.

All the parts, including the penlight cell, may be mounted on a Bud CB-1616 chassis, or equivalent. Terminals are provided for connections to the oscilloscope and to the base current meter. The tran-

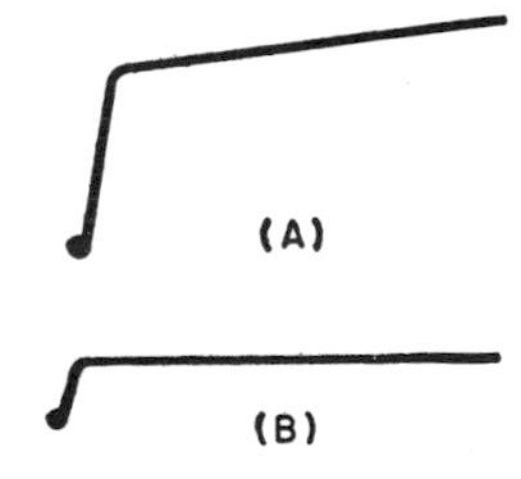

Fig. 6.7. Collector characteristic curve for (A) base current of 100 μa, and (B) for base current of 20 μa.

sistor socket may be a standard subminiature tube socket, a terminal strip to which the transistor leads may be temporarily soldered, a screw-type terminal strip, or permanently mounted spring clips. However, care must be taken not to overheat the transistor if the leads are soldered into position.

The device was designed to obtain the characteristic curves of P-N-P junction transistors over a fairly limited range of collector voltages. Another transformer may be substituted for T_1, having a larger secondary voltage, such as 12.6 v or 25.2 v, when larger changes in collector voltage are required.

When ordinary point-contact transistors are to be tested, a different transformer may be substituted for T_1 as mentioned above. For measuring N-P-N junction transistors, the connections to the battery B_1 and to the selenium rectifier RECT._1 should be reversed. This may be accomplished by suitable switches, or by making the battery and the selenium rectifier plug-in units, suitably marked P-N-P and N-P-N, which may be reversed in their jacks. These reversals are necessary to provide voltages of the proper polarity for the transistor electrodes.

In operation, the transistor is inserted in its socket (or connected in the circuit), and the required base current, as indicated by the meter M_1, is obtained by varying R_1. The desired image size on the oscilloscope is produced by adjusting the vertical gain and horizontal gain controls.

For accurate results, the scope should be calibrated to read actual milliamperes current and applied voltage by placing a transparent graph scale over the screen and adjusting the vertical gain and horizontal gain to known values. A known alternating voltage is applied to the vertical input and horizontal input terminals of the scope, and the vertical gain and horizontal gain controls, respectively, are adjusted for a given deflection. No changes should be made in the settings of the horizontal gain and vertical gain controls while a characteristic curve (or family of curves) is being run, after the above controls have been set.

5. *Quick evaluation of junction transistor characteristics by oscilloscopic display*[4]

This curve tracer displays two voltage-current curves of a junction transistor simultaneously on an oscilloscope by the switching action of a relay. The interpretation of the curves is simple, and can be done quickly.

On the oscilloscope screen, the voltage applied between the collector of a transistor and either the base or the emitter is displayed as the abscissa and the current flowing through the collector is displayed as the ordinate. Also, the abscissa itself ($I_c = 0$) is shown.

For the first curve, the transistor is connected in the grounded-base circuit with open emitter. A rectified 60 cps signal is then applied between collector and base. The I_c versus V_c characteristic is displayed in the usual manner on an oscilloscope as shown in Fig. 6.8. The distance from the $I_c = 0$ line is I_{co}, the collector current for zero emitter current. The slope of this curve is approximately $1/r_c$. The

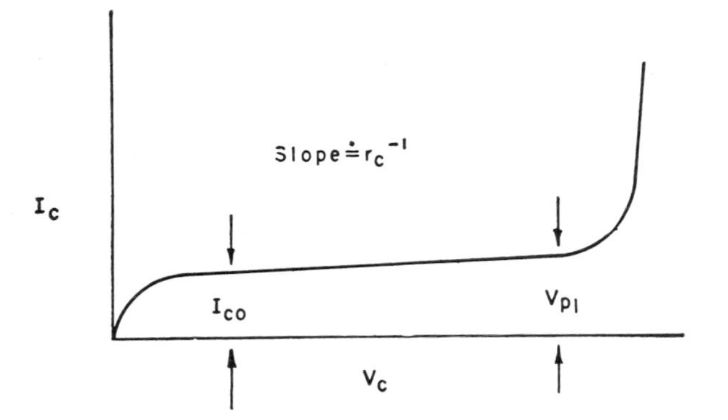

Fig. 6.8. I_c versus V_c characteristic for $I_e = 0$.

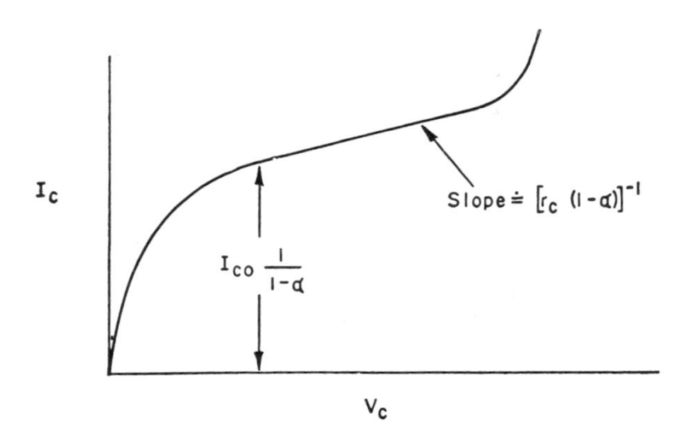

Fig. 6.9. I_c versus V_c characteristic for $I_b = 0$.

voltage at which the collector diode breaks down is the peak inverse voltage V_{PI} which appears in the display as an abrupt change in slope.

For the second curve, the transistor is connected in the grounded-emitter circuit with open base, and hence another I_c versus V_c characteristic is obtained as represented in Fig. 6.9. The distance from the zero axis is $I_c = I_{co}/(1 - a)$ and the slope is $1/r_c(1 - a)$.

Combining the scope patterns produced by these two circuits gives us a great deal of information about the transistor being tested. Figure 6.10 shows the pattern on the scope. The ratio of the ordinate of curve E at any voltage to the ordinate of curve B is

$$\frac{I_{co}/(1 - a)}{I_{co}} = \frac{1}{1 - a}$$

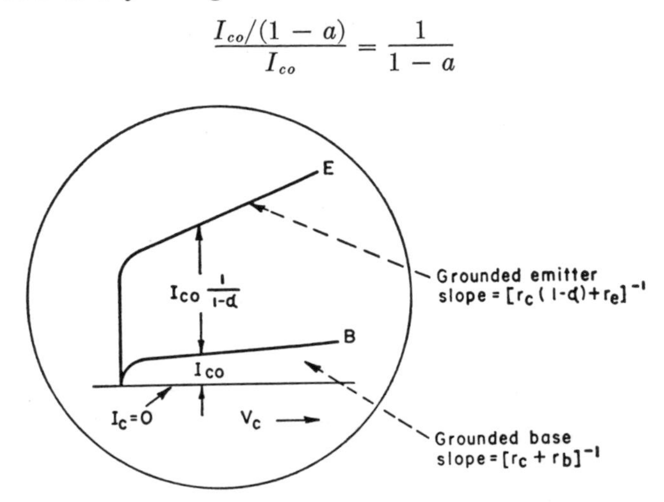

Fig. 6.10. Scope pattern produced by transistor under test.

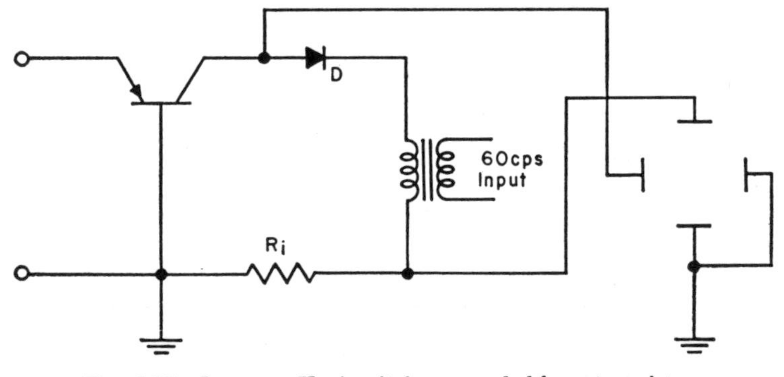

Fig. 6.11. I_c versus V_c circuit for grounded-base transistor.

from which we may determine $a/(1 - a)$, the current amplification of the grounded-emitter stage, if the approximation is not already good enough.

The variation of $1/(1 - a)$ or r_c with operating voltage is shown and the position of the knee is indicated.

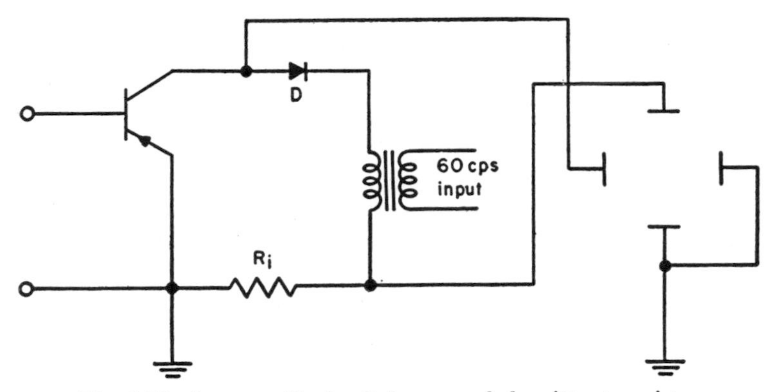

Fig. 6.12. I_c versus V_c circuit for grounded-emitter transistor.

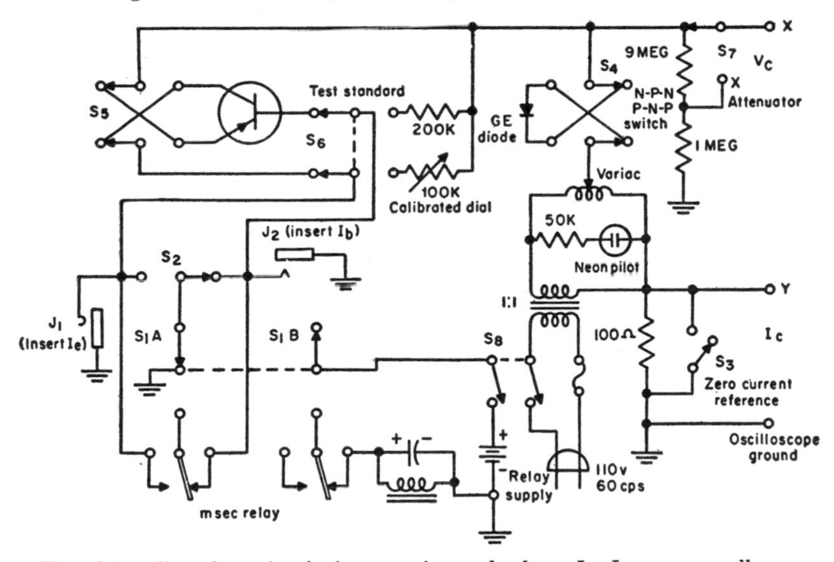

Fig. 6.13. Complete circuit for transistor checker. J_1, J_2 are normally open jacks: S_1 is a manual relay (D.P.D.T.); S_2, manual operation (S.P.D.T.); S_3, zero current (S.P.S.T., spring return); S_4, P-N-P/N-P-N (D.P.D.T.); S_5 is to reverse transistor (D.P.D.T.); S_6, test, standard (D.P.D.T.); S_7, an X attenuator (S.P.D.T.); S_8, power.

With this information we can choose a reasonable operating point for the transistor, properly limit the maximum inverse voltage for the collector diode, and decide whether the parameters and the linearity of the transistor are satisfactory for a given circuit.

Figure 6.11 shows the basic circuit for displaying the I_c versus V_c curve for grounded base. The diode D cuts off the collector current when the 60 cps sweep biases the transistor collector in the forward direction. We can feed in any desired value of emitter current at the input, or leave the emitter open to give the I_{co} curve for the grounded-base transistor. Figure 6.12 indicates similarly the grounded-emitter circuit. Once more the diode D prevents large currents from flowing through the transistor when the collector is driven positive. Figure 6.13 gives the complete circuit for a curve tracer designed to display the above curves.

The 100 kilohm calibrated potentiometer provides a known slope to compare with the value of $r_c(1 - a)$ for the transistor under test. The 200 kilohm resistance permits a rough comparison with the r_c of the transistor.

6. *Measurement of input impedance of transistor amplifier*

Figure 6.14 illustrates the circuit employed in measuring the input impedance of a transistor amplifier. A generator frequency of 1000

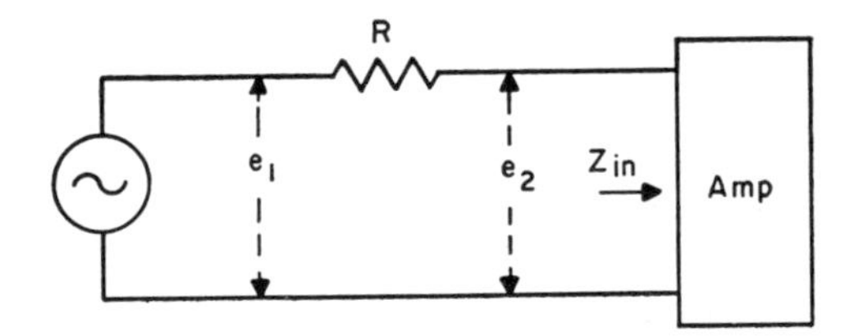

Fig. 6.14. Circuit for measuring input impedance of transistor amplifier.

cps is convenient for audio frequency amplifiers. The voltage e_2 normally should not exceed about 0.1 v rms. There are two variations of this method. In both schemes, R is a fixed resistor whose resitance is accurately known. For example, it might be 1000 ohms. The voltage e_2 is measured with a calibrated oscilloscope or a high-impedance a-c vacuum-tube voltmeter, and then the voltage across R is similarly read. By proportion, $Z_{in}/e_2 = R/\text{voltage across } R$, or

$$Z_{in} = \frac{e_2}{\text{voltage across } R} R \tag{3}$$

where Z_{in} = input impedance.

Where it is not feasible to remove one connection of the scope or vacuum tube voltmeter from ground to measure the voltage across R, the voltage e_1 may be measured instead. Then

$$Z_{in} = \frac{e_2}{e_1 - e_2} R \tag{4}$$

This method assumes that Z_{in} is essentially resistive.

7. *A transistor noise test set*[5]

The application of junction transistors to low input level audio amplifiers, such as hearing aids, requires the evaluation of the noise level under conditions simulating actual use. Hence we should operate a transistor under test in a circuit equivalent to that of the application.

Noise level is preferably expressed as *noise figure*. This is approximately equal to the total noise power in the output divided by that portion of the output noise power that results from thermal agitation in the input resistance.

Typical instantaneous characteristics of transistor noise and thermal noise are indicated in Fig. 6.15, which is sketched from observation of scope patterns. When first connected into a circuit a transistor has a noise level of a certain starting value. The noise level of some transistors increases appreciably within the first hour of operation. Figure 6.15 indicates such an increase. If we break the collector current even for an instant, the noise generally returns to the starting value. "Pips" occur in some transistors. They are very annoying to a listener but make little difference in the reading of an average indicating voltmeter such as a Ballantine Model 300.

The lower portion of Fig. 6.15 shows thermal noise. It has a definite statistical pattern, in which the equivalent rms voltage is a little less than one-third of the peak voltage.

Previously, transistor noise, like thermal noise, has been measured on an rms meter or on an average reading meter calibrated in rms volts for sinusoidal waveforms. This is obviously unsuited to evaluating the annoyance factor of pips. Therefore the peak-to-peak Ballantine Model 305 meter is utilized.

The peak value of transistor noise is compared to the peak value of a sine wave voltage inserted in the input. The frequency band is not limited to 100 cps but is extended to include the hearing aid band as nearly as possible.

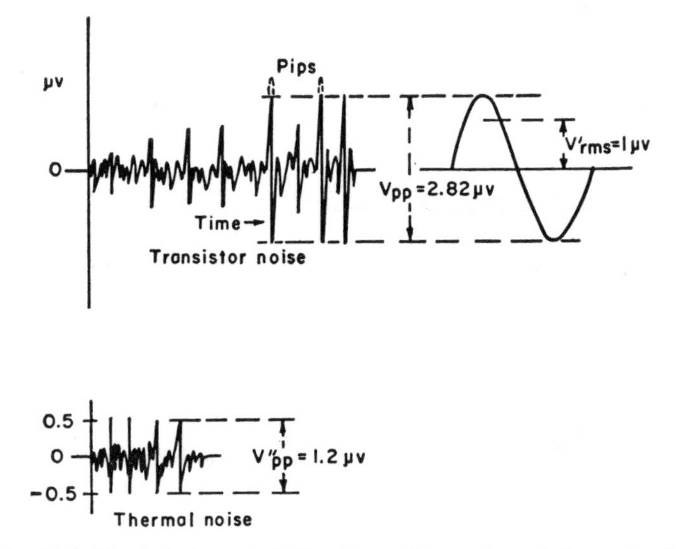

Fig. 6.15. Typical characteristics of transistor noise and thermal noise.

A block diagram of the noise measurement system is shown in Fig. 6.16. A calibrated insert voltage generator is excluded by the comparison switch when the noise alone is observed. An insert voltage 20 db above transistor noise voltage is utilized to obtain a reading unaffected by noise. The generator has a specific impedance, for which we can calculate the theoretical thermal noise voltage.

A block indicates the transistor circuit complete with its power supply. To establish a suitable aging cycle, several transistors are operated on individual circuits, and then inserted one at a time into the test system.

An amplifier having a gain of about 40 db, such as the Ballantine Decade Amplifier Model 220-A, is required. This is followed by a band limiting filter.

We can read the insert voltage at the same point of the meter scale as the corresponding noise voltage, by attenuating the output 20 db when reading the insert voltage. The second circuit of the comparison switch does this automatically.

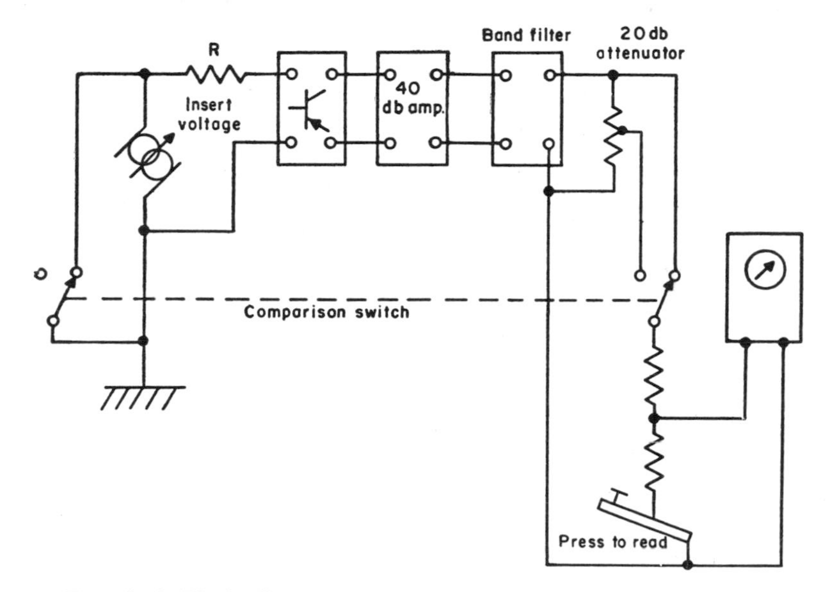

Fig. 6.16. Block diagram of transistor noise-measurement system.

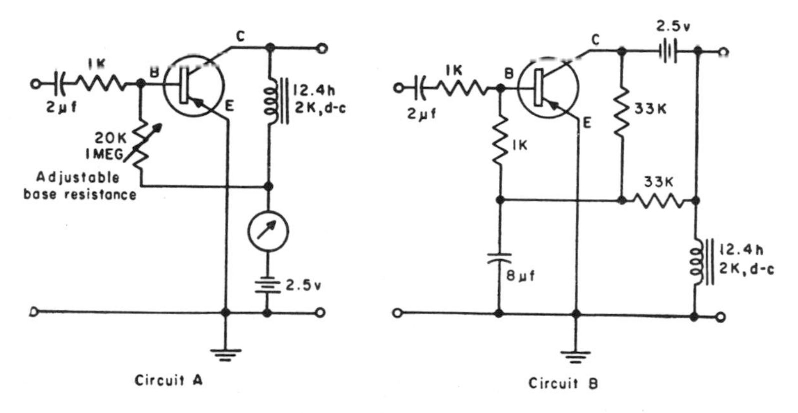

Fig. 6.17. Two alternative circuits for the transistor box in the block diagram.

A press-to-read key with a resistor network across the voltmeter keeps it from deflecting off scale during the switching operation.

We thus compare transistor noise and insert noise on an equal peak-to-peak basis at the output of the transistor. Hence we may compare the equivalent transistor noise referred to the input, the insert sinusoidal voltage, and the thermal noise voltage with each other as if they all occurred in the input loop.

Two alternative circuits for the transistor box in the block diagram are shown in Fig. 6.17. Each employs a grounded-emitter circuit with the battery supply polarized for the particular type of transistor. In circuit *A* we adjust the collector current individually to an assumed value of 0.5 ma. In circuit *B* the collector current is self-compensated to approximately 0.5 ma for the inspection of a large number of units.

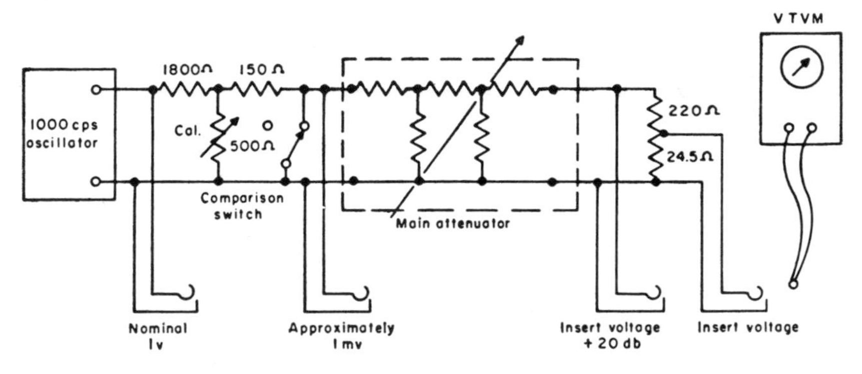

Fig. 6.18. Complete insert voltage control system.

Figure 6.18 shows the complete insert voltage control system. This includes a 1000 cps oscillator which is set arbitrarily at 1 v, a network by which we can adjust the input to the main attenuator to approximately 1 mv, a 45 db attenuator with 30 steps, and a resistance load which is divided to attenuate the output of the attenuator exactly 20 db. This divider provides a point at which to check the insert voltage without a high gain amplifier. We connect the meter across the total load and thus read 20 db above the insert voltage. We measure this with the same peak-to-peak meter used for noise, and allow for the 2.82 to 1 or 9 db difference between peak-to-peak and rms voltage. The main attenuator is calibrated with an inner scale indicating the rms insert voltage, and an outer scale indicating the noise level as 20 db below the rms insert voltage.

The absolute calibration, in relation to thermal noise, requires an evaluation of the equivalent frequency band.

The frequency band filter and amplifier is shown in Fig. 6.19. Part of the filter precedes the amplifier and the rest follows it. The top of this figure also gives the overall frequency characteristic of this

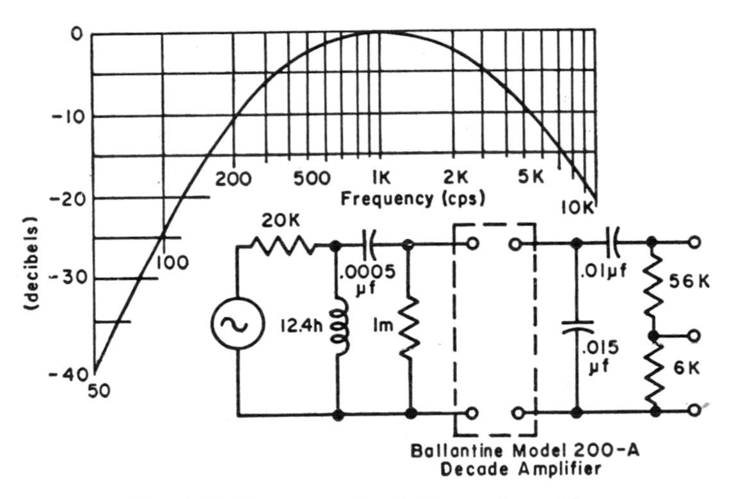

Fig. 6.19. Frequency band filter and amplifier.

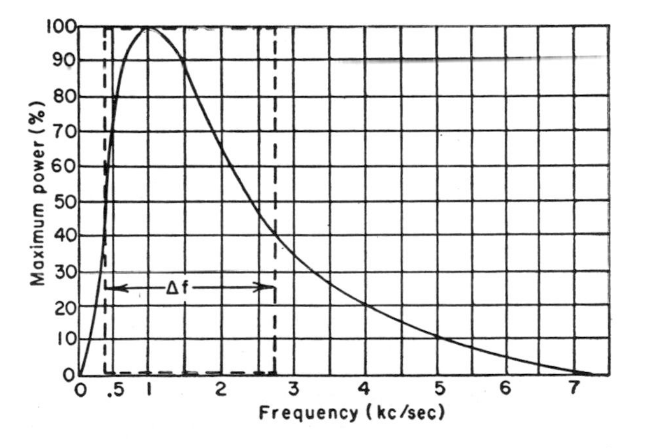

Fig. 6.20. Equivalent rectangular pass band of thermal noise.

network. The lows are attenuated 40 db at 50 cps and the highs are down 20 db at 10,000 cps.

Figure 6.20 represents the equivalent frequency band for thermal noise which was determined graphically. The abscissa has a linear frequency scale, because thermal noise power is directly proportional to bandwidth. The ordinate is the relative power as a function of frequency. The equivalent pass band was determined by graphical integration to select lower and upper limits, between which the integrated power was the same as that for the original characteristic. The equivalent pass band is 2300 cps wide, extending from 450 to 2750 cps.

We can calculate the thermal or Johnson noise as

$$V''_{\text{rms}} = 2\sqrt{KTR(\Delta f)} \tag{5}$$

where k equals Boltzmann's constant of 1.347×10^{-23} joules per degree absolute, T equals absolute temperature and is assumed to be 300°K, R equals source resistance of 1000 ohms, and Δf equals equivalent bandwidth of 2300 cps. Substituting the above values, V''_{rms} equals 0.193 μv rms. The statistical properties of thermal noise are fairly well known. The peak-to-peak value is approximately

$$\begin{aligned} V''_{\text{p-p}} &= 2 \times 3.1\ V''_{\text{rms}} \\ &= 2 \times 3.1 \times .193 \times 10^{-6} \\ &= 1.2 \times 10^{-6} \text{ v or } 1.2\ \mu\text{v}. \end{aligned} \tag{6}$$

We must now calculate the ratio of transistor noise power to thermal noise power. Normally this is taken as the ratio of mean square transistor noise voltage to mean square thermal noise voltage and is called the noise figure. However, since the ratio of peak-to-rms voltage of actual transistor noise is not a fixed value for every transistor, root-mean-square values are not feasible. The ratio of peak-to-rms voltage is known for thermal noise. Therefore we can express the relative noise powers as the squares of the respective peak voltages, or

$$\left(\frac{\text{Peak of transistor noise voltage}}{\text{Peak of thermal noise voltage}}\right)^2 \tag{7}$$

We can now evaluate numerical values for the condition given in Fig. 6.15 where the attenuator dial reads 0 db, corresponding to 1 μv rms and to 2.82 μv peak-to-peak. The above ratio thus becomes

$$\left(\frac{2.82}{1.2}\right)^2 = 5.5 \quad \text{or} \quad 7.4 \quad \text{db}$$

The dial reading on the main attenuator corresponding to the reference value of thermal noise is hence -7.4 db with reference to 1 μv rms.

A practical limit for first stage transistors has been set at 5 db or 1 μv which corresponds to a peak noise figure of 12.4 db. Some of the transistors measured had a peak noise figure as low as 2 to 4 db. We can relate these peak noise figures to the narrow band noise figures if we know the spectral distribution of noise and the ratio of peak-to-rms noise. If we assume a spectral distribution of noise power inversely proportional to frequency and a ratio of peak-to-rms noise voltage the same as for thermal noise, the 1 kc/sec narrow band noise figures are found to be 2 db higher than the peak noise figures expressed above.

This noise measurement system simulates the conditions of the amplifier application accurately and permits grading of transistors for the various stages of an audio amplifier.

References

1. R. Johnson, D. Humez, and G. Knight, Jr., "Precision Transistor Test Equipment," *Tele-Tech and Electronic Industries*, Vol. XIII, No. 2, Feb. 1954, pp. 74–75.
2. H. L. Armstrong, "Transistor Tester," *Radio and Television News*, Vol. LI, No. 5, May 1954, p. 39.
3. Warren Philbrook, "Obtaining Transistor Characteristic Curves," *Radio and Television News*, Vol. L, No. 3, Sept. 1953, pp. 66–67.
4. V. P. Mathis, and J. S. Schaffner, "Quick Evaluation of Junction Transistor Characteristics by Oscilloscopic Display," *Convention Record IRE*, 1953, Part 9, pp. 72–74.
5. Richard W. Carlisle, Harry A. Pearson, and William H. Greenbaum, "A Simple Transistor Noise Test Set," *Convention Record IRE*, 1954 National Convention, Part 10, pp. 88–91.

Chapter 7

METHODS OF ANALYSIS OF TRANSISTORS AND TRANSISTOR CIRCUITS

1. *The three basic transistor amplifier circuits*

Since the ordinary transistor has three electrodes, there are three possible ways of connecting it in a circuit. The grounded-base circuit[1] (or common-base circuit) is shown in Fig. 7.1. This circuit has a low input impedance and a high output impedance. The emitter of a tran-

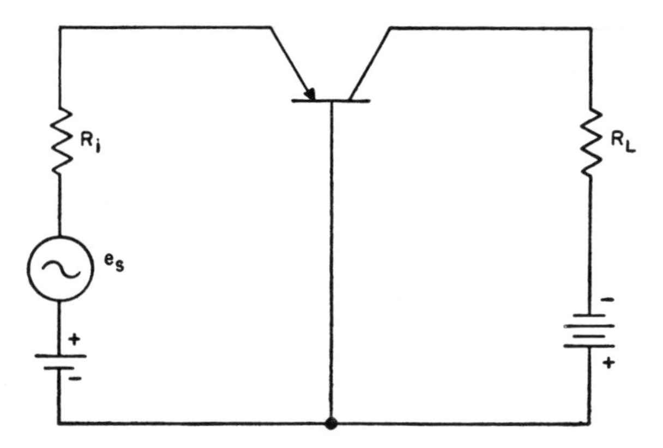

Fig. 7.1. Grounded-base transistor amplifier circuit.

sistor is somewhat similar to the cathode of a vacuum tube, because the emitter is the source of the current carriers in the transistor. Likewise, the base of the transistor resembles the grid of the vacuum tube. The collector is like the plate of a vacuum tube. In this circuit the phase of the signal remains unchanged. Therefore, aside from the low input impedance, the grounded-base circuit of the transistor corresponds to the grounded-grid circuit of a vacuum tube.

Figure 7.2 describes the grounded-emitter circuit[2] (or common-emitter circuit) which has moderate input and output impedances. This circuit resembles the common or grounded-cathode vacuum tube configuration. Like its vacuum tube counterpart it gives a phase reversal to the signal, and negative feedback is produced by insertion of resistance in the emitter lead.

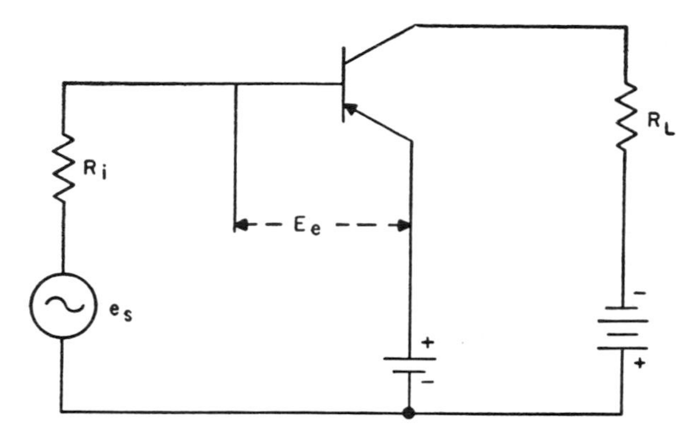

Fig. 7.2. Grounded-emitter transistor amplifier circuit.

Figure 7.3 represents the grounded-collector circuit[2] (or common collector circuit). This has a high input impedance and a low output impedance, and thus is similar to the grounded-plate or cathode-follower vacuum tube connection. This circuit is quite unusual in that it is a bilateral amplifier, with no phase reversal of the signal in the forward direction, and a phase reversal in the reverse direction.

It should be noted that the above circuits are biased for ordinary

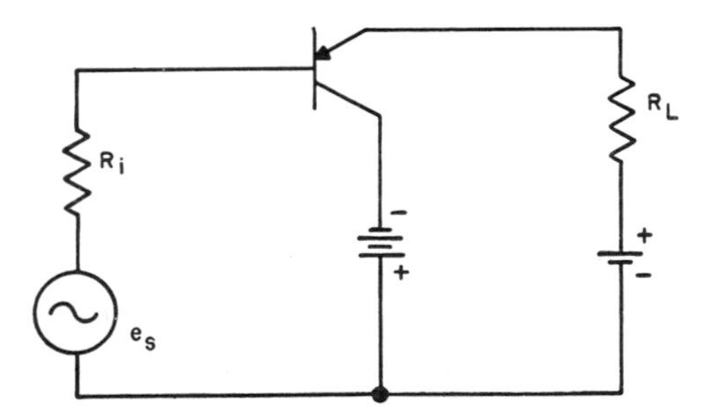

Fig. 7.3. Grounded-collector transistor amplifier circuit.

point-contact transistors and P-N-P junction transistors. These circuits may also be employed for N-P-N junction transistors if the bias polarities are reversed.

2. *Small signal equivalent circuits*[3]

Junction transistors are unconditionally stable with all terminations, because α is normally less than unity. Hence one may employ matched terminations without having to worry about stability. Moreover, one may connect the transistor in the grounded-base, grounded-emitter, or grounded-collector circuit to obtain a variety of input and output impedances. In this section consideration will be

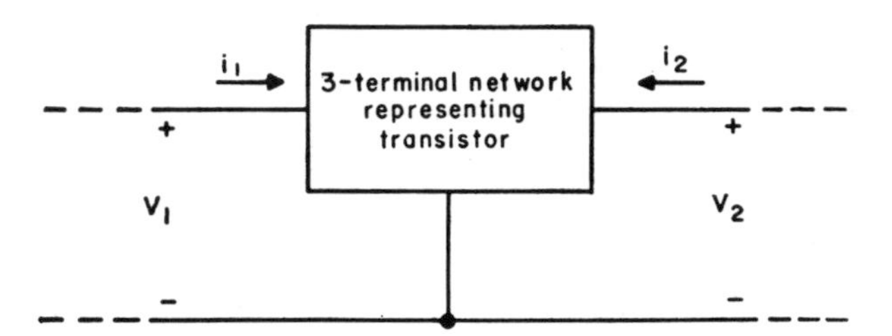

Fig. 7.4. Three-terminal network representing transistor in all possible connections with convention of signs.

given to the characteristics of these various amplifiers, and to ways of supplying the necessary biases and couplings to the stages. Although the bias batteries in the circuits which follow in this section are for N-P-N junction transistors, one may utilize P-N-P junction transistors by simply reversing the polarities of these power supplies.

The following general relationships will apply to all possible connections of the transistor. Figure 7.4 represents the transistor by a box. The equations for the signal voltages and currents at low frequencies are

$$\left.\begin{aligned} R_{11}i_1 + R_{12}i_2 &= v_1 \\ R_{21}i_1 + R_{22}i_2 &= v_2 \end{aligned}\right\} \qquad (1)$$

If, as shown in Fig. 7.5, one connects a generator of open-circuit voltage v_g and internal resistance R_g to the input terminals of the transistor,

$$v_1 = v_g - i_1R_g \qquad (2)$$

and if one connects a load resistance R_L to the output terminals,

$$v_2 = -R_L i_2 \tag{3}$$

By combining Eqs. (1), (2), and (3) one obtains for the circuit of Fig. 7.5 the following equations:

$$\left.\begin{aligned}(R_{11} + R_g)i_1 + R_{12}i_2 &= v_g \\ R_{21}i_1 + (R_{22} + R_L)i_2 &= 0\end{aligned}\right\} \tag{4}$$

Solving for the voltage drop across the load, the following equation results:

$$v_2 = \frac{R_L R_{21}}{(R_{11} + R_g)(R_{22} + R_L) - R_{12}R_{21}} v_g \tag{5}$$

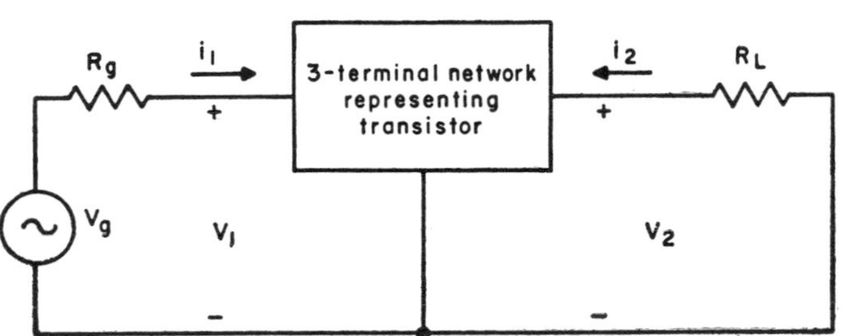

Fig. 7.5. Transistor three-terminal network with generator and load.

The power gain in the circuit equals the quotient of the power delivered to the load (v_2^2/R_L) and the power available from the generator ($v_g^2/4R_g$). Applying Eq. (5) we have

$$G = \frac{4R_g R_L R_{21}^2}{[(R_{11} + R_g)(R_{22} + R_L) - R_{12}R_{21}]^2} \tag{6}$$

where G is the power gain in the circuit.

The gain is a function of R_g and R_L and will have its maximum value when these terminations match the input and output impedances of the transistor circuit. However, R_L affects the input impedance and R_g influences the output impedance as shown in the equations

$$\text{input impedance} = R_i = R_{11} - \frac{R_{12}R_{21}}{R_{22} + R_L} \tag{7}$$

$$\text{output impedance} = R_o = R_{22} - \frac{R_{12}R_{21}}{R_{11} + R_g} \tag{8}$$

Maximum gain is obtained for the conditions that the impedances are matched at the input and output terminals, or $R_i = R_g$ and $R_0 = R_L$. These conditions give

$$\text{matched input impedance} = R_{im} = R_{11}\sqrt{1 - R_{12}R_{21}/R_{11}R_{22}} \quad (9)$$

$$\text{matched output impedance} = R_{om} = R_{22}\sqrt{1 - R_{12}R_{21}/R_{11}R_{22}} \quad (10)$$

$$\text{maximum available gain} = \text{M.A.G.} = \frac{R_{21}^2}{R_{11}R_{22}} \frac{1}{(1 + \sqrt{1 - R_{12}R_{21}/R_{11}R_{22}})^2} \quad (11)$$

In the following discussion the proper 4-pole r's will be substituted into Eqs. (4) through (11) to determine relations for the impedances and gains. These r's are the measured values of a particular transistor having the operating point $V_c = 4.5$ v, and $I_c = 1$ ma, and are $r_e = 25.9$ ohms, $r_b = 240$ ohms, $r_c = 13.4$ megohms, $r_c - r_m = 0.288$ megohm, and $\alpha = 0.9785$.

The grounded-base stage is illustrated in Fig. 7.6. The grounded-base connection is adaptable for operation between a low-impedance

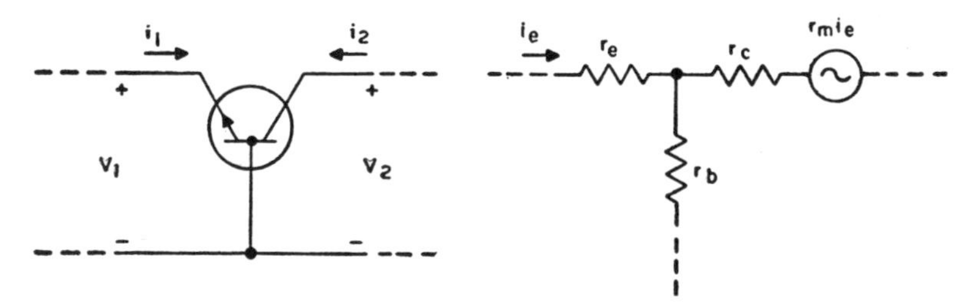

Fig. 7.6. The grounded-base connection of a transistor.

generator and a high-impedance load. Input impedances of about 100 ohms and output impedances of 1 or more megohms are common. This configuration may give large voltage amplification, but can produce only a current amplification less than unity. Matched impedances may yield power gains of about 40 to 50 db. Even if the load resistance is decreased to a few thousand ohms so that the current gain becomes nearly unity, the power gain may still be appreciable.

Then the transistor characteristics which vary from unit to unit have little effect on the stage gain. No phase reversal results in this circuit.

The equivalent circuit relationships for the grounded-base amplifier of Fig. 7.6 are as follows:

$$\left.\begin{aligned} R_{11} &= r_e + r_b = 266 \text{ ohms} \\ R_{12} &= r_b = 240 \text{ ohms} \\ R_{21} &= r_m + r_b = 13.1 \text{ megohms} \\ R_{22} &= r_c + r_b = 13.4 \text{ megohms} \\ \alpha &= \frac{r_m + r_b}{r_c + r_b} = \frac{r_m}{r_c} = 0.9785 \end{aligned}\right\} \quad (12)$$

Since r_b is very small compared with r_m and r_c, it may be neglected. Then Eq. (5) may be transformed to

$$v_2 = \frac{\alpha R_L v_g}{(r_e + r_b + R_g)(1 + R_L/r_c) - \alpha r_b} \quad (13)$$

If R_L is made very large, an enormous voltage amplification may be obtained. If R_L is infinite and $R_g = 0$,

$$v_2 = v_g \frac{r_m}{r_e + r_b} \quad (14)$$

For the above transistor this gives

$$v_2 = 49{,}300$$

To realize this voltage amplification the load resistance would have to be very large compared with the r_c of 13.4 megohms, but large voltage gain may be achieved with moderate load impedances.

When R_L is small compared with r_c, the last of Eq. (4) may be converted to

$$i_2 = \frac{-r_m}{r_c} i_1 = -i_1 \quad (15)$$

or the load current approximatly equals the generator current.

It is informative to consider the ranges over which the input and output impedances may vary for this particular transistor. If the load impedance is varied from zero to infinity, the input impedance changes from 31.1 ohms to 266 ohms. As the input impedance varies from zero to infinity, the output impedance variation is from 1.56 megohms to 13.4 megohms.

Equation (9) gives a matched input impedance of about 91 ohms, whereas Eq. (10) indicates that the matched output impedance is approximately 4.58 megohms. The maximum available gain with matched impedances from Eq. (11) equals 27,000 or 44.3 db.

Although the above matched output impedance is prohibitively large, useful gain may be achieved with moderate values of R_L. With R_L equal 200,000 ohms and R_g equal 25 ohms, the power gain from Eq. (6) becomes 5300 or 37.2 db.

When one wishes to cascade stages of this kind, one should couple each collector to the following emitter with a step-down transformer. Otherwise, the gain per stage would be less than unity, because the transistor current amplification factor is slightly less than unity for junction transistors.

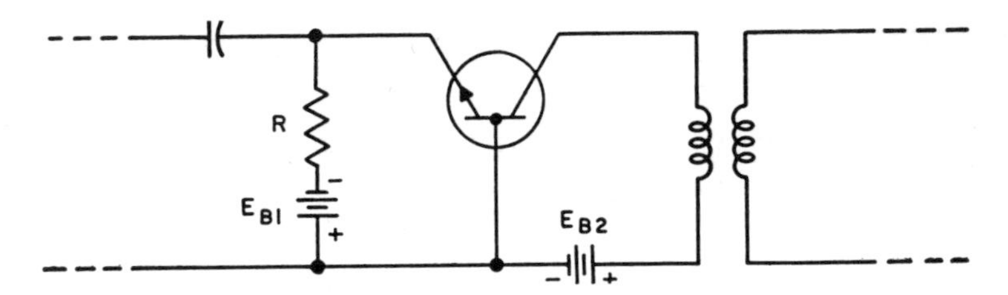

Fig. 7.7. A practical grounded-base transistor amplifier stage.

Figure 7.7 describes a practical arrangement for a grounded-base amplifier. The resistor R will have the approximate value

$$R = \frac{E_{B1}}{I_c} \tag{16}$$

where I_c is the operating collector current and E_{B1} is the emitter-bias battery voltage. For example, if $I_c = 1$ ma, then one could employ $E_{B1} = 1.5$ v and $R = 1500$ ohms.

Figure 7.8 shows the grounded-emitter connection of a transistor. This is the configuration generally employed for junction transistor amplifiers. Power gains as large as 50 db may be achieved. The interstage coupling problem is less troublesome because the output impedance is much lower than that of the grounded-base circuit, whereas the input impedance is somewhat larger. The output impedance may be several hundred thousand ohms and the input impedance a few hundred ohms. Both current and voltage amplification are realized, the phase of the signal is reversed, and with no interstage coupling transformers power gains of about 30 db or larger per stage can be produced. Alpha greatly affects the input and output impedances, which may show considerable variation in different units.

The relationships between the R's and the r's for the grounded-emitter stage are

$$\left.\begin{aligned} R_{11} &= r_e + r_b = 266 \text{ ohms} \\ R_{12} &= r_e = 25.9 \text{ ohms} \\ R_{21} &= r_e - r_m = -13.1 \text{ megohms} \\ R_{22} &= r_e + r_c - r_m = 0.288 \text{ megohm} \end{aligned}\right\} \tag{17}$$

When these values are substituted in Eq. (5), v_2 has the opposite polarity of v_g, showing that the grounded-emitter stage gives a phase reversal like the grounded-cathode electron tube amplifier.

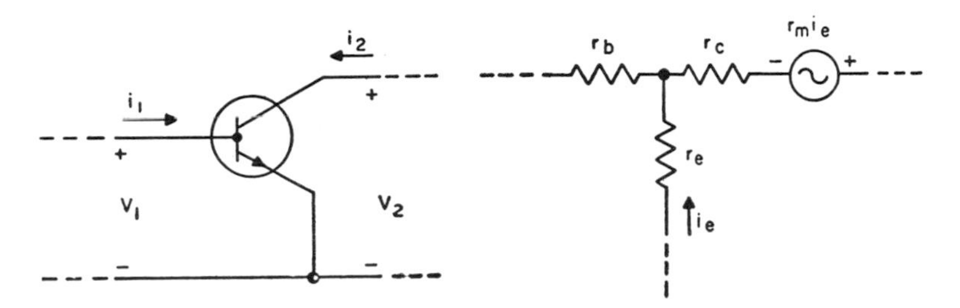

Fig. 7.8. The grounded-emitter connection of a transistor.

When R_g equals 0 and R_L is infinite,

$$v_2 = v_g \frac{r_e - r_m}{r_e + r_b} = -49{,}300 v_g$$

This is numerically the same as for the grounded-base circuit. If $R_L = 0$, the second expression of Eq. (4) leads to

$$i_2 = \frac{r_m - r_e}{r_e + r_c - r_m} i_1 \tag{18}$$

$$= \frac{\alpha}{1 - \alpha} i_1 = 45.5 i_1 \tag{19}$$

Hence considerable current amplification may be obtained from the grounded-emitter amplifier, especially when alpha nears unity.

The output impedance variation is from 1.56 megohms when R_g equals 0, to 0.288 megohm when R_g is infinite.

The input impedance of the circuit varies from 1440 ohms when R_L equals 0, to 266 ohms when R_L is infinite.

The matched input impedance is 619 ohms, whereas the matched output impedance is 0.671 megohms.

The matched input impedance becomes larger and the matched output impedance gets smaller when alpha increases toward unity. The limits become

$$R_{im} = \sqrt{(r_b + r_c)(r_e + r_b)} \tag{20}$$

$$R_{om} = \sqrt{(r_b + r_c)/(r_e + r_b)} \tag{21}$$

as $\alpha \to 1$. For this transistor, if alpha equals 1 (r_m made equal to r_c), the matched impedances would become

$$R_{im} = 59{,}700 \text{ ohms}, \qquad R_{om} = 5800 \text{ ohms}$$

These figures show how rapidly the impedances change with alpha as alpha approaches unity.

The maximum available gain with matched impedances for the grounded-emitter stage is 202,000 or 53 db.

The maximum available gain equals r_c/r_e when alpha is 1 and if r_e and r_b are small compared with r_c. When alpha is sufficiently near 1, the power gain does not increase rapidly with alpha. For example, the gain increases only 4.1 db when alpha is increased from 0.9785 to 1. Since the approximate stage gain varies directly with r_c and inversely with r_e, it may be increased by higher emitter current operation, or by employing a transistor with a larger r_c and higher alpha to prevent the output impedance from becoming excessively large.

The matched output impedance has been shown to be large compared with the input impedance, or a ratio of 671,000 to 619 ohms. This indicates that step-down interstage transformers must be employed to achieve the maximum available gain in cascaded stages. However, considerable gain may be realized without interstage impedance matching due to the large short-circuit current amplification. This is approximately

$$\frac{\alpha}{1 - \alpha}$$

or 45.5 for this transistor. The iterative gain per stage is 33.2 db without impedance transformation.

Figure 7.9 describes one practical arrangement of biasing a grounded-emitter stage. One battery supplies both the emitter and collector voltages. The collector voltage is approximately equal to the supply voltage, since V_e is normally a small fraction of a volt. With no d-c connection to the base, this electrode floats above ground

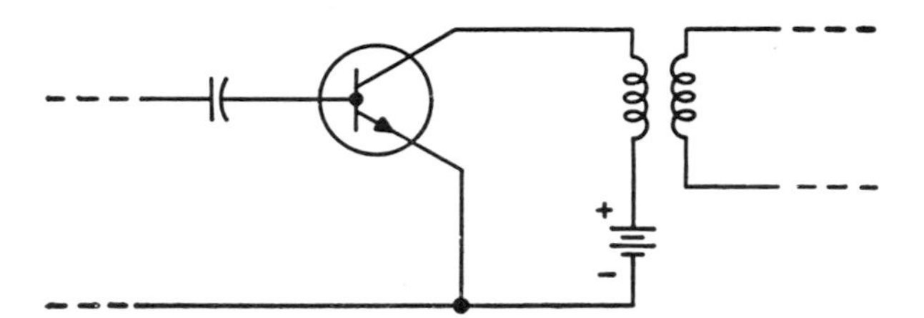

Fig. 7.9. One practical circuit for biasing a grounded-emitter stage.

at the potential V_e, and the emitter current equals the collector current. These currents are given by the equation

$$I_e = I_c = \frac{I_{co}}{1 - \alpha} \tag{22}$$

where I_{co} is the collector current for zero emitter current, and equals about 20 μa for this transistor. The emitter and collector currents vary rapidly with alpha, and equal approximately 465 μa in the numerical example.

If one desires to operate with a smaller current to decrease the battery power consumption, a small current must flow out of the base.

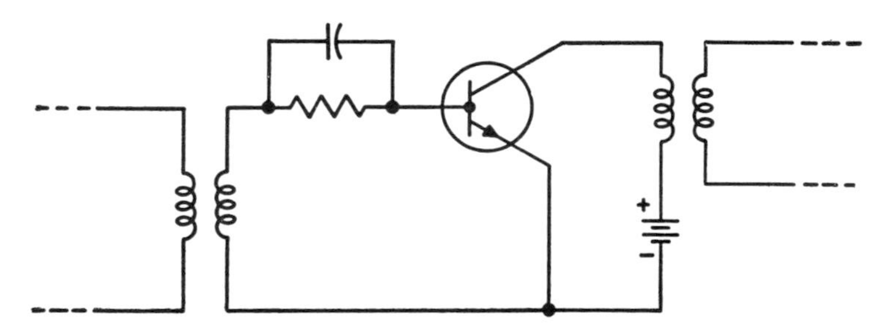

Fig. 7.10. Circuit to obtain lower collector current.

Since the collector current will decrease by $1/(1 - \alpha)$ μa for each microampere from the base, the required base current is small. Figure 7.10 gives one way of obtaining this base current. A resistive path is provided between the base and ground. This arrangement produces a base current of the correct direction to decrease the collector current, since the base is at a positive voltage to ground. The collector current will decrease to that for zero emitter voltage, as one decreases the series resistance to zero. A resistor connected between the emitter and ground will decrease the collector current still further.

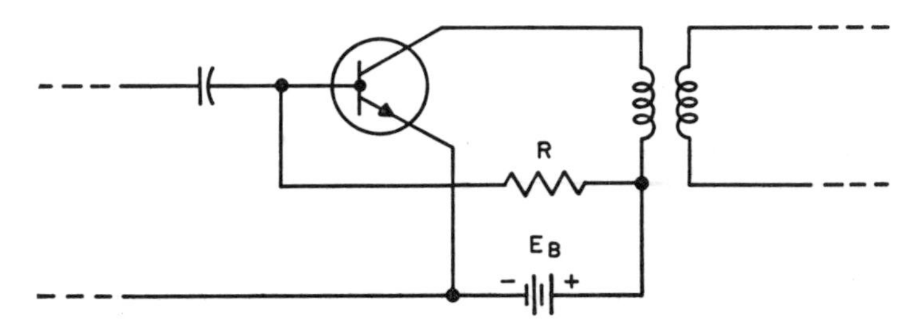

Fig. 7.11. Circuit to obtain higher collector current.

Figure 7.11 indicates a circuit for increasing the collector current to a larger value than that for zero base current. A high-resistance path is connected between the positive supply voltage and the base. For each microampere which flows through this bias resistor, the collector current will increase by $1/(1 - \alpha)$ μa. When the required collector current is known, one can easily calculate the bias resistor value, since the bias resistor current is approximately E_B/R.

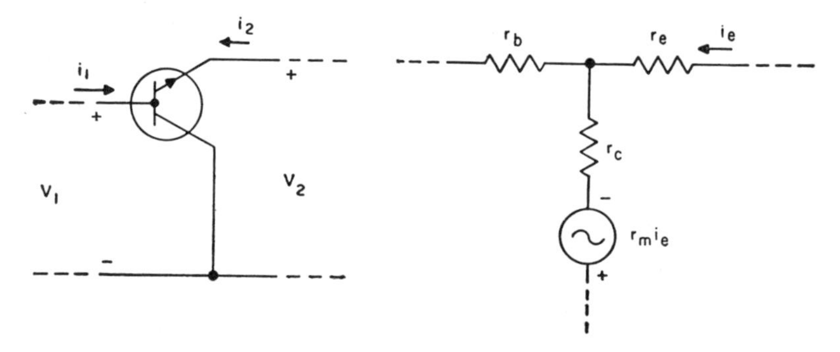

Fig. 7.12. The grounded-collector connection of a transistor.

Figure 7.12 represents the grounded-collector connection of a transistor. This circuit has a comparatively large input impedance and a low output impedance, although the power gain is only about 15 to 20 db. The input impedance may be several megohms, if the load impedance is fairly large. The output impedance may be about 25 ohms or lower, if the source impedance is moderately low, say a few thousand ohms.

The equivalent circuit relationships are

$$\left.\begin{aligned} R_{11} &= r_b + r_c = 13.4 \text{ megohms} \\ R_{12} &= r_c - r_m = 0.288 \text{ megohm} \\ R_{21} &= r_c = 13.4 \text{ megohms} \\ R_{22} &= r_e + r_c - r_m = 0.288 \text{ megohm} \end{aligned}\right\} \tag{23}$$

If $R_g = 0$ and R_L is infinite,

$$v_2 = v_g \left(\frac{r_c}{r_b + r_c}\right) \doteq v_g \tag{24}$$

The output voltage is less than the input voltage, and like the cathode follower there is no phase reversal of the signal.

When R_L equals 0,

$$i_2 = -i_1 \frac{r_c}{r_e + r_c - r_m} \tag{25}$$

$$\doteq -i_1 \frac{1}{1 - \alpha} = -46.5 i_1 \tag{26}$$

Hence the circuit can produce a good current gain.

The input impedance varies from 1445 ohms when R_L equals 0, to 13.4 megohms when R_L is infinite. It is apparent that the input impedance is large when the load impedance is high just like the cathode follower.

The output impedance changes from 31.1 ohms when R_g equals 0, to 0.288 megohm when R_g is infinite.

The matched input impedance is 139,000 ohms, whereas the matched output impedance is 2990 ohms.

The maximum available gain of the grounded-collector stage with matched impedance as alpha approaches unity becomes approximately

$$\text{M.A.G.} = r_c/4r_e \tag{27}$$

However, as long as $r_e \ll r_c - r_m$, the following equation is a good approximation:

$$\text{M.A.G.} = 1/(1 - \alpha) = 46.5 \text{ or } 16.7 \text{ db} \tag{28}$$

The problem of biasing a grounded-collector stage is similar to that already described for the grounded-emitter circuit. If, as shown in Fig. 7.13, the base is permitted to float, Eq. (22) previously given

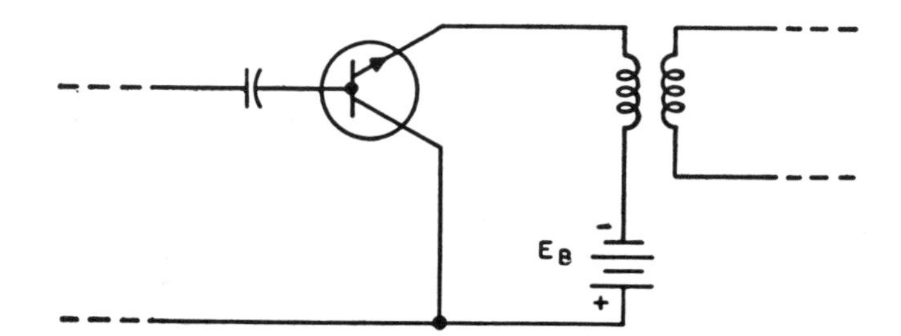

Fig. 7.13. A practical arrangement for a grounded-collector amplifier.

for the grounded-emitter stage will give the collector current. Moreover, it may be best to let the base float if one wishes to obtain the largest input impedance. Figure 7.14 illustrates the circuit used to decrease the collector current by placing a resistance between the base and the negative side of the battery. Should one desire to increase the collector current, remove the above resistance and connect a high resistance between the base and ground.

Although the T equivalent circuit has been employed most fre-

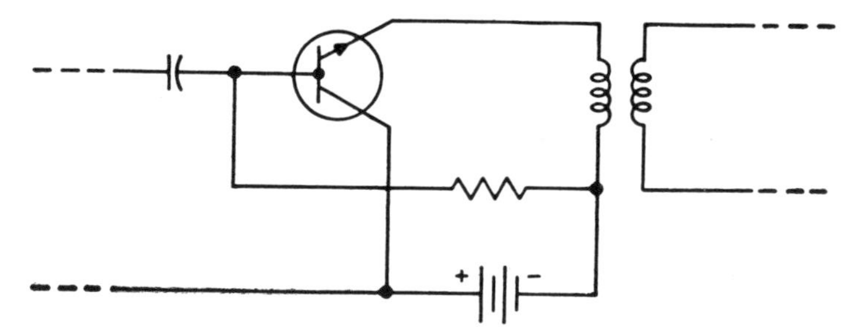

Fig. 7.14. Circuit to obtain a lower collector current. To increase the collector current, remove the resistance shown and connect a high resistance between the base and ground.

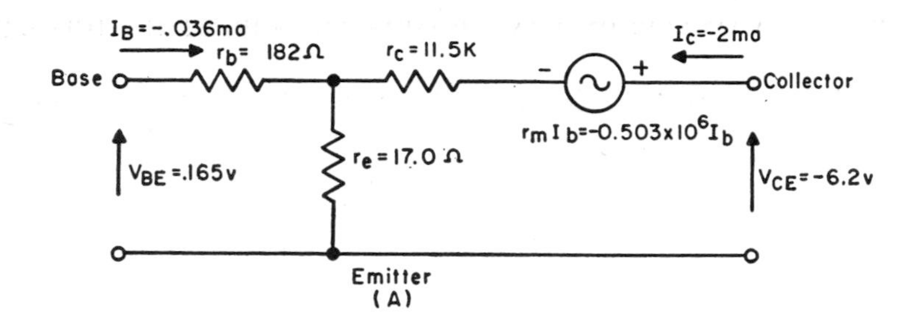

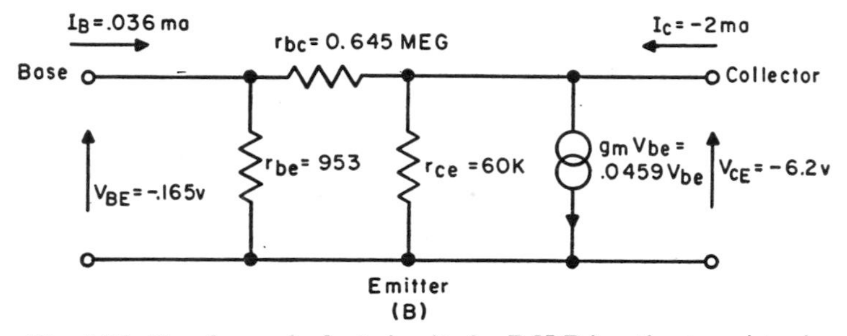

Fig. 7.15. T and π equivalent circuits for P-N-P junction transistor in common-emitter stage.

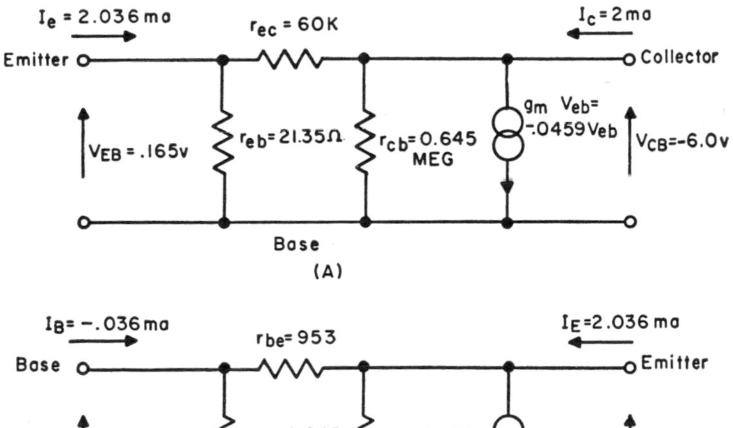

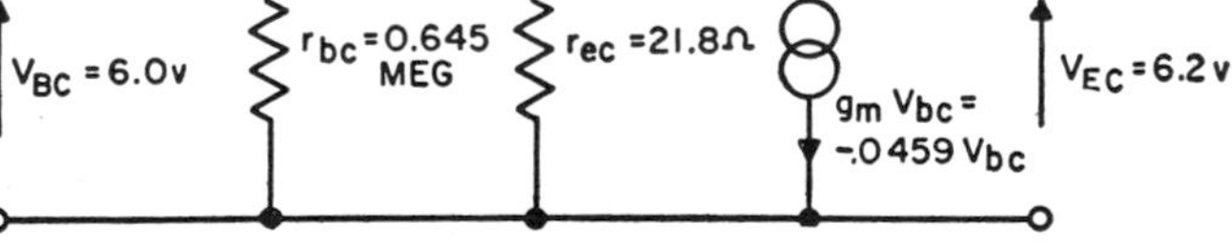

Fig. 7.16. π equivalent circuits for P-N-P junction transistor in (A) common-base stage and (B) common-collector stage.

quently for transistors, the π equivalent circuit has generally been utilized for grounded-cathode vacuum tubes.[4] Figure 7.15(A) shows the T equivalent circuit for the common-emitter connection for an experimental P-N-P junction transistor. Figure 7.15(B) is the equivalent π network for the same transistor shown in Figure 7.15(A). The T equivalent circuit has been converted to a π network by the theory of Peterson.[5]

Figure 7.15(B) indicates that the resistance between the input and output, although not infinite as in an electron tube, is sufficiently large that the input and output circuits may be considered to be approximately independent of each other. It is interesting to compare this circuit with the π equivalent circuits for the common-base and the common-collector circuits given in Fig. 7.16.

3. *Large signal analysis*[6]

Large signals are those which involve extensive variations over the electrical characteristics of the transistor and cannot be considered small changes about a given operating point. The set of static characteristics of the transistor supply a convenient means for the study of large signals.

Figure 7.17 includes a set of characteristics[7] representing the Type A1698 point-contact transistor operation. This consists of four graphs, one of each of the electrode voltages versus each of the currents with the other current held constant. Unlike vacuum tubes, the currents are the independent variables instead of the voltages. This is done to prevent short-circuit unstable transistors from oscillating with constant voltage biases, and also to avoid double-valued voltage-dependent characteristics.

The dashed lines in graph *D* represent discontinuities which are found in some of the A1698 transistors currently being manufactured. A discontinuity can be defined as a condition in the output characteristics when, for a fixed value of emitter current, the collector voltage can be a multiple-valued function of collector current or the collector current can be a double-valued function of collector voltage. Operation of the transistor as a linear device in the region of emitter biases between voltage cutoff and saturation is not recommended due to discontinuities which appear in this region.

These characteristics have a direct relationship to the open circuit impedances; the open circuit resistances are the slopes of these static characteristics. The reactive components are not represented because the static characteristics do not contain the reactive data.

Since there are five other pairs of small signal parameters which we could have selected, there are five other ways in which we could have described the static characteristics. For special purposes these other curves may prove more convenient, or may be more closely related to certain large signal circuits.

One may measure these characteristics by the usual point-by-point plots or by oscilloscopic display. Such equipment is described in Chapter 6.

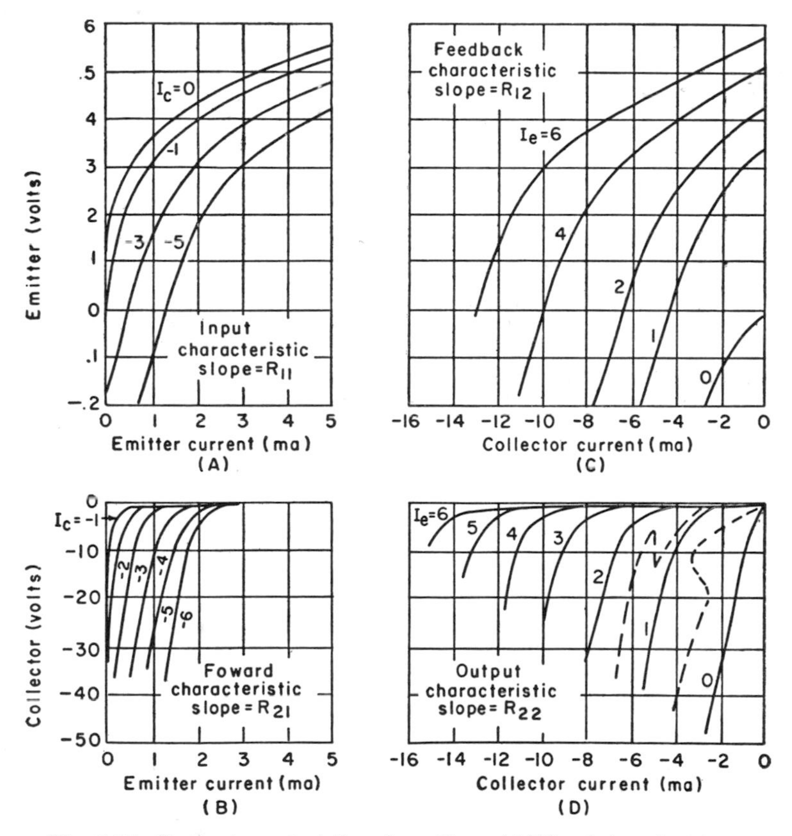

Fig. 7.17. Static characteristics of the Type A1698 point-contact transistor.

Occasionally an oscilloscope presentation does not give the same results for the static characteristics as a slow point-by-point plot because of thermal effects. For the normal region of operation of the A1698 transistor these thermal effects are small, but excessive power dissipation may cause appreciable heating.

4. *The principle of duality*[8]

A comparison of the transistor with a vacuum tube triode indicates many important differences. For example, the grounded-base transistor is basically a current-amplifying device with a low input impedance and a comparatively high output impedance, whereas the grounded-cathode electron tube is essentially a voltage amplifier with a high input impedance and a relatively low output impedance. Moreover, high gain transistors tend to be unstable with short-circuit terminations, whereas high gain vacuum tubes tend to be unstable with open-circuit terminations.

The properties of the two devices are so unlike that the development of the transistor has created a host of new circuit design problems. When one replaces the vacuum tubes in a given circuit with transistors and changes the bias voltages accordingly, one generally finds that the transistor does not operate efficiently nor does the circuit perform satisfactorily. When new circuits are devised especially for the transistor, some of them only slightly resemble the vacuum tube circuits which perform the same purpose.

In spite of the great difference between the electrical properties of vacuum tubes and transistors, there exists a simple approximate relationship between them. One may start with a known vacuum tube circuit and transform it into a completely different circuit suitable for transistors. Such circuits take advantage of the peculiarities of the transistor, and in some instances have given good performance.

The properties of a transistor are related to those of a vacuum tube triode through an interchange of current and voltage; transistor currents act like vacuum tube voltages and vice versa. The discussion is limited to the frequency range in which circuit operation is determined by static characteristics, and applies especially to the large-signal behavior of the two devices.

The emitter-base input terminals of a transistor may be compared to the grid cathode input terminals of a triode. Each device acts like a diode rectifier which the biases applied to the third electrode (collector or plate) affect only to a minor degree. The emitter conducts when biased in the forward direction and fails to conduct when biased in the reverse direction. The same can be said for the grid. Moreover, either device exhibits a low impedance when biased in the forward direction and a comparatively high impedance when biased in the reverse direction.

However, the transistor is most effective as an amplifier when the emitter is biased in the forward direction, whereas the vacuum tube is most effective when the grid is biased in the reverse direction. The basic difference, then, is between "forward" and "reverse," or an interchange of current and voltage.

In addition, the emitter is normally given a moderate current bias at which the emitter voltage is approximately zero, whereas the grid is ordinarily given a moderate voltage bias at which the grid current is essentially zero. Moreover, the principal nonlinearity in the emitter circuit occurs when the emitter current is allowed to rise, whereas the principal nonlinearity in the grid circuit occurs when the grid voltage is permitted to swing through zero, with the result that grid current begins to increase.

When the collector-base output circuit of the transistor is compared with the plate-cathode output of the triode, the effects of emitter and grid biases cause a complication. If we apply zero bias ($i_e = 0$ and $v_g = 0$) to the input circuits, both the collector and plate act like diode rectifiers, and conduct heavily when biased in the forward direction and poorly when biased in the reverse direction. However, when input biases are applied to the emitter only the reverse part of the collector circuit characteristic is affected, whereas when input biases are applied to the grid only the forward part of the plate circuit characteristic is affected.

Hence the emitter and collector are normally biased in the forward and reverse directions, respectively, such that the transistor input impedance is low and the output impedance is relatively high. However, the grid and plate are normally biased in the reverse and forward directions, respectively, such that the vacuum tube input impedance is high and the output impedance is comparatively low.

Transistor properties may be compared with those of the vacuum tube by the aid of Fig. 7.18. Figure 7.18(A) shows the plate characteristics of a vacuum tube triode, whereas Fig. 7.18(B) displays the collector characteristics of a transistor. The axes in these figures have been selected to compare transistor currents with vacuum tube voltages and vice versa. The two families of curves appear quite similar. The quantities which are interchanged are $-i_c$ and v_p, $-v_c$ and i_p, i_e and $-v_g$, and, not shown, v_e and $-i_g$.

The above difference in signs between transistor and vacuum tube quantities applies only for transistors made from N-type semiconductors (P-N-P transistors). There is no difference in signs between these transistors and vacuum tube quantities when the transistor is made of P-type material (N-P-N transistors).

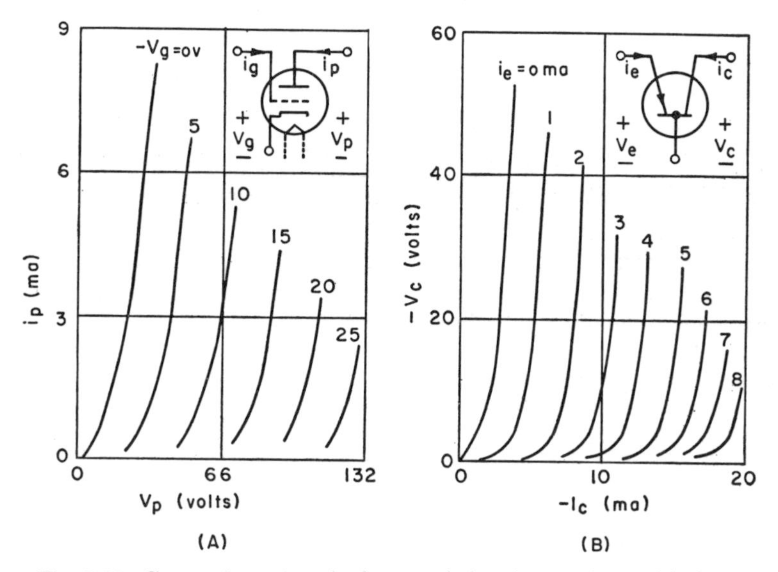

Fig. 7.18. Comparison of static characteristics of a transistor with those of a vacuum tube triode.

Figure 7.18(A) illustrates that a negative bias voltage applied to the grid essentially shifts the plate characteristics to the right along the v_p axis. The change in plate voltage produced by a 1 v change on the grid is known as the voltage amplification factor μ of the triode. Likewise, Fig. 7.18(B) demonstrates that a positive current bias applied to the emitter simply shifts the collector characteristic to the right along the $-i_c$ axis. The change in milliamperes of collector current caused by a change of 1 ma of emitter current is called the current amplification factor α of the transistor. Hence the transistor α corresponds to the vacuum tube μ. Moreover, the gross nonlinearities in the transistor collector circuit have their counterparts in the vacuum tube plate circuit. For example, collector voltage cutoff corresponds to plate current cutoff.

If the transistor is compared with a suitable vacuum tube, a quantitative as well as a qualitative relationship may be established. This requires that α of the transistor equal the μ of the vacuum tube, and both devices must have the same dissipation ratings. The vacuum tube and transistor of Fig. 7.18(A) and (B) roughly satisfy these conditions. From these characteristics one may see that 1 ma of current in the transistor corresponds to 6.6 v in the vacuum tube and vice versa. Hence one may relate transistor currents to vacuum tube voltage by a "transformation resistance," r, which is

$$r = \frac{6.6 \text{ v}}{0.001 \text{ amp}} = 6600 \text{ ohms} \tag{29}$$

If a transistor is substituted for a vacuum tube and the circuit performance (as it applies to the terminals of the transistor or vacuum tube) is to be kept high, the external circuit must be revised. Since the transistor produces an interchange of currents and voltages compared with those of the vacuum tube, the external network of the vacuum tube should also be replaced by a new network for the transistor, which facilitates this interchange.

Networks which cause this kind of interchange are called duals,[9] one of the other. The duals of most practical circuits can be found and physically realized. When a network is transformed into its dual, it will normally have the same number of circuit elements, since each element is transformed into a new element which is its dual. However, the transformed elements are connected together in a different way than the original ones. Parallel elements become series elements and vice versa. Loops convert into nodes and nodes into loops.

When mutual inductances or nonlinear elements appear in a network, or if one cannot draw the network on a flat surface without crossovers, complications may arise. Bode[10] has discussed some of these problems.

Table 4 illustrates a number of network elements and their duals related by the transformation resistance r.

One network element is the dual of another if the role of voltage

TABLE 4. SOME COMMON CIRCUIT ELEMENTS AND THEIR DUALS

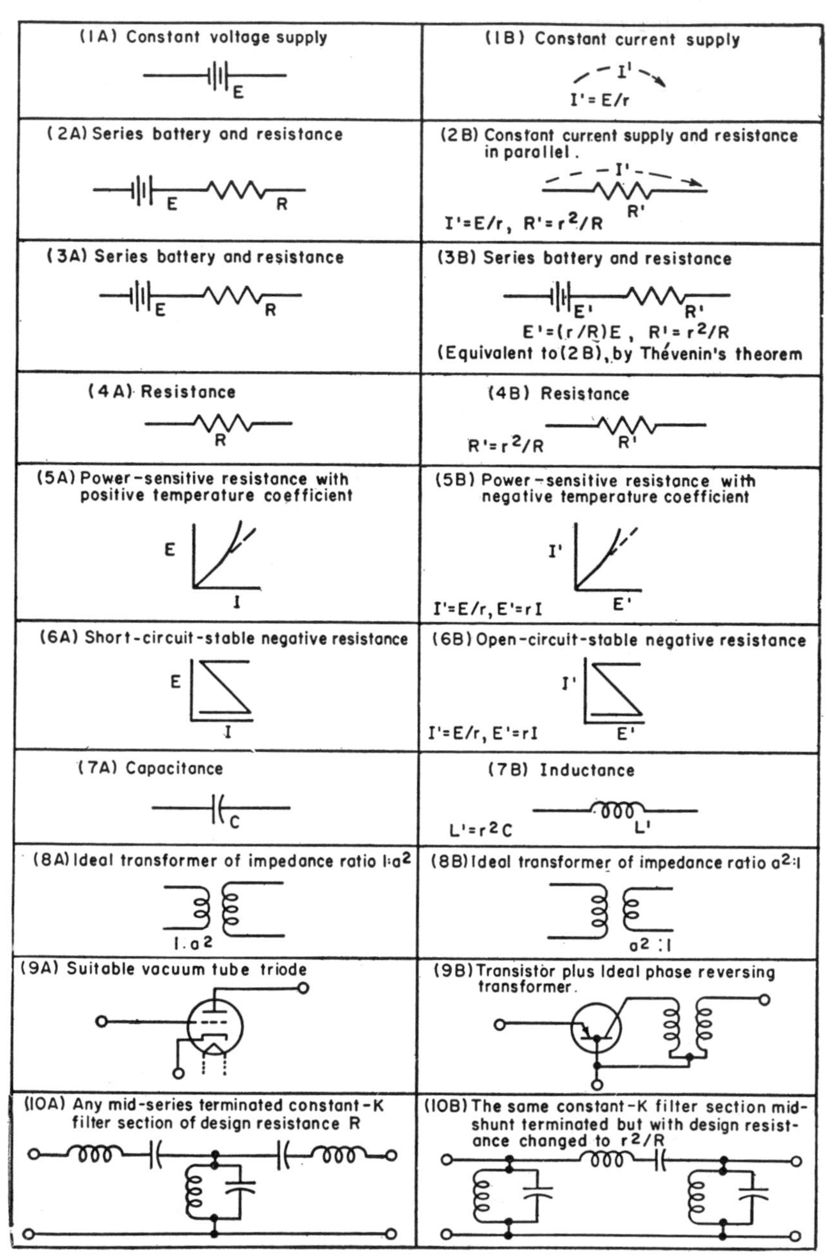

A	B
(1A) Constant voltage supply E	(1B) Constant current supply I' I' = E/r
(2A) Series battery and resistance E R	(2B) Constant current supply and resistance in parallel. I' R' I'=E/r, R'=r²/R
(3A) Series battery and resistance E R	(3B) Series battery and resistance E' R' E'=(r/R)E, R'=r²/R (Equivalent to (2B), by Thévenin's theorem
(4A) Resistance R	(4B) Resistance R'=r²/R R'
(5A) Power-sensitive resistance with positive temperature coefficient E I	(5B) Power-sensitive resistance with negative temperature coefficient I' I'=E/r, E'=rI E'
(6A) Short-circuit-stable negative resistance E I	(6B) Open-circuit-stable negative resistance I' I'=E/r, E'=rI E'
(7A) Capacitance C	(7B) Inductance L'=r²C L'
(8A) Ideal transformer of impedance ratio 1:a² 1.a²	(8B) Ideal transformer of impedance ratio a²:1 a² :1
(9A) Suitable vacuum tube triode	(9B) Transistor plus Ideal phase reversing transformer.
(10A) Any mid-series terminated constant-K filter section of design resistance R	(10B) The same constant-K filter section mid-shunt terminated but with design resistance changed to r²/R

in one is played by current in the other and vice versa. For example, in a capacitance the voltage and current are related by the equation

$$e = \frac{1}{j\omega C} i \tag{30}$$

To interchange the roles of voltage and current, replace e by $i'r$ and i by e'/r. The voltage across the capacitor which corresponds to 1 amp through its dual is determined by the value of r. When the above substitutions are made,

$$i' = \frac{1}{j\omega Cr^2} e' \tag{31}$$

It is apparent that this is like the equation between the current through an inductance and the voltage across it. Therefore the dual of a capacitance C is an inductance,

$$L' = r^2C \tag{32}$$

Hence in finding the dual of a network, one transforms each capacitance in the original circuit to an inductance in the dual network in the above way.

Conversely, each inductance L has for its dual a capacitance C', such that

$$C' = L/r^2 \tag{33}$$

One may find the dual of a resistance R in the same manner. For a resistance

$$e = Ri \tag{34}$$

Substituting ri' for e and e'/r for i,

$$i' = \frac{e'}{r^2/R} \tag{35}$$

Hence a resistance R becomes a resistance R' or

$$R' = r^2/R \tag{36}$$

Other circuit elements may be converted into their duals in the same way.

An excellent example of what duality may achieve is the push-pull class B amplifier of Fig. 7.19. Figure 7.19(A) illustrates the conventional vacuum tube amplifier and its Kirchhoff equations, whereas

Fig. 7.19(B) presents the transformed equations and the dual transistor circuit. Here the selection of the operating point is fully as important as the circuit. In the class B vacuum tube amplifier the grids of the tubes are biased highly negative, such that with no input signal of the plate currents are almost zero but the plate voltages are quite large. However, in the transistor dual, the emitters have a large positive emitter current bias such that without an input signal the

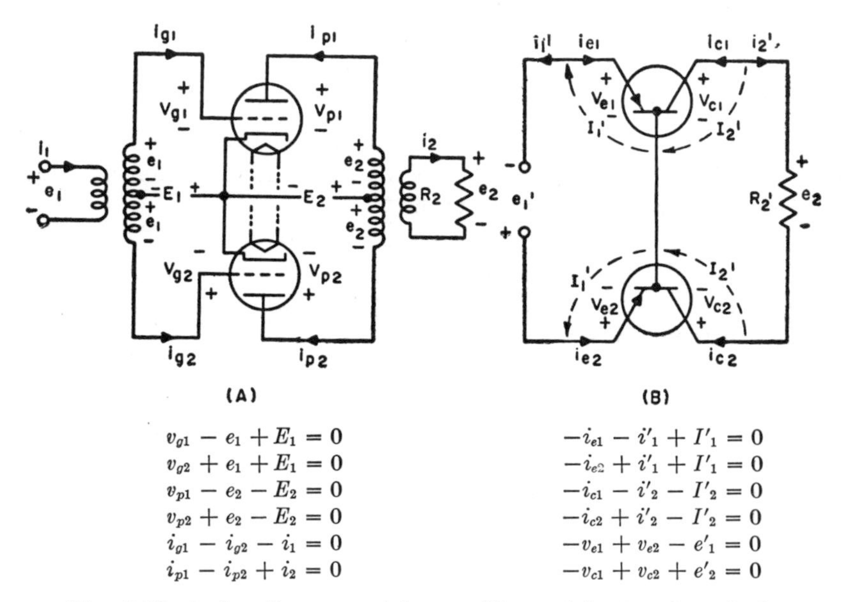

$$v_{g1} - e_1 + E_1 = 0 \qquad -i_{e1} - i'_1 + I'_1 = 0$$
$$v_{g2} + e_1 + E_1 = 0 \qquad -i_{e2} + i'_1 + I'_1 = 0$$
$$v_{p1} - e_2 - E_2 = 0 \qquad -i_{c1} - i'_2 - I'_2 = 0$$
$$v_{p2} + e_2 - E_2 = 0 \qquad -i_{c2} + i'_2 - I'_2 = 0$$
$$i_{g1} - i_{g2} - i_1 = 0 \qquad -v_{e1} + v_{e2} - e'_1 = 0$$
$$i_{p1} - i_{p2} + i_2 = 0 \qquad -v_{c1} + v_{c2} + e'_2 = 0$$

Fig. 7.19. A class-B vacuum tube amplifier and its transistor dual.

collector voltages are nearly zero but the collector currents are quite large. When the input voltage is on a positive half cycle, the upper vacuum tube plate circuit conducts, and its plate current varies through a positive half cycle while the plate current in the lower tube stays essentially at zero. During this half cycle the output transformer couples the plate current of the upper tube to the load, while the lower tube is cut off and acts like an open circuit in parallel with the load and the upper tube. However, in the transistor amplifier a positive half cycle of the input current causes the collector voltage of the upper transistor to go through a negative half cycle, whereas the collector voltage of the lower transistor remains essentially zero.

All the collector voltage swing of the upper transistor is applied directly to the load since the lower transistor acts as a short circuit in series with the load and the upper transistor during this half cycle. During the negative half cycle the lower tube and the lower transistor contribute to the load in a similar manner.

When the circuit of Fig. 7.19(B) was employed with two typical point-contact transistors, each rated at 200 mw collector dissipation, it was possible to achieve an audio output of 400 mw at a collector circuit efficiency of 60 per cent. When the same transistors were utilized in a grounded-base amplifier similar to the conventional circuit of Fig. 7.19(A), an output of only 25 mw could be obtained.

The transistor duals of many different kinds of vacuum tube circuits may be obtained by the principle of duality.

Other methods of analysis of transistors and transistor circuits include graphical analysis,[11] matrix methods,[12] and transient analysis.[13] However, these are beyond the scope of this chapter.

References

1. J. Bardeen and W. H. Brattain, "The Transistor, A Semi-Conductor Triode," *Phys. Rev.*, Vol. LXXIV, No. 2, July 15, 1948, p. 230.
2. W. M. Webster, E. Eberhard, and L. E. Barton, "Some Novel Circuits for the Three Terminal Semi-Conductor Amplifier," *RCA Review*, Vol. X, No. 1, March 1949, pp. 5–16.
3. R. L. Wallace, Jr. and W. J. Pietenpol, "Some Circuit Properties and Applications of N-P-N Transistors," *Proc. IRE*, Vol. XXXIX, No. 7, July 1951, pp. 753–767.
4. L. J. Giacolletto, "Junction Transistor Equivalent Circuits and Vacuum-Tube Analogy," *Proc. IRE*, Vol. XL, No. 11, Nov. 1952, pp. 1490–1493.
5. Liss C. Peterson, "Equivalent Circuits of Linear Active Four-Terminal Networks," *Bell System Tech. J.*, Vol. XXVII, No. 4, Oct. 1948, pp. 593–622.
6. R. M. Ryder and R. J. Kircher, "Some Circuit Aspects of the Transistor," *Bell System Tech. J.*, Vol. XXVIII, July 1949, pp. 367–401.

7. *Western Electric Transistor, Development Model A1698,* Western Electric Co., Inc., New York, May 21, 1954.
8. R. L. Wallace, Jr., and G. Raisbeck, "Duality as a Guide in Transistor Circuit Design," *Bell System Tech. J.*, Vol. XXX, April 1951, pp. 381–418.
9. E. A. Guillemin, *Communication Networks,* Vol. 2, John Wiley & Sons, Inc., 1935, pp. 246–251.
10. H. W. Bode, *Network Analysis and Feedback Amplifier Design,* D. Van Nostrand Company, Inc., 1945, p. 196.
11. Lloyd P. Hunter, "Graphical Analysis of Transistor Characteristics," *Proc. IRE,* Vol. XXXVIII, No. 12, Dec. 1950, pp. 1387–1391.
12. L. Lawsine, "Analysis of Transistors by Matrix Methods," *National Bureau of Standards Report 2520,* May 27, 1953.
13. W. F. Chow and J. J. Suran, "Transient Analysis of Junction Transistor Amplifiers," *Proc. IRE,* Vol. XLI, No. 9, Sept. 1953, pp. 1125–1129.

Chapter 8

TETRODE AND PENTODE TRANSISTORS

1. *Crystal-tetrode mixer*[1]

For many years crystal devices have been employed as demodulators and mixers. The point-contact transistor can also be utilized as a mixer, and exhibits a conversion gain similar to that of the triode vacuum tube.

A crystal mixer with three whiskers has several advantages over the crystal diode or transistor triode mixer, although such a tetrode has many other applications. The advantages of the transistor tetrode mixer are good conversion gain with high conversion transconductance, low interaction between input circuits, and operation at much higher input frequencies than the triode transistor can amplify. Compared with ordinary vacuum tube mixers, this tetrode transistor equals their conversion transconductance and, in addition, is physically small, requires less power, and operates with input signals up to at least 200 mc/sec.

Figure 8.1 shows the construction of an early type of crystal tetrode suitable for a mixer. Since either the whiskers or the crystal semiconductor can easily be changed, this construction is especially good

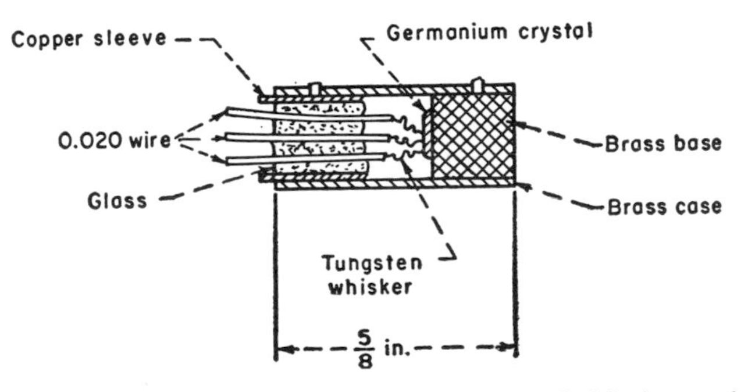

Fig. 8.1. Construction of early crystal tetrode suitable for a mixer.

for experimental work. A simpler construction is employed for production units, and will be described later. The three whiskers are spaced about 0.002 in. from each other in a triangular formation. Most of these early tetrodes were made of germanium crystals of the type utilized in 1N34 diodes. These were processed like the crystals for triode transistors.

Figure 8.2 is the circuit of the crystal tetrode as a mixer. The input voltages are fed to emitters 1 and 2. Normally, emitter 1 connects to the local oscillator and requires no bias battery because self-bias can

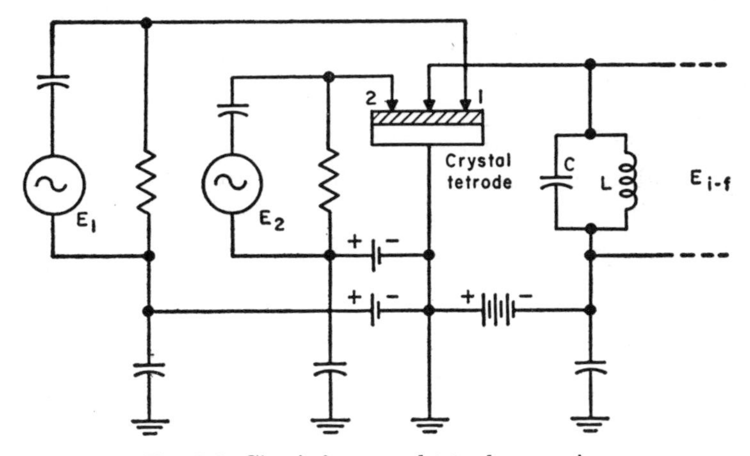

Fig. 8.2. Circuit for crystal tetrode as a mixer.

be obtained by adjusting the local oscillator voltage to the correct level. The load in the collector circuit consists of a resonant circuit, LC, tuned to the intermediate frequency, or a frequency equal to $f_2 - f_1$.

The effectiveness of a mixer is usually described by its conversion transconductance. Vacuum tube mixers have conversion transconductances ranging from 200 to 600 μmhos. For example, a 6SA7 pentagrid converter has a g_c of 425 μmhos at a plate voltage of 100 v and a cathode current of 12.3 ma. Compare these figures with typical operating values for the crystal mixer, which are a collector voltage of 30 v, a collector current of 2 ma, and a g_c of 300 μmhos. A g_c as large as 1100 μmhos, and a conversion power gain of +1 db have been achieved.

Figure 8.3 illustrates the variation of g_c with collector current for a typical crystal mixer. Although it requires lower voltages and currents than vacuum tube mixers, the crystal tetrode mixer has a conversion transconductance comparing favorably with that of common vacuum tube types.

Figure 8.4 indicates the degree of isolation that can be attained between the emitter circuits of the crystal tetrode. It is apparent that excellent signal isolation can be had, so that the signal applied to each

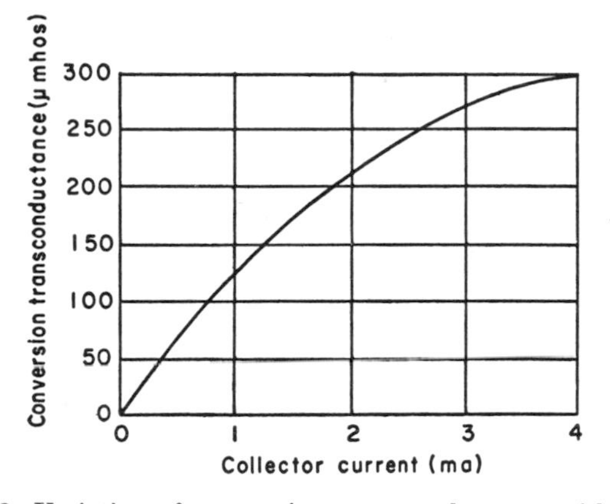

Fig. 8.3. Variation of conversion transconductance with collector current. f_{signal} is 3.7 mc/sec; $f_{i\text{-}f}$ is 530 kc/sec; E_{signal} is 0.10 v; E_{local} is 2.0 v.

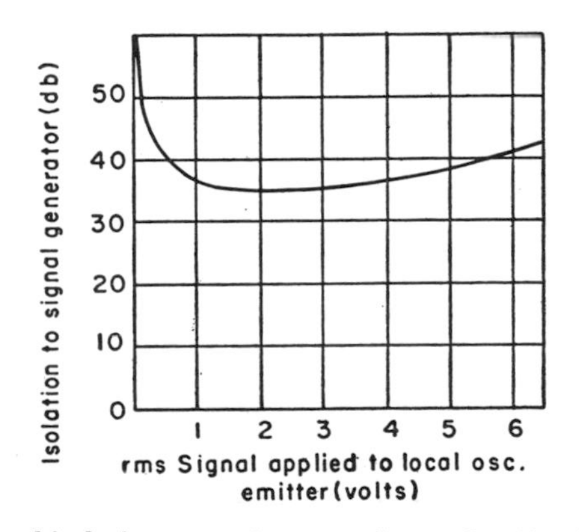

Fig. 8.4. Signal isolation curve for crystal tetrode. f is 3.70 mc/sec; I_e is 2.0 ma.

emitter is not transmitted strongly to the other. Likewise, neither emitter circuit is greatly affected by the heterodyne frequency.

Figure 8.5 presents a typical crystal tetrode interaction transconductance characteristic. This curve shows the good isolation between emitters in the relation between the current in one emitter caused by the voltage applied to the other. For example, the interaction transconductance for a typical operating point on the curve is 570 μmhos. This compares with the normal input conductance of either emitter of approximately 10,000 μmhos, indicating that the signal interaction is small.

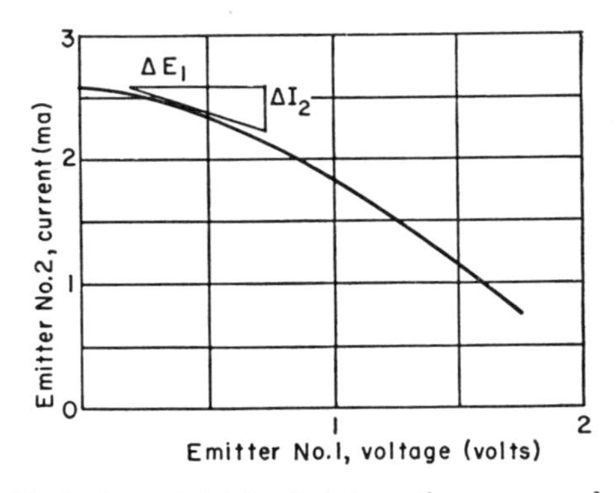

Fig. 8.5. Typical crystal-tetrode interaction transconductance characteristic. $E_e{}^2$ is constant at 0.5 v; V_c is constant; $\Delta E_1/\Delta I_2$ is 570 μmho at $E_1 = 0.4$ v.

The crystal-tetrode mixer operates with very high frequency input signals. Because of transit-time losses the triode transistor is normally limited to frequencies below about 5 megacycles as an amplifier. This also holds true for the tetrode when either emitter is utilized with the collector as an amplifier. However, if the intermediate frequency of the mixer does not exceed the upper range of the unit as an amplifier, the two input frequencies can be much larger than 5 megacycles without any loss in conversion efficiency. Input signals greater than 100 mc/sec have been applied to crystal tetrodes, giving an intermediate frequency of 500 kc/sec with a conversion transconductance higher than that shown at much lower frequencies. For example, a typical mixer with an intermediate frequency of 600 kc/sec gave a conversion voltage gain of 2.5 and a conversion transconductance of

430 μmhos at a frequency of 150 mc/sec. The frequency characteristics for several coupling methods are given in Fig. 8.6.

The noise in the collector circuit of a crystal tetrode is no larger than that of an ordinary point-contact transistor according to experiment. When the input signal was reduced to 2 μv the signal output was about equal to the noise output in some units.

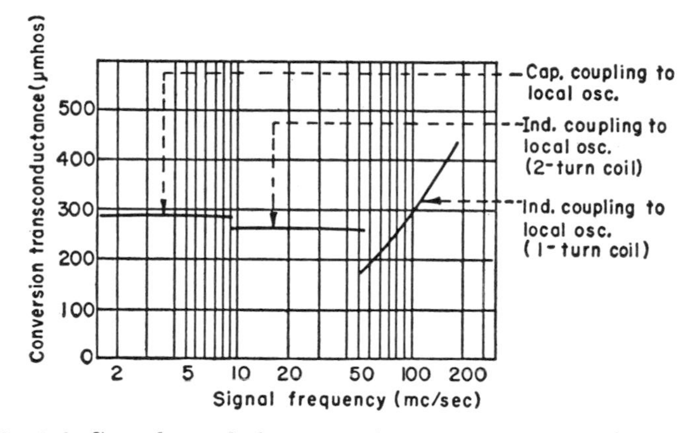

Fig. 8.6. Crystal-tetrode frequency characteristic for several coupling methods. $Q_{i\text{-}f}$ is 10; i-f is 595 kc/sec; E_{signal} is 0.1 v; I_c is 0.2 ma.

2. *Type 3N21 point-contact tetrode transistor*[2]

The Type 3N21 point-contact tetrode transistor is the latest version of the crystal-tetrode mixer. The new construction is illustrated in Fig. 8.7. The germanium crystal and the 3 catwhisker mounting posts are supported upon a glass base in which the four leads of the tetrode transistor are sealed. The dome-shaped envelope consists of a cast resin proportioned to give the required dissipation.

The electrical characteristics of the Type 3N21 tetrode transistor are listed in the Appendix. This transistor is designed primarily for small signal and switching applications. Signal uses include modulation, audio or low radio frequency mixer circuits, signal translation, and as a push-pull detector with gain analogous to two triodes with the grids connected in push-pull and the plates connected in parallel. Switching applications consist of a logical "or" circuit for binary computers, and for control and sequencing operations; gating circuits, and as a ring counter consisting of a two-input diode.

Figure 8.8 gives a logical "or" circuit for binary counters employing the 3N21 transistor tetrode.

It is anticipated that in a number of applications one tetrode will do the work of two triode transistors. The net result will be simplified circuitry in electronic equipment, more compact units, and substan-

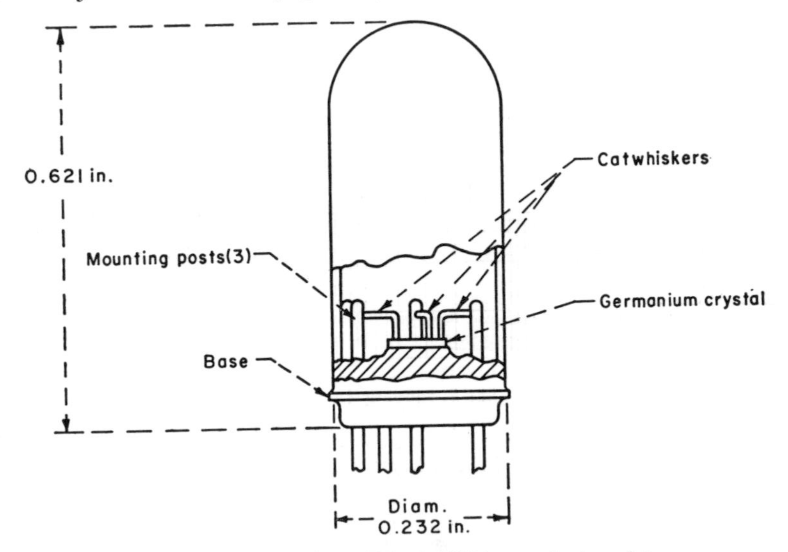

Fig. 8.7. Construction of Type 3N21 tetrode transistor.

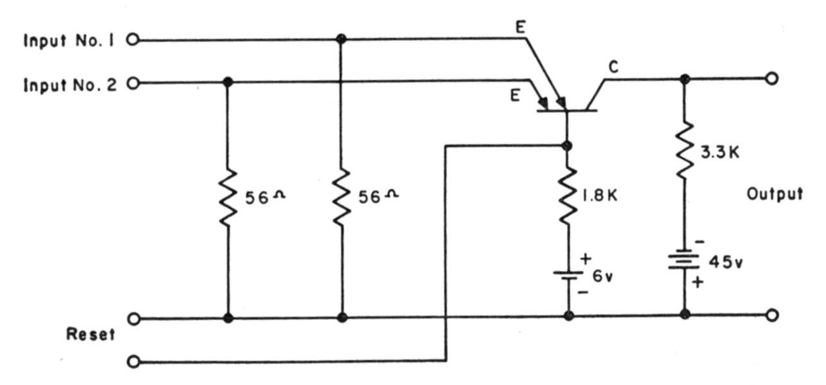

Fig. 8.8. Logical "or" circuit for binary counter employing tetrode transistor.

tially lower cost of manufacture. Long life of the transistor will cut maintenance expense, and low power requirements will reduce current or battery costs of portable equipment.

3. *Junction transistor tetrode for high-frequency use*[3]

If to a conventional junction transistor there is added a fourth electrode which is properly biased, the base resistance of the transistor is greatly reduced. This reduction in base resistance enables the transistor to operate at frequencies ten times or more higher than it otherwise could.

Two other factors that aid in improving the high-frequency response are thinner P layers to increase the cutoff frequency of the current gain alpha, and the decrease of the collector junction area to about 10^{-4} sq in. to reduce the collector capacitance.

Figure 8.9 represents the structure of the junction tetrode. The fourth electrode b_2 is attached to the P layer like the base connection except that it is connected to the opposite side of the bar.

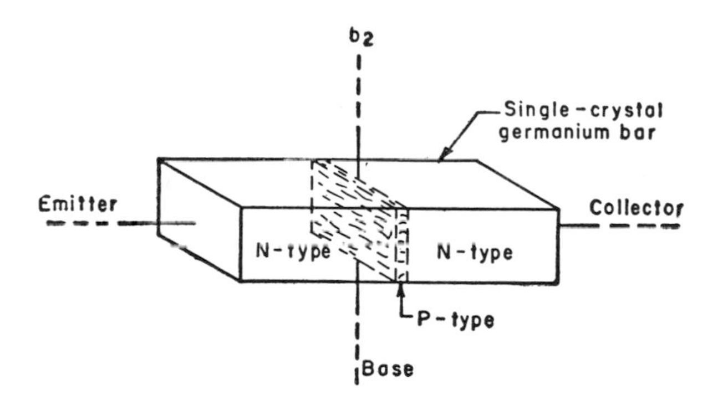

Fig. 8.9. Construction of junction tetrode.

In the discussion which follows, it is assumed that the tetrode transistor has a fixed current bias I_{b2} applied between the base and the added electrode. For this condition the potential of b_2 is about -6 v with respect to the base. The emitter and collector biases are approximately the same as for triode junction transistors.

That part of the emitter junction near b_2 is biased in the reverse direction and does not emit electrons into the P layer. The only part of the emitter junction biased in the proper direction to function as an emitter is that part of the emitter junction near the base contact. Therefore all transistor action occurs in the immediate vicinity of the base contact, reducing the base resistance r_b and improving the high-frequency operation. The b_2 bias current is not critical for good high-frequency performance. Values between 1 and 2 ma have proved satisfactory.

For example, one junction transistor tetrode has a base resistance of 1100 ohms with no b_2 bias. When $-I_{b2}$ was raised to 2 ma, r_b fell to only 40 ohms. At the same time the current gain α decreased from 0.99 to approximately 0.75, increasing the bandwidth with a loss of gain.

The bias applied to b_2 reduced the collector resistance r_c in the direction of decreasing gain. As $-I_{b2}$ increases from 1 to 2 ma, the emitter resistance r_e increases, but not greatly.

When considering the variation of α with frequency, it is convenient to define an α cutoff frequency $f_{c\alpha}$, as the frequency at which the magnitude of α has been reduced from its low-frequency value by a factor of $1/\sqrt{2}$. This frequency is about 15 to 20 mc/sec.

Shockley[4] has shown that $f_{c\alpha}$ should be inversely proportional to the square of the thickness of the P layer and should be about 20 mc/sec for the P layers of roughly 0.0005 in. employed in these transistors.

Figure 8.10 is the circuit of the transistor tetrode in a grounded-base amplifier between a generator of internal resistance R_G and a load resistance R_L. The characteristics of the transistor were $r_e = 6.9$ ohms, $r_b = 92.5$ ohms, $r_c = 0.825$ megohms, $\alpha_0 = 0.82$, $f_{c\alpha} = 18.5$ mc/sec, and $C_c = 1.5$ $\mu\mu$f. It can be shown that the gain of such a grounded-base transistor amplifier will be down 3 db at a frequency f given by

$$\frac{f}{f_{c\alpha}} = 1 - \frac{\alpha_0 r_b}{r_e + r_b + R_G} \tag{1}$$

where $f_{c\alpha}$ is the cutoff frequency for α and α_0 is the low frequency value of α.

When $r_b = 0$ the response is 3 db down for $f = f_{c\alpha}$. For a typical tetrode transistor and $R_G = 25$ ohms, when the fourth electrode is inoperative, the cutoff frequency is at $f = 0.055 f_{c\alpha}$. However, with normal bias current flowing into b_2, the gain is 3 db down for $f = 0.603 f_{c\alpha}$. The cutoff frequency of the amplifier has been increased eleven times by the effect of the tetrode bias. The reductions of both r_b and α_0 are responsible for this rise in the cutoff frequency.

Figure 8.11 indicates the measured and computed gains for the circuit of Fig. 8.10. A gain of 22.3 db is achieved and $f_{c\alpha}$ is 5 mc/sec for $R_L = 5100$ ohms. This compares favorably with the performance of

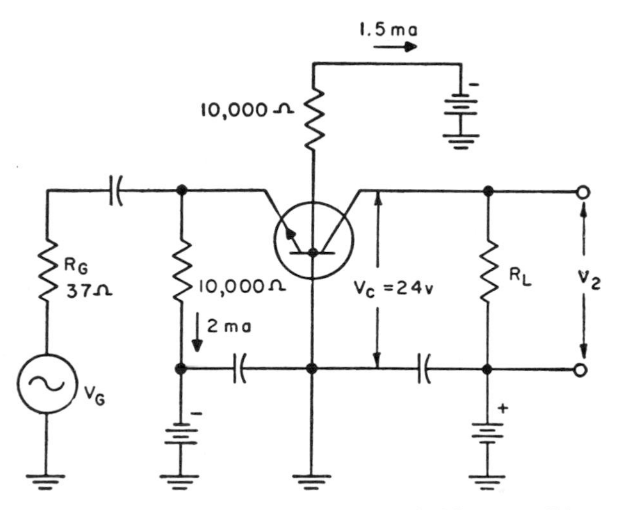

Fig. 8.10. Transistor tetrode in grounded-base amplifier.

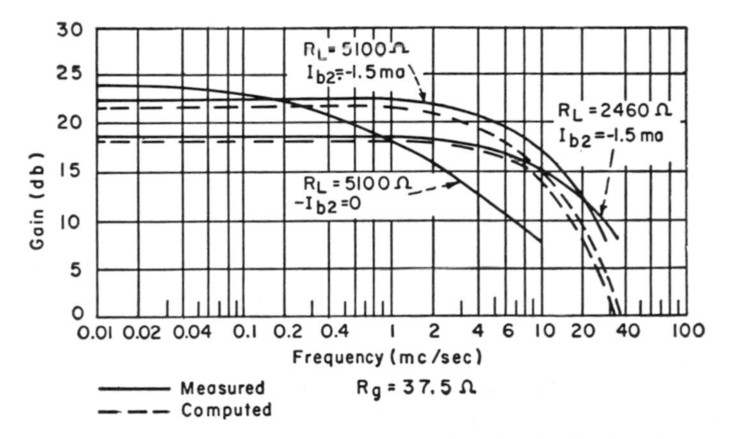

Fig. 8.11. Measured and computed gains for the circuit of Fig. 8.10.

good vacuum tubes. If the transistor is converted to a triode by reducing $-I_{b2}$ to 0, the cutoff frequency falls to only about 0.5 mc/sec.

As the lower solid curve of Fig. 8.11 shows, the cutoff frequency rises to 10 mc/sec and the low-frequency gain decreases to 18.4 db, when R_L is reduced to 2460 ohms.

If a resistive generator feeds a grounded-base amplifier, the output impedance may be represented by a capacitance and a resistance in parallel. When, as illustrated in Fig. 8.12, the amplifier load consists

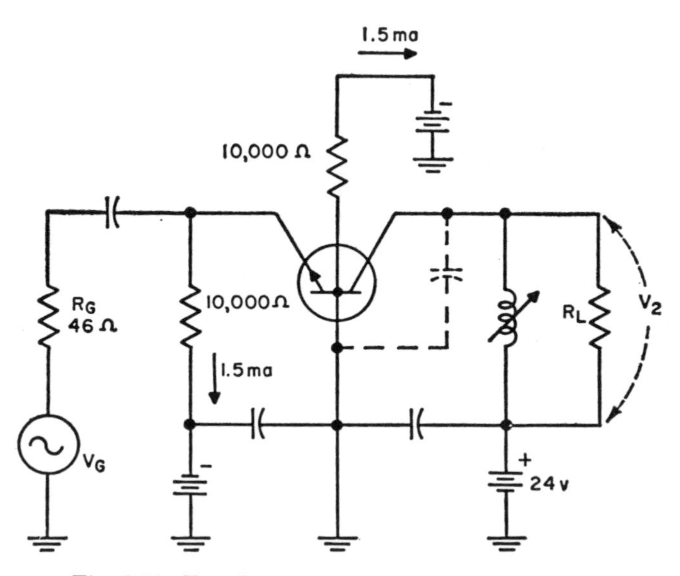

Fig. 8.12. Tuned-transistor tetrode-amplifier circuit.

of a shunt inductance and resistance, the output capacitance will resonate with the inductance, giving a peaked response. If one adjusts R_L for matched impedances, one can achieve maximum gain at the frequency of resonance.

Figure 8.13 presents the curves obtained by changing the load inductance to get various resonant frequencies and adjusting R_L at each frequency for maximum gain. At 50 mc/sec the measured gain was 11.8 db. The equivalent parallel resistance and capacitance of the measured output impedance of the amplifier are shown in Fig. 8.14.

Since the output capacitance and resistance of Fig. 8.14 are com-

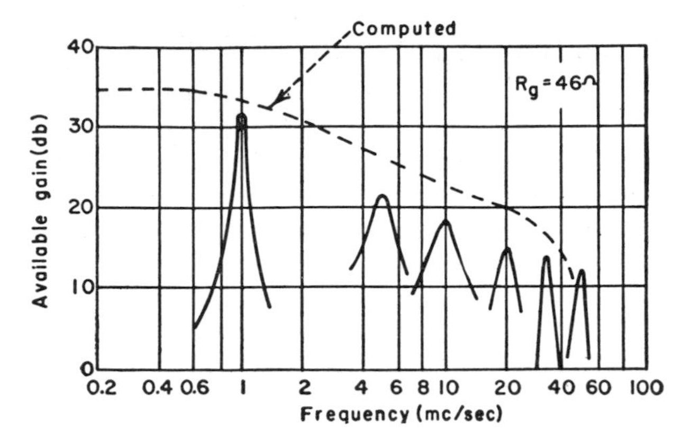

Fig. 8.13. Measured and computed available gain for the circuit of Fig. 8.12.

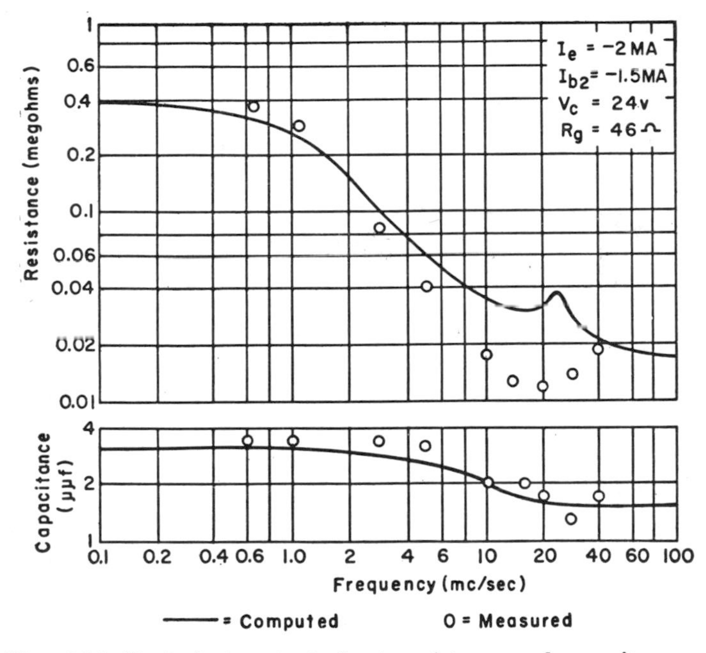

Fig. 8.14. Equivalent output shunt resistance and capacitance of grounded-base amplifier.

paratively low, it would seem that one could construct fairly wide bandpass amplifiers without sacrificing too much of the gain obtained in the narrow-band stages of Fig. 8.13. Accordingly, the circuit of Fig. 8.15 was designed for a 9 mc/sec bandwidth centered around 32 mc/sec. A gain of 15 db was achieved with a gain-band product of 280 mc/sec.

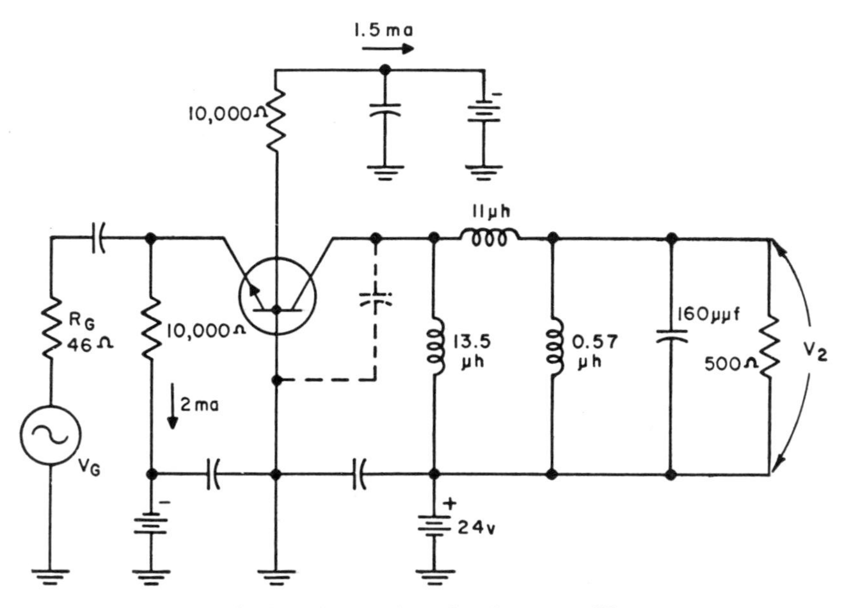

Fig. 8.15. Tetrode-transistor bandpass amplifier stage.

The performance of tetrode transistors as oscillators at high frequencies was observed in the circuit of Fig. 8.16. At higher frequencies, the input impedance at the emitter becomes inductive, and therefore provision is made for adjusting the capacitor in the feedback path to the emitter.

Most tetrodes oscillated sinusoidally in this circuit up to frequencies of 80 to 100 mc/sec, with some at 100 to 130 mc/sec. During these measurements the collector dissipation was kept at about 30 mw. The measured output for one transistor between 40 and 75 mc/sec was approximately 1 mw. At 100 mc/sec the output was 0.25 mw, and at 115 mc/sec it was 0.06 mw.

An interesting application of a junction tetrode transistor is in a miniature coaxial amplifier[5] designed and constructed by Bell Telephone Laboratories to study some of the problems involved in making a wide-band amplifier which could be inserted in small coaxial cables. Such a combination of amplifiers and cables might be utilized for transmitting broad-band signals, such as television, over short distances.

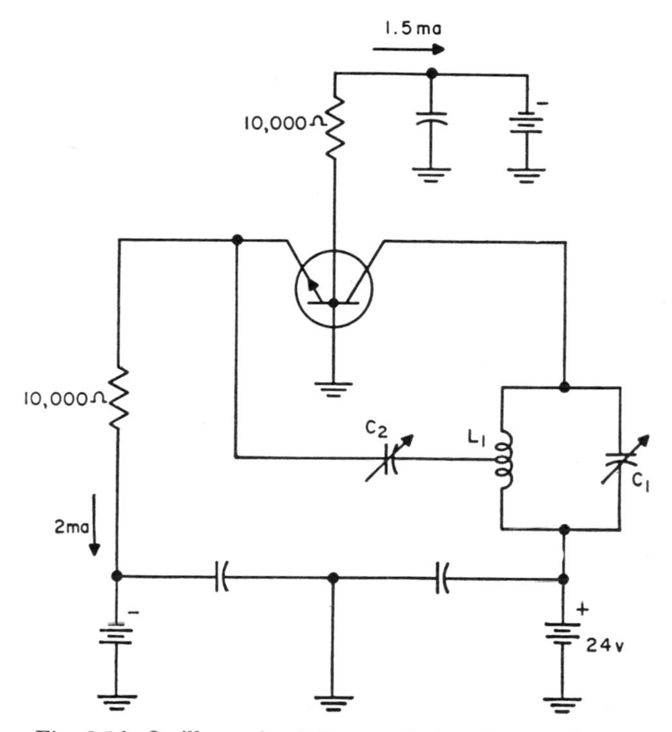

Fig. 8.16. Oscillator circuit for tetrode-junction transistors.

Although this amplifier contains two transformers, one inductor, four resistors, one capacitor, two voltage-regulating diodes, two coaxial jacks, and a junction tetrode transistor, it is only 0.15 in. in diameter and 1.5 in. in length. It has a bandwidth extending from 0.4 mc/sec to 11 mc/sec, and achieves a gain of 22 db flat within 0.1 db over this range.

4. *Four-terminal transistor for trigger service*[6]

A patent has been granted on a special four-terminal transistor for trigger service. Three metal electrodes are plated on the crystal. There is a control element in addition to the usual emitter, collector, and base. No catwhiskers are employed. As shown in Fig. 8.17, such

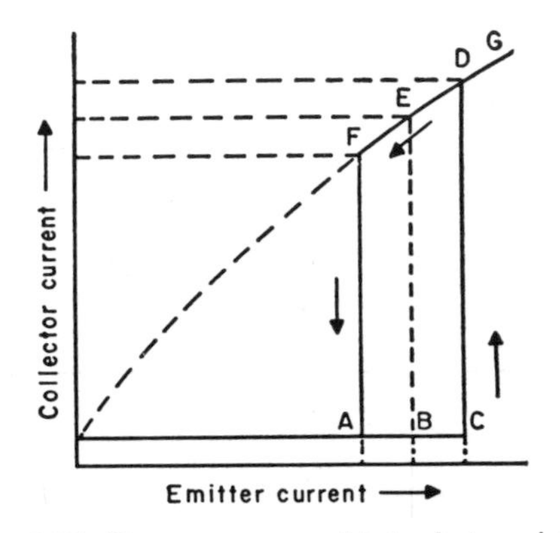

Fig. 8.17. Response curve of tetrode transistor.

a device exhibits a collector characteristic similar to that of hysteresis.

Normally the operating point is centered at *B*, where the collector current is low. If the emitter bias is increased, as by a positive pulse, the operating point moves to *C*, and the collector current rises abruptly to *D* (and then increases gradually to *G* as the emitter current

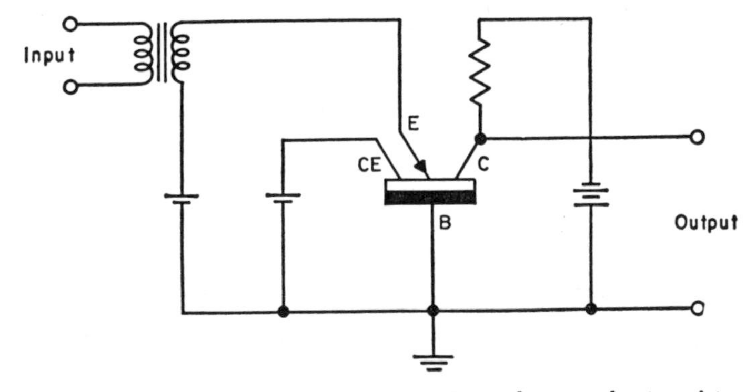

Fig. 8.18. Trigger circuit for plated-electrode tetrode transistor.

continues to increase). When the pulse dies out, the current will fall off to point *E*. On the arrival of a negative pulse, the collector current follows the path *EF*, then drops abruptly to *A*. The operating point returns to *B* at the end of the pulse.

Figure 8.18 indicates the tetrode transistor circuit. The control element *CE* is biased at a few volts. This voltage determines the actual shape of the hysteresis curve. The other elements function like those of a conventional transistor.

5. *Pentode transistors*[2]

The first commercially available pentode transistor is of the point-contact type. It has four catwhisker wires, three for the emitters and one for the collector, making contact with the germanium crystal. It is expected that in a number of potential applications one pentode will do the work of three triodes.

This pentode transistor is designed primarily for switching and also finds application as a mixer or modulator. Basically, the unit is a regular transistor with provisions for three inputs. This permits controlling the switching action of the transistor from three sources, as well as allowing mixing of three signals with only one transistor. In this way circuit simplifications can be affected and more compact equipment can be built.

Maximum ratings include -60 v collector voltage, 100 mw collector dissipation, -50 v emitter voltage on the three emitters, 30 mw emitter dissipation (for each emitter), and an ambient temperature of 50°C. For switching applications, the unit has a rise time of 0.2 μsec and a turn-off of 0.5 μsec.

References

1. Rowland W. Haegele, "A Crystal Tetrode Mixer," *The Sylvania Technologist*, Vol. II, No. 3, July 1949, pp. 2–4.
2. Sylvania Electric Products, Inc., "Transistors with Multiple Elements," *Electrical Manufacturing*, Vol. LII, No. 3, Sept. 1953, pp. 163–164. Copyright 1953 by the Gage Publishing Co.
3. R. L. Wallace, Jr., L. G. Schimf, and E. Dickten, "A Junction Transistor Tetrode for High-Frequency Use," *Proc. IRE*, Vol. XL, No. 11, Nov. 1952, pp. 1395–1400.

4. W. Shockley, M. Sparks, and G. K. Teal, "P-N Junction Transistors," *Phys. Rev.*, Vol. LIII, No. 1, July 1951, p. 151.

5. R. L. Wallace, "Smallest Amplifier," *Radio-Electronics*, Vol. XXV, No. 2, Feb. 1954, p. 95. Copyright 1954 by Gernsback Publications.

6. Charles De Boismaison White, "4-Terminal Transistor," *U. S. Patent 2,624,016*, assigned to International Standard Electric Corp., New York, *Radio-Electronics*, Vol. XXIV, No. 8, Aug. 1953, p. 86. Copyright 1953 by Gernsback Publications.

Chapter 9

PHOTODIODES AND PHOTOTRANSISTORS

1. *Introduction*

Quantum mechanics as well as the physical theory of transistors indicates that a bright light flashed on a germanium crystal can momentarily disturb the valence-bond structure. A high-energy photon will eject an electron from one of the bonds, and this electron is then free to move through the crystal lattice. The hole thus created can also move, since an electron from an adjoining bond may move into it, producing a net displacement of the hole. Hence light can create electron-hole pairs, which can act as current carriers in the germanium crystal. Light can be considered to perform the same function as the emitter in a transistor.

Just as there are point-contact and junction transistors, so there are point-contact and junction phototransistors.

2. *The point-contact phototransistor*[1]

The absorption of light can charge-produce the exciting signal in a transistor. A photoconductivity cell, known as the phototransistor, was a by-product of the development of the transistor. Figure 9.1

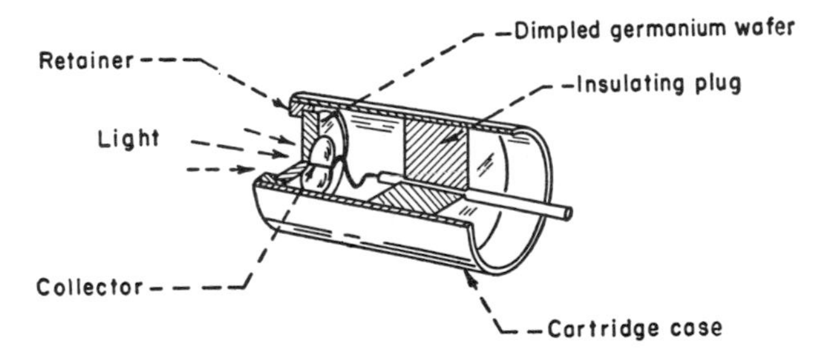

Fig. 9.1. Longitudinal section of the phototransistor.

shows a longitudinal section of the point-contact phototransistor. A pill-shaped wafer of germanium has a spherical "dimple" ground in one side so that the wafer is about 0.003 in. thick at the center. Clean surfaces are obtained by etching the wafer as is done for germanium diodes. The periphery of the wafer is held by a retaining ring which is forced into one end of a metal cartridge. The collector electrode consists of a 0.005 in. phosphor bronze pointed wire which bears upon the germanium at the center of the dimple. The wire is attached to a metal pin embedded in an insulating plug which fits into the other end of the cartridge.

When the germanium absorbs light, the resistance of the germanium element between the peripheral contact and the collector decreases. If a d-c circuit is formed by connecting the phototransistor in series with a load resistance and battery, a small current will flow with the photocell in the dark. However, if light falls on the unit, the current will increase in proportion to the amount of light. The current increase caused by the light is known as the photocurrent.

Only when light falls in the immediate vicinity of the collector on the illuminated surface of the germanium is a substantial photocurrent response obtained. Figure 9.2 indicates the change in the collec-

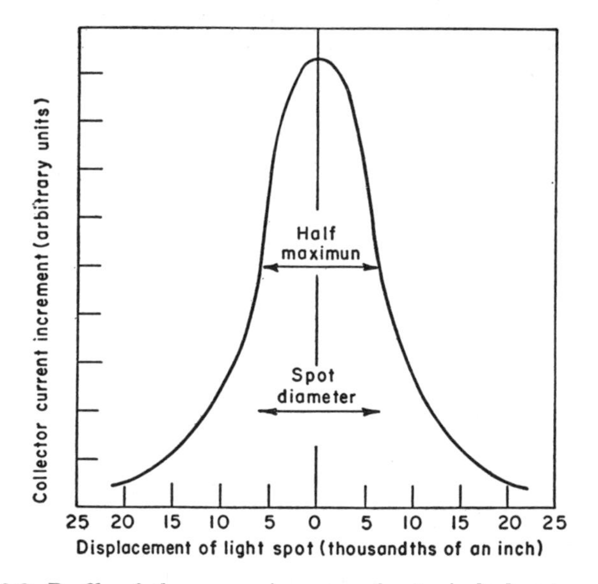

Fig. 9.2. Profile of the responsive area of a typical phototransistor.

tor current increment with the displacement of the light spot from the center of the responsive area of a typical point-contact phototransistor. The width of the sensitive area at half maximum is found to be about 0.008 in., when the diameter of the spot of light is taken into consideration.

If light is permitted to fall uniformly over the germanium surface, a large percentage of the light will be wasted, and the spatial resolving power of the phototransistor will not be realized. Therefore lenses should be provided for these cells to focus the available light onto the responsive areas. This may be accomplished by fitting a small lens into one end of the cartridge mounting. The cartridge is made sufficiently long to accommodate the focal distance of the lens. The phototransistor has a high spatial resolving power because of the small size of its responsive area.

Figure 9.3 gives the static collector characteristics for a phototransistor. These represent the variation of collector current with collector voltage for various values of steady light flux. In each instance the light flux was focused well within the responsive area of the cell. The dark current should be as small as possible for best observation and utilization of the photocurrent. The cell is biased as a crystal diode in the reverse direction to make the dark current small. For N-type germanium the collector voltage should be negative with respect to the cell cartridge. The "dark" curve is simply the reverse characteristic of a germanium diode, whereas the other curves represent the modification of this characteristic caused by different light fluxes.

When operated with time-varying light flux, the cell is connected in series with a load resistor of from 10,000 to 30,000 ohms for good impedance matching. The dashed line in Fig. 9.3 represents a load line of 20,000 ohms. The collector voltage and current for each light flux are shown by the intersections of the load line with the curves for the various values of light falling on the cell. The difference between the applied voltage and the voltage drop across the 20,000 ohm load is the collector voltage. The current output response in this instance is about 0.07 ma per millilumen. This is equivalent to an alternating current output of about 5 mw for a light fluctuation from dark to 20 millilumens.

The output of the cell is essentially constant up to at least 200 kc with fluctuating light.

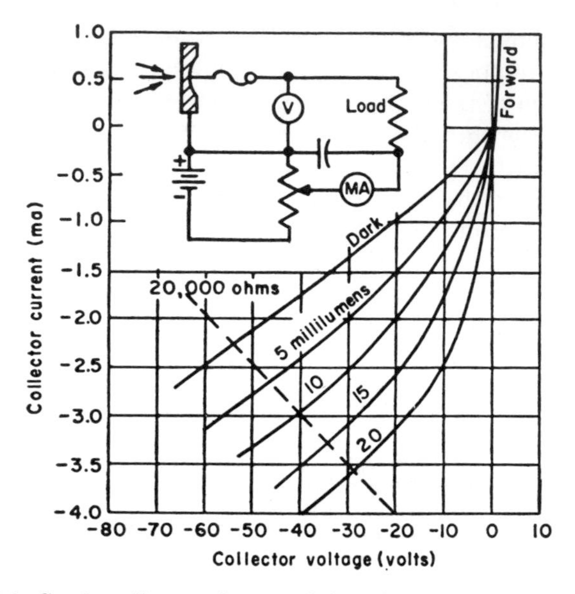

Fig. 9.3. Static collector characteristics of a point-contact phototransistor.

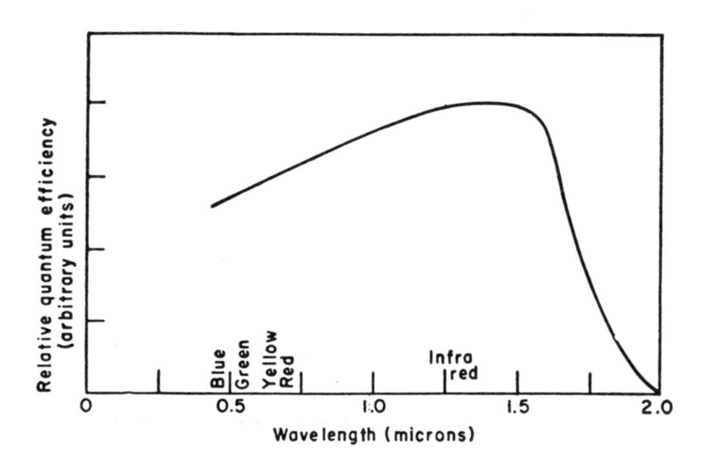

Fig. 9.4. Variation of relative quantum efficiency with spectral wavelength for a point-contact phototransistor.

The germanium phototransistor has a responsive area limited to the immediate vicinity of the collector contact in the center of the germanium wafer for the following reasons. The distribution of bias current flow lines in the semiconductor concentrates the electric field near the collector. When holes and electrons are liberated here, the charges are separated and collected before recombination can occur. However, if such electron-hole pairs are produced near the periphery of the wafer where the electric field is weak, the charges recombine and disappear before they can be collected.

Figure 9.4 represents the relative quantum efficiency versus the spectral wavelength for a point-contact phototransistor. The long wavelength limit is in the neighborhood of 2.0 microns. This wavelength corresponds to a quantum energy of 0.61 electron volt, which represents the least energy that can create a free electron-hole pair in germanium. It may therefore be considered the activation energy for the photoprocess. The sensitivity is greatest in the spectral region from 1.0 to 1.5 microns. Fortunately, this is the same region in which the quantum emission from ordinary incandescent lamps is the largest. Therefore the germanium cell is especially useful with such sources of light.

3. *The M-1740 P-N junction photocell* [2]

Figure 9.5 shows a sectional drawing of the M-1740 P-N junction photocell. A bar of single-crystal germanium, about 0.030 by 0.030

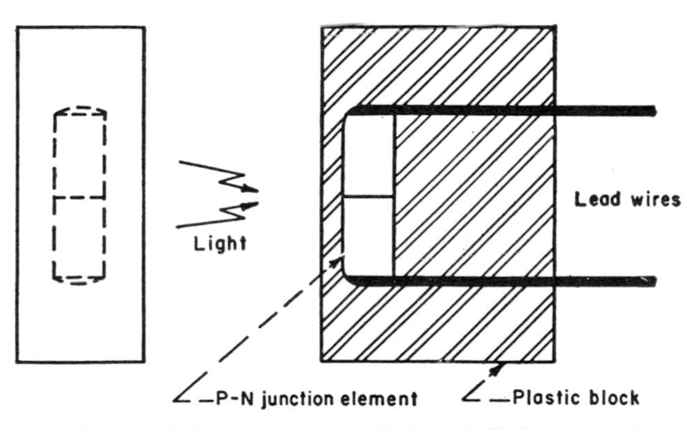

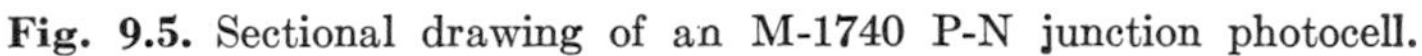

Fig. 9.5. Sectional drawing of an M-1740 P-N junction photocell.

by 0.125 in. in size, forms the photoelectric element, which has a P-N junction in the middle between its two ends. Each end of the bar has a terminal lead attached to it. A small rectangular block of plastic measuring $\frac{1}{4}$ by $\frac{3}{16}$ by $\frac{3}{32}$ in. protects the element. One of the $\frac{1}{4}$ by $\frac{3}{32}$ in. sides of the block permits light to fall upon the element, and the leads are taken out of the opposite side. The lateral surfaces of the block are covered with black paint, and a red dot on the side of the block indicates the positive lead wire for the biasing circuit.

The usual circuit consists of the cell in series with a direct voltage biasing source and a load resistance across which the output signal is developed. The P-N barrier is biased in the reverse direction (P-type end negative). With the cell in the dark a small reverse leakage current flows. The reverse current increases when light falls on the cell.

Light must be carefully focused upon the P-N junction area if the best response of the element is to be obtained. The light must fall within a few tenths of a millimeter of the junction line to be effective. Figure 9.6 indicates the sensitivity of a typical M-1740 photocell versus the position of a small spot of light when it moves across the germanium along a line perpendicular to the junction. At half maximum the width of this response curve is about 0.75 mm.

There is a simple physical explanation for the shape of the above curve. The photocurrent is the result at the P-N junction of the collector of minority carriers (electrons in the P-region and holes in the N-area) liberated at and near the junction by the photoelectric process. The electric field is negligible except in the junction layer itself, and most of the carriers diffuse to the junction. The farther away from the junction they are liberated the farther they must diffuse to be collected, and the more probable it is that they will disappear by recombination on the way. This explains the decrease of sensitivity on each side of the maximum, which coincides with the junction.

There is a noticeable asymmetry in the curve of Fig. 9.6. This is partly because holes and electrons have different diffusion mobilities, and partly because of the difference in the lifetimes of holes in N-type material and electrons in P-type material. Analysis of this curve gives a lifetime of 17 μsec for electrons on the P side and 30 μsec for holes on the N side of the photoelement.

Figure 9.7 represents the current-voltage characteristics of the M-1740 photocell. The data for ten typical cells were averaged to obtain these characteristics. The curves show the performance for darkness and for several different incident light fluxes. To obtain these data the light was focused into a spot about 0.5 mm in diameter, centered on the P-N junction by manipulating the position of the cell relative to the light spot for maximum output. A tungsten filament operated at about 2400°K color temperature constituted the light source.

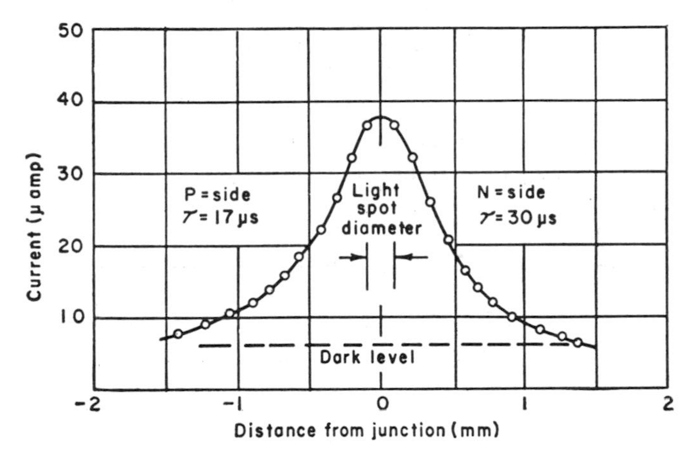

Fig. 9.6. Spatial distribution of sensitivity for a typical M-1740 photocell.

The maximum dark current of the M-1740 photocell at 90 v is 20 μa. The dark currents of most M-1740 units range from 1 to 5 μa at room temperatures. The constant thermal generation of new minority charges in the germanium within a few diffusion lengths of the junction, and their diffusion into and collection by the junction, cause these reverse leakage currents across the junction.

It should be noticed that the characteristics of Fig. 9.7 display a current saturation in the region from 1 to 100 v. This comes about because the diffusion of photocurrent carriers from their generation point to the junction takes place in substantially field-free space irrespective of the voltage drop across the terminals of the bar, most of which appears as the drop across the junction. In this saturation section the slopes of the curves of Fig. 9.7 represent a-c impedance of about 10 megohms.

Figure 9.8(A) is an equivalent circuit which describes these characteristics. This equivalent circuit consists of a germanium body resistance r_b in series with a junction resistance r_c shunted by a current generator kl, where k is a constant of proportionality and l is the effective light flux on the photocell. The constant k is usually given in milliamperes per millilumen, and the flux l is generally expressed in millilumens at a specified color temperature. The equation for the short-circuit output current is

$$i_c = kl \frac{r_c}{r_c + r_b} = Kl \tag{1}$$

where K is a new constant of proportionality easily accessible to external measurement. Since r_b is about 100 ohms compared with several megohms for r_c, then K and k are nearly equal for all practical purposes.

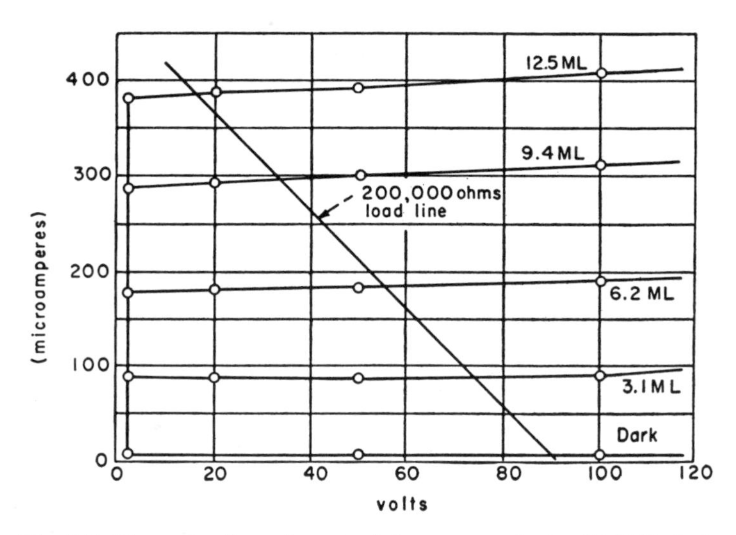

Fig. 9.7. Current voltage characteristics, average for ten M-1740 photocells.

When k (or K), r_c, and r_b are determined, the P-N junction photocell is specified. The barrier resistance r_c is best determined from the slopes of the static characteristics, since it is too large to measure conveniently by dynamic methods. The resistance r_b can be measured by biasing the junction in the forward direction and determining the asymptotic resistance approached with increasing voltage, or can be computed from the resistivities and geometry of the germanium element.

In practice it is seldom necessary to know r_b and r_c. The former is much smaller than any load resistance which is likely to be employed with this photocell, whereas r_c is much larger than any such load. Therefore an approximate equivalent circuit will have $r_b = 0$ and $r_c =$ infinity. Thus the a-c generator kl operates directly into the output load. This approximation is accurate to within 5 per cent for a load from 2000 ohms to 0.5 megohm. Hence it is necessary only to determine the k of the photocell. (For the approximate equivalent circuit K and k are the same.) The direct current is measured with a short-circuit load, first with the device in the dark and then with a known light flux upon the junction, the difference equal to kl. The standard practice is to utilize a 90 v bias and a flux of 6.25 millilumens of 2400°K color temperature light focused into a spot of 0.5 mm diameter centered on the junction line. Typical values for k are from 0.03 to 0.04 ma per millilumen.

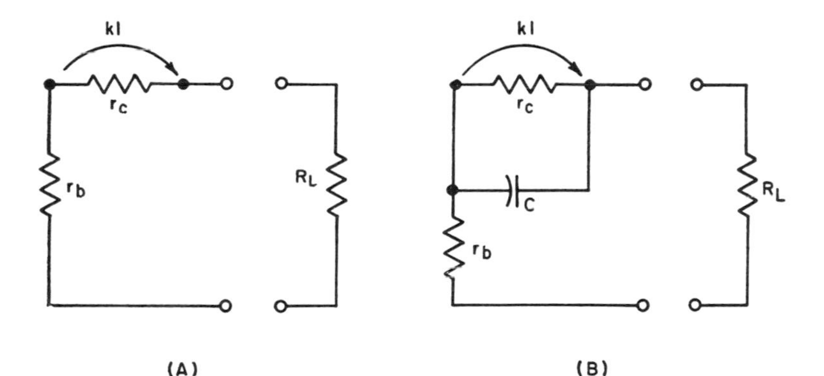

Fig. 9.8. (A) Low-frequency a-c equivalent circuit, and (B) high-frequency equivalent circuit.

When step-function light inputs or a-c light signals having frequencies of about 100 kc or higher are applied to the photocell, one must consider the effect of the barrier capacitance. In Fig. 9.8(B), which gives the high-frequency equivalent circuit, this capacitance is shown in parallel with r_c. A simple analysis enables one to solve for the load current. Once again, assume that for all practical purposes R_L is much larger than r_b and much smaller than r_c; then the load current may be expressed as

$$i \approx \frac{kl}{1 + j\omega CR_L} \tag{2}$$

At low frequency this equation reduces to kl, with increasing frequency it remains essentially constant until the second term in the denominator becomes appreciable compared with unity, and with further increase in frequency it decreases inversely with frequency, in quadrature with the light input.

It has not been feasible to measure directly the barrier layer capacitances of M-1740 photocells. However, capacitances of a few micromicrofarads for such junctions back-biased at 50 v have been determined by calculations based on the P-N junction theory of Shockley.[3] At frequencies of about 1 megacycle the term ωCR_L becomes comparable with unity for a load resistance of 0.1 megohm.

In practice the effects of diffusion transit time of the carriers usually override the simple barrier capacitance effects. When liberated some distance away from the junction, holes or electrons may require microseconds or tens of microseconds to diffuse into the barrier and be collected. This process causes an additional time lag to that produced by the barrier capacitance. Anderson measured the delay in response to short, steep light pulses incident upon a photocell at various distances from the junction. He found that as the illuminated spot was moved farther away from the junction the current collection pulses were more delayed, more attenuated, and more spread out. The shape of the light flashes and other experimental limitations caused these experiments to lack resolution in time below about 2 μsec. However, these indicate that the delay in response can be reduced to the above values, by masking down the photocell window so that light can fall no farther away than about 0.010 in. from the junction.

For a temperature change from 20°C to 55°C the dark current of a germanium P-N junction photocell increases approximately 10 times. This increase seems to be independent of the actual room temperature dark current. The measurements of dark and light currents for six cells at the above temperatures are presented in Table 5. The conditions for these tests were 24 v (direct) and a flux of 6.25 millilumens for the light currents.

TABLE 5. DARK AND LIGHT CURRENTS FOR SIX M-1740 PHOTOCELLS AT 20°C AND 55°C

Unit No.	Dark current, μa		Light current, μa	
	20°C	55°C	20°C	55°C
1	3.7	35	190	270
2	8.6	91	160	240
3	1.8	19	180	252
4	3.1	26	206	292
5	12.4	108	196	268
6	4.7	52	164	242

These data demonstrate that the temperature rise caused a larger increase in the light current than in the dark current for the same cell. Hence raising the temperature increases the sensitivity. This results from temperature variations of mobility, diffusion constant, and minority carrier lifetime.

Montgomery has made measurements of noise in P-N junction photocells. He determined the short-circuit noise alternating current in a 1 cps band at 1000 cps. Table 6 gives the values for a typical photocell for two bias direct voltages and several light-flux conditions.

Although the direct current may increase almost 100 times from the dark to the greatest light condition for a given bias voltage, the change in the noise current could hardly be distinguished from the uncertainties of measurements. When the appearance of the noise of these junction photocells was examined on an oscilloscope, no irregularities were observed over a total of several hours. The noise exhibited no bursts or spikes larger than a smooth distribution would warrant.

TABLE 6. NOISE MEASUREMENTS FOR A TYPICAL M-1740 PHOTOCELL

Supply direct voltage	Dark		Light		More light	
	d-c μa	noise μμa	d-c μa	noise μμa	d-c μa	noise μμa
45	6.7	30	154	25	620	50
90	7.6	45	144	55	600	60

The noise power available from a typical M-1740 P-N junction photocell is about 2×10^{-15} w per cycle at 1000 cps as calculated from Table 2. This compares with about 10^{-13} w per cycle for a point-contact photocell, or the junction unit has a 17 db lower noise power.

When the M-1740 photocell is exposed to a high-humidity environment for a prolonged period of time, an upward drift of dark current occurs. The higher the temperature, the greater is the rate of increase. However, one may reverse this effect and restore the initial characteristics by drying out the unit, provided that the increase is not carried too far. Operation above 60°C should be avoided. A permanent upward shift in dark current may result from shipping and storage exposure at temperatures of 70°C or higher for more than a few days.

An operational life test for more than two years under conditions of ordinary room temperature and humidity showed that these photocells did not depart essentially from their initial characteristics. The same favorable results were obtained from other tests with different electrical and optical conditions but under the same environmental conditions over shorter periods of time.

The heat dissipation of the unit is restricted because of its small size. One should select a load resistance large enough to limit the continuous dissipation in the photocell to less than 50 mw, for applications with large supply voltages and photocurrents of 1 ma or more. However, in switching transitions the instantaneous dissipations may exceed 1 w for a few milliseconds.

4. *Type 1N188 germanium P-N junction photodiode*[4]

The Type 1N188 germanium P-N junction photodiode was designed to be a light detector, especially in the near infrared region. It may be coupled with an a-c amplifier provided that a mechanical or electromechanical light chopper is combined with it to supply a pulse signal for alternating current flow. The current is then a function of the light intensity. This photosensitive diode is responsive to frequencies as high as 25 kc/sec.

The electrical characteristics are 175 v maximum applied voltage, less than 40 v average applied voltage, 20 μa maximum dark current with 40 v applied, and 10 μa per millilumen minimum sensitivity.

The unit is housed in a miniature metal case in which the sensitive element is suspended in a transparent plastic which provides complete protection from humidity. The light-sensitive region is approximately 0.5 sq mm.

Figure 9.9 shows typical characteristics at 25°C for the Type 1N188 germanium P-N junction photodiode.

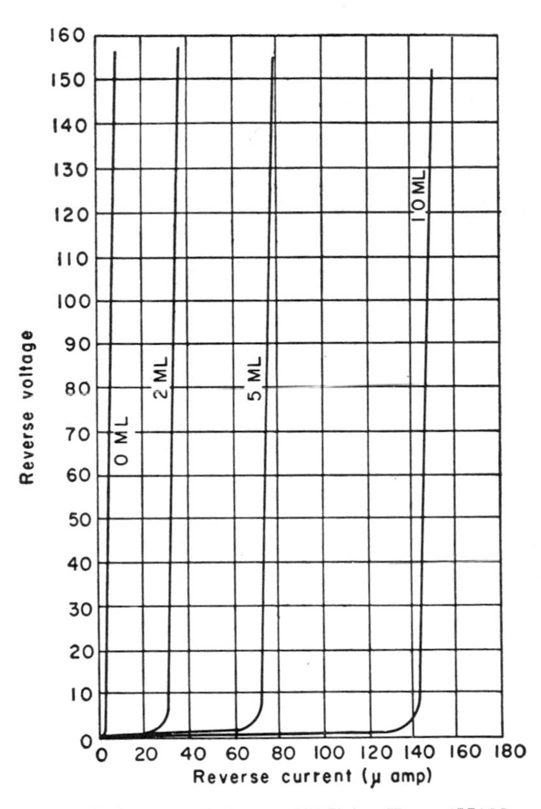

Fig. 9.9. Typical characteristics at 25°C for Type 1N188 germanium P-N junction photodiode.

5. *Type X-25 germanium N-P-N junction phototransistor*[5]

The Type X-25 germanium N-P-N junction phototransistor has sufficient power output to operate a relay. The power output is about

60 mw. The X-25 may be considered as a light-sensitive device with an incorporated amplifier.

All sides of the unit are opaque except the light-sensitive $\frac{3}{16}$ in. by $\frac{11}{32}$ in. face located on the side opposite the connecting wires. Figure 9.10 gives the average estimated characteristics for experimental X-25 phototransistor.

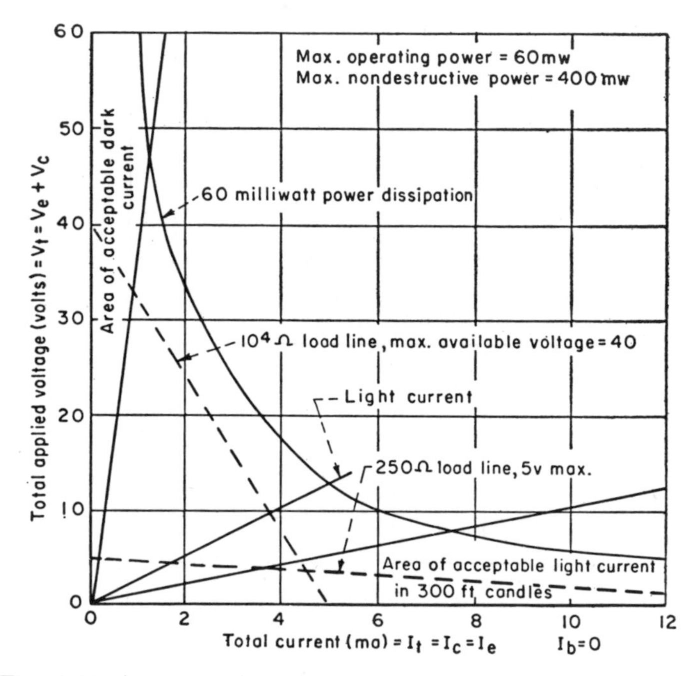

Fig. 9.10. Average estimated characteristics for experimental X-25 phototransistor.

6. *Device characteristics and applications*[6]

The advantages of photodiodes and phototransistors are as follows:

1. Low power consumption
2. Small power loss (high efficiency)
3. Exceedingly low operating voltages
4. Low noise level
5. Large optical sensitivity
6. Small physical size

7. High optical resolving power
8. Simple associated circuitry
9. Reasonable cost
10. Physical ruggedness
11. Long life.

The disadvantages of photodiodes and phototransistors are:

1. Protection against moisture required
2. Temperature sensitivity
3. Some lack of production uniformity.

A typical characteristic curve for a photodiode is shown in Fig. 9.11. The absolute light sensitivity is approximately 35 μa per millilumen. This property may vary from 15 to 70 μa per millilumen. The dark current is often specified to be less than 20 μa at 40 v. Although the theoretical dynamic dark resistance is almost infinite, in practice a

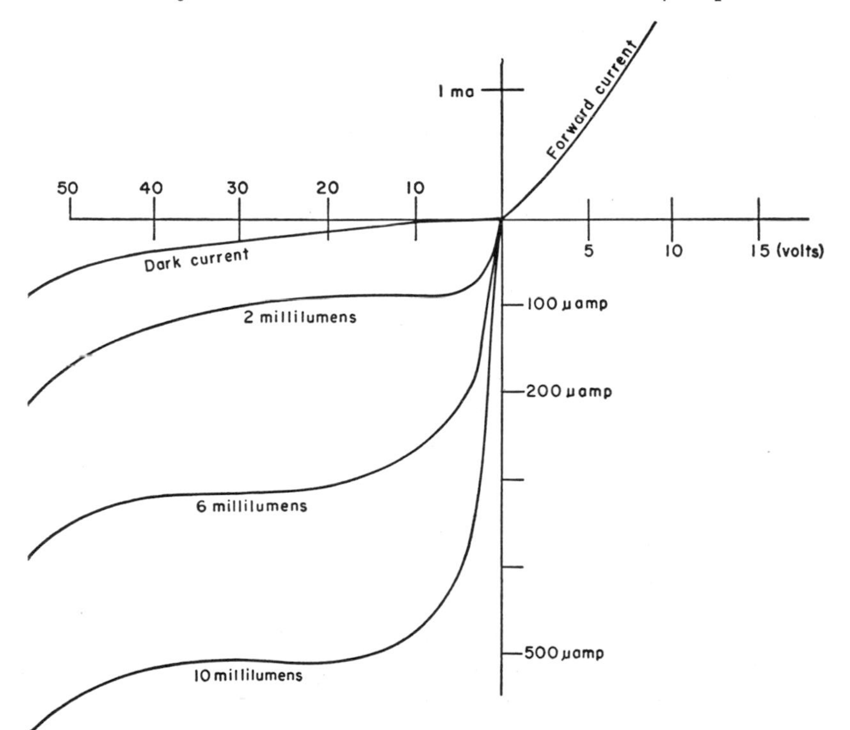

Fig. 9.11. A typical characteristic curve for a photodiode.

value of about 2 megohms is achieved. Also, the light resistance should be almost infinite, but its values are similar to those of the dark resistance.

The maximum operating power level is about 60 mw and is limited by the amount of internally generated heat (I^2R) which can be dissipated without significant temperature rise. Within limits the elements can be heated above the point of operation, permitted to cool, and returned to normal working conditions. The minimum destructive power level is approximately 400 mw, beyond which there is no return. The maximum applied voltage is determined by the dark current and the Zener voltage. It is normally about 40 to 125 v.

Theoretically the photodiode should respond to interrupted light that flashes with a frequency greater than 100 kc/sec. Actual tests with a flashing neon tube have shown a response up to 8000 cps.

Photodiodes are temperature sensitive. Operation above 50°C is not recommended, and operation above 100°C may destroy the unit. With proper care the life of a photodiode should be long.

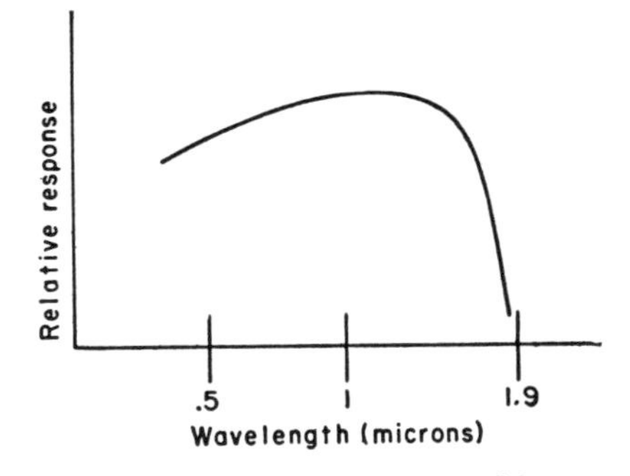

Fig. 9.12. Relative light response versus spectral frequency for a photodiode.

The sensitive region is limited to the area near the junction, and hence is small. A typical junction bar measures 1 mm by 1 mm by 4 mm. The sensitive region is only 0.1 mm wide and 1 mm long. Figure 9.12 gives the relative light response versus the spectral frequency.

Many of the previous statements apply also to phototransistors. The latter have the great advantage of tremendously increased sensitivity of about $1/(1 - \alpha)$, or from 50 to 500 times that of photodiodes.

The photodiode or phototransistor can be employed in nearly every application which now utilizes other kinds of light sensitive elements. Some of these are:

1. Photoelectric controls
2. Optical tape read out
3. Punch card optical read out
4. Telegraphic optical read out
5. Infrared burglar alarms
6. Liquid level controls
7. Automatic automobile headlight dimmers
8. Moving picture variable density sound read out
9. Automatic brillance controls on TV receivers.

7. *Basic circuits of photodiodes and phototransistors*[7]

Germanium photodiodes or phototransistors can be employed to advantage in practically any device now utilizing photoemissive vacuum diodes or gas filled diodes. One must analyze the available light and the amount of light falling on the sensitive region of the

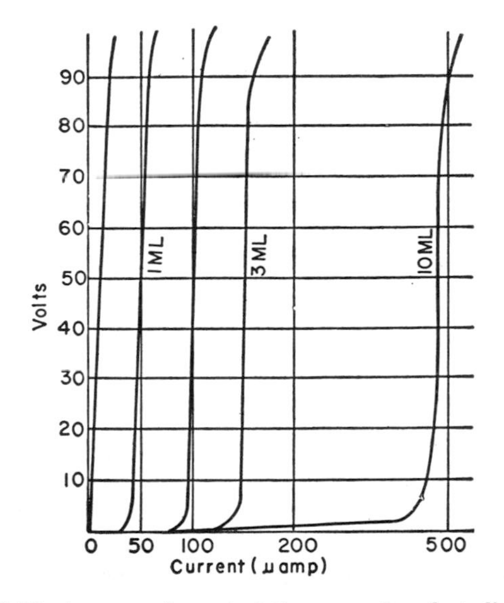

Fig. 9.13. Average characteristic curves for photodiodes.

unit. Since the sensitive area of these germanium photoelements is generally smaller than 0.01 sq in., a collecting lens is necessary. This can be a simple double convex lens costing no more than 50 cents. However, the light must be collected and focused on the sensitive area of the unit; the germanium photoelements cannot be simply substituted for a gas filled photodiode in the latter's physical layout. The next step is to analyze the output of the device by referring to typical characteristic curves for photodiodes and phototransistors as shown in Figs. 9.13 and 9.14, respectively.

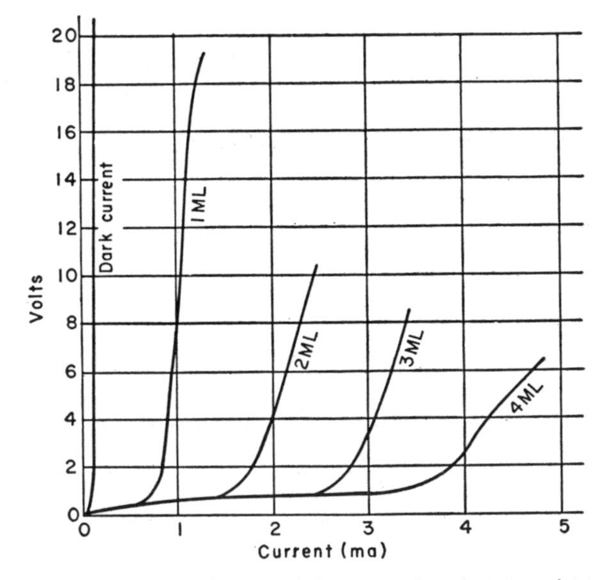

Fig. 9.14. Average characteristic curves for phototransistors.

Several fundamental ways of employing photodiodes and phototransistors are as follows:

1. Simple d-c output
2. Simple a-c output
3. D-c output plus d-c amplifier
4. A-c output plus a-c amplifier.
5. Balanced bridge circuits with either d-c or a-c outputs.

The above circuits may utilize point-contact transistor amplifiers, junction transistor amplifiers, or vacuum tube amplifiers.

Although photosensitive germanium elements can yield a continuously variable output current as a linear function of a continuously variable light input, immediate applications should preferably be restricted to off-on types. This allows a greater safety factor to compensate for temperature effects and variations due to lack of production uniformity. The light intensity can produce at the output of the device an output voltage, an output current, or an output power.

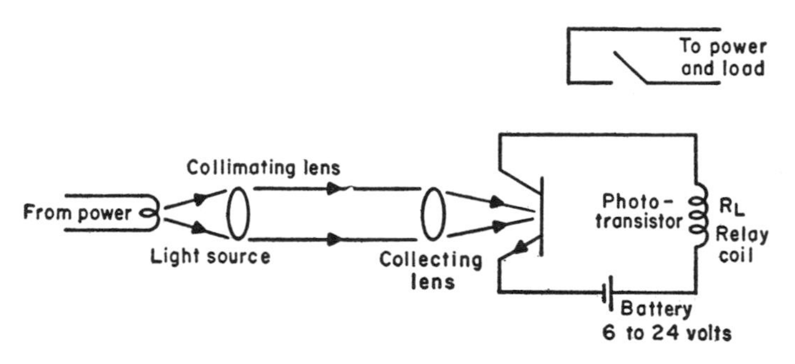

Fig. 9.15. Phototransistor relay circuit.

Figure 9.15 gives the simplest type of circuit where the load is a relay. In such circuits phototransistors have sufficient output to operate a moderately sensitive relay. The relay is energized or deënergized by interruption of the light beam. A battery power supply or the 115 v a-c line with a proper stepdown transformer and a rectifier may provide the low-voltage supply for the phototransistor. There are three parameters which one can vary in this simple circuit; the amount of light, the load resistance, and the applied voltage.

The operating characteristics of a phototransistor with a 15 v power supply, 3000 ohm load line, 20 mw dissipation curve, and 3 millilumens of incident radiation are represented by Fig. 9.16. In the dark the operating point is at A ($V = 15$ v, $I = 0.06$ ma), whereas in the light the operating point is at B ($V = 5.5$ v, $I = 3.2$ ma). Note the striking resemblance of these curves to the characteristic curves for the grounded-emitter operation of an ordinary transistor. Many production units have larger dark currents than that shown in Fig. 9.16 which represents a first-grade phototransistor.

In some instances alternating voltage may be applied directly to the terminals of these units. Then the dark current must be about

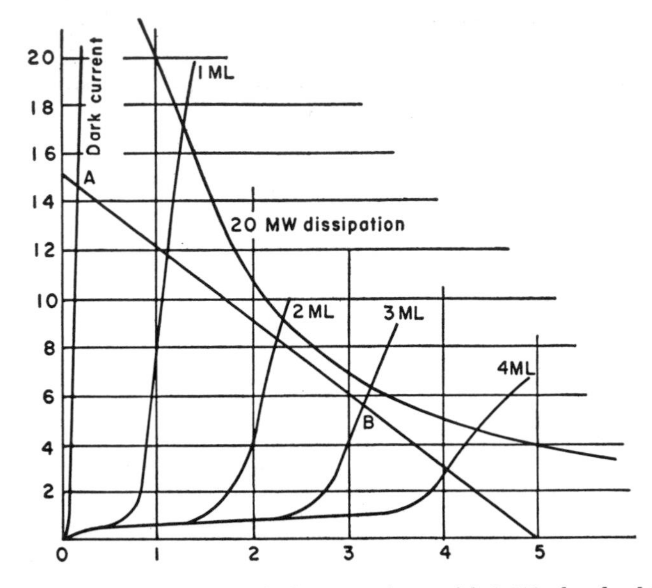

Fig. 9.16. Characteristics of phototransistor with 3,000 ohm load line and 20 mw dissipation curve.

the same regardless of the polarity of the applied voltage. Most production transistors meet this requirement. A transformer is generally required since most phototransistors cannot withstand the 115 v line voltage.

Figure 9.17 presents a simple d-c detector plus a d-c transistor amplifier. The sensitive element is a phototransistor, but a photodiode will work equally well. Figure 9.18 shows a direct-coupled amplifier utilizing complementary symmetry. This circuit finds application

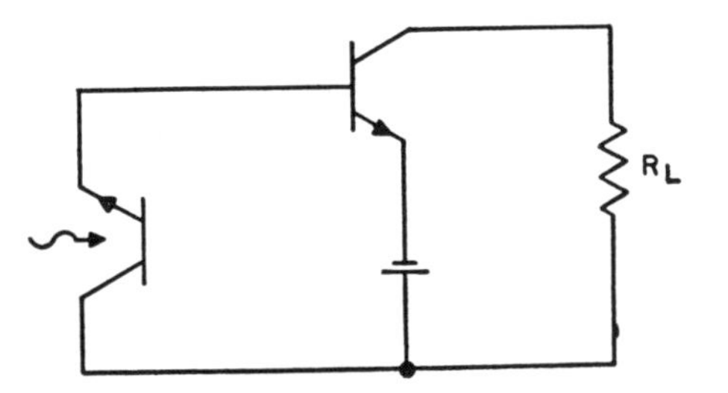

Fig. 9.17. Simple d-c detector with a d-c transistor amplifier.

when several stages of amplification are needed to give more than 40 db gain.

Alternating current circuits have the advantages of easy, low cost amplification, and elimination of dark current. Chopping or modulating the light beam results in an a-c signal without dark current. An ordinary neon bulb operated by a simple oscillatory power supply forms a convenient source of modulated light for frequencies up to

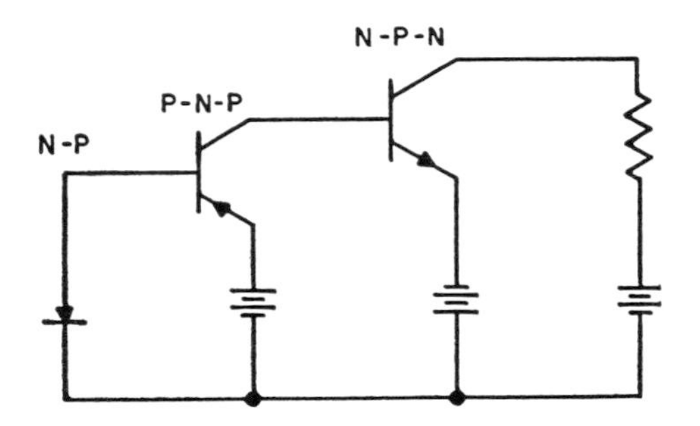

Fig. 9.18. Two-stage d-c amplifier employing complementary symmetry.

6000 cps. The dark current is not eliminated by chopping the output electric signal mechanically with a vibrator or electromagnetically, because the dark current is also chopped and then amplified with the signal. In addition, one may tune the a-c amplifier to the chopper frequency. Again, one may utilize a phase-sensitive detector when a low-level intensity is troublesome. Figure 9.19 is the circuit of a simple a-c detector and amplifier. This diagram illustrates the condition of low signal levels or small currents where it may be necessary

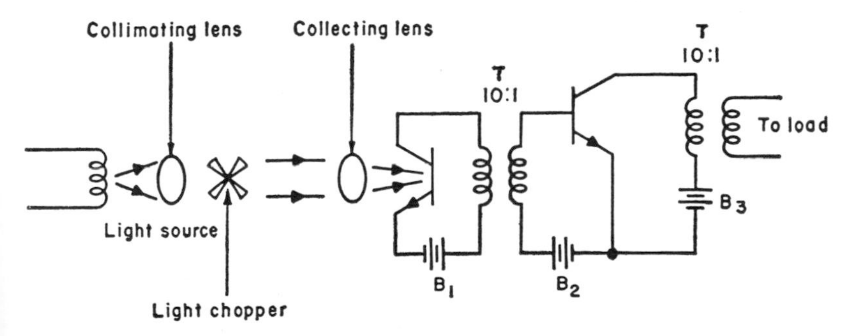

Fig. 9.19. An a-c detector and amplifier arrangement.

to bias the transistor to a suitable operating area, particularly when point-contact transistors are employed.

The balanced bridge circuit of Fig. 9.20 is helpful where dark current is troublesome and where small currents must be detected. The bridge is balanced when the phototransistor is dark. The equation for balance is

$$(R_{PT} \text{ in dark})/R_1 = R_3/R_2 \qquad (3)$$

This represents the condition where no current flows through the load. When light falls on the unit, its effective resistance is greatly decreased, the bridge becomes unbalanced, and a large current flows through R_L.

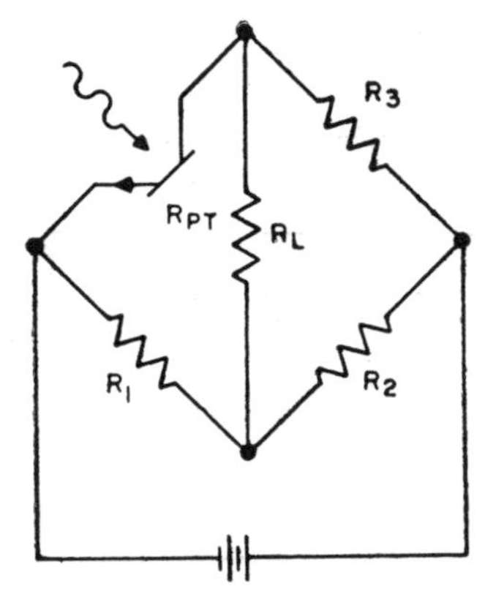

Fig. 9.20. Balanced bridge circuit for eliminating dark current and detecting small currents.

A balanced bridge can largely compensate for the temperature sensitivity of phototransistors. To accomplish this, one replaces resistor R_1 with a second transistor which is kept dark. Since the temperature effects would be the same in both units, the bridge would stay balanced. To reduce the expense of employing two phototransistors, one may utilize for R_1 a semiconductor thermistor with temperature properties similar to those of the phototransistor.

8. *Photovoltaic cells*[7]

A photovoltaic cell is a device which generates electric power from the incident light energy. Hence the unit generates current which depends upon the amount of incident light. The N-P germanium diodes act as excellent photovoltaic cells.

The sensitivity of these germanium photovoltaic cells is remarkable, a current sensitivity of 40 μa per millilumen having been observed. This value is nearly 80 per cent of that achieved by the photodiode with voltage applied. Figure 9.21 demonstrates the varia-

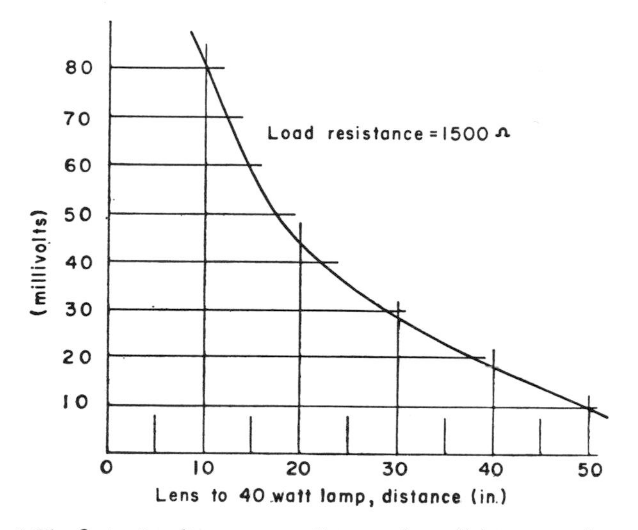

Fig. 9.21. Output voltage versus distance from light source for a germanium photovoltaic cell.

tion of the voltage across a 1500 ohm load in series with a photovoltaic cell with distance from a 40 w light source and 2 in. collecting lens. The disadvantage of these cells is their small sensitive area. They have the advantage of low noise level compared with ordinary selenium photovoltaic cells.

9. *Photoconducting germanium cells*[7]

A photoconducting device is a linear resistive circuit element, whose resistance value is affected by the amount of light falling on the element. The X-47 photoconducting germanium cell consists of a bar of 20 ohm-cm resistivity single-crystal germanium. This device is enclosed in plastic and is sensitive over the entire surface area which is about 1 by 1 by 6 mm. Typical dark resistance values are 1800 to 2000 ohms. Figure 9.22 gives average X-47 characteristics.

The current sensitivity approaches that of a germanium photodiode. The disadvantage of this device is the large dark current resulting from the low dark resistance. However, a balanced bridge similar to that shown in Fig. 9.20 can largely compensate for this large dark current. Also the technique previously mentioned may take care of temperature effects.

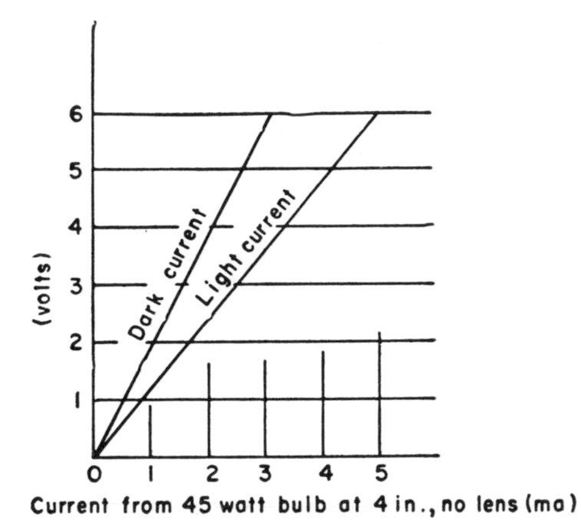

Fig. 9.22. Average characteristics for Type X-47 germanium photoconducting cells.

10. *Transistors in 4A toll crossbar switching*[8]

The 4A toll crossbar switching system is a great advance in the automatic handling of toll telephone calls. The card translator is the heart of this system. It stores the information required to route a call to any one of the toll or local offices in the United States and Canada. It selects a pattern of light beams having the necessary routing information. Determination of the routing information is made by detecting which light beams, called channels, are present during each translation.

The card translator employs phototransistors to detect which channels are illuminated. These phototransistors require only about 12 millilumens of light for satisfactory operation. A single 500 w projection-type lamp operating on half voltage to insure long life supplies the light for the 118 channels of the card translator. A motor-driven perforated disk interrupts the light from this lamp at a 400 cps rate. Interrupted light is utilized since it is easier to build a-c than d-c amplifiers, and also because the ratio between the light and dark currents of the phototransistor is more reliable than the absolute value of either.

When making a translation, the light of an illuminated channel falls on the phototransistor of that particular channel. Figure 9.23 gives the circuit diagram. The light acts as the emitter of the photo-

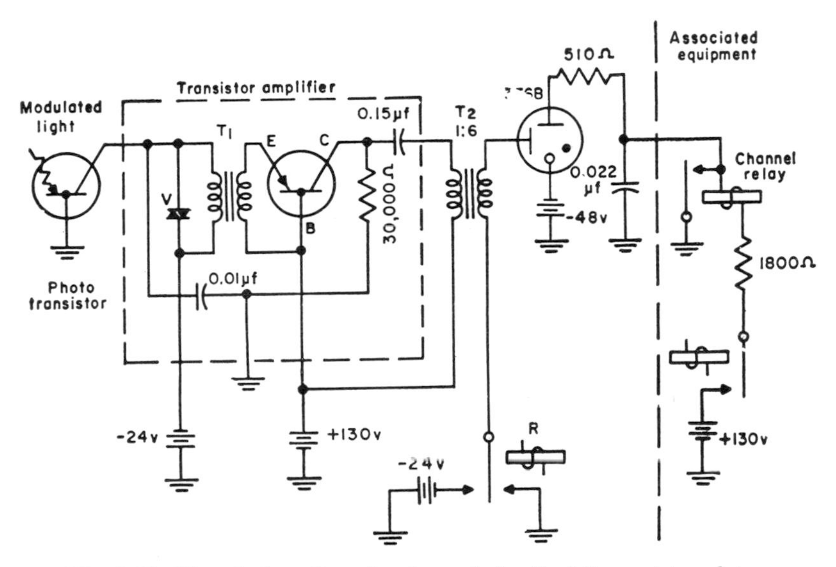

Fig. 9.23. Electrical section of a channel circuit of the card translator.

transistor. The collector is similar to that of point-contact transistors and is biased in the high impedance direction like grounded-base circuits. When dark, the phototransistor has a collector impedance of approximately 10,000 ohms, but when illuminated this is decreased to about 3000 ohms.

The transistor amplifier receives the a-c signal from the phototransistor. Matching of impedances and separation of bias voltages are performed by transformer *T*1. The common-base amplifier gives a voltage gain of 40 to 100. A phototransistor amplifier combination is rejected if its positive peak output voltage falls below 38.5 v.

The output of the transistor amplifier triggers a cold-cathode gas tube. An auxiliary checking circuit operates relay R to change the bias and increase the operating margin, when a translation is to be made. The associated equipment applies the positive 130 v through its channel relays, and the gas tubes of the illuminated channels transfer to their main gaps, operating their associated channel relays.

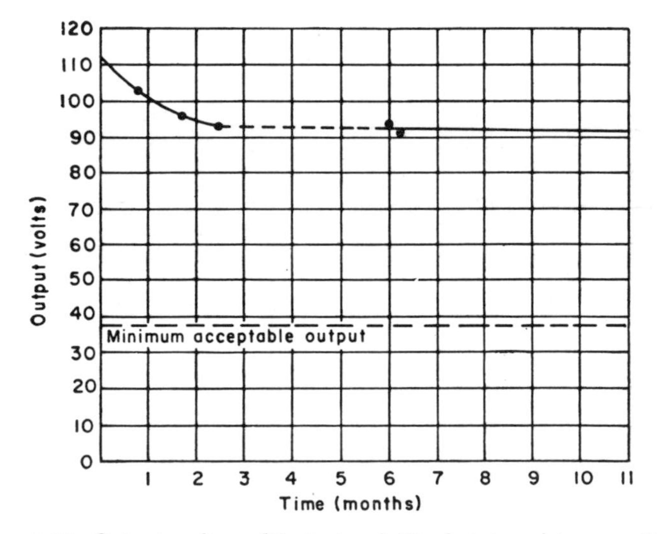

Fig. 9.24. Output voltage life tests of 96 phototransistor amplifier combinations.

This circuit was tested in the laboratory for reliable operation by installing three card translators equipped with 272 channel circuits. Negligible failures occurred in a total of 28,000,000 translations, each of which required many channel operations. In addition, a life test of the output voltage was conducted. The average output voltage of 96 phototransistor-amplifier combinations versus time in months is presented in Fig. 9.24. The above tests indicate that the transistor and its associated circuits in the card translator appear to have a satisfactory service life and are reliable.

References

1. J. N. Shive, "The Phototransistor," *Bell Lab. Record,* Vol. XXVIII, No. 8, Aug. 1950, pp. 337–342.

2. John N. Shive, "Properties of the M-1740 P-N Junction Photocell," *Proc. IRE,* Vol. XL, No. 11, Nov. 1952, pp. 1410–1413.

3. W. Shockley, "The Theory of P-N Junctions In Semiconductors and Junction Transistors," *Bell Sys. Tech. J.*, Vol. XXVIII, May 1949, p. 435.

4. *Data Sheet, Type 1N188 Germanium P-N Junction Photodiode,* Transistor Products, Inc., Boston, Mass., Jan. 1954.

5. *Data Sheet, Type X-25 Germanium N-P-N Junction Phototransistor,* Transistor Products, Inc., Boston, Mass.

6. Richard G. Seed and Roland B. Holt, "Photodiodes and Phototransistors," *Electronic Design,* Vol. I, No. 9, Sept. 1953, pp. 8–9.

7. Richard G. Seed and Roland B. Holt, "Photodiodes and Phototransistors-II," *Electronic Design,* Vol. I, No. 11, Nov. 1953, pp. 10–11.

8. P. Mallery, "Transistors in 4A Toll Crossbar Switching," *Electrical Engineering,* Vol. LXXIII, No. 2, Feb. 1954, p. 129.

Chapter 10

SOME PRACTICAL CONSIDERATIONS IN TRANSISTOR CIRCUITS

1. *Care of transistors*[1]

Although transistors are mechanically rugged they may be burned out easily in experimental circuits unless the proper precautions are taken. It is important to observe the correct polarity for the bias voltages applied to transistors. If the polarity of the plate voltage of a vacuum tube is reversed no harmful effect results other than rendering the circuit inoperative. However, if the polarity of the collector voltage of a transistor is reversed, the transistor will be immediately burned out.

When the emitter voltage of a transistor is reversed, no harm is done to the transistor but the circuit will no longer operate properly as an amplifier.

Ordinary point-contact transistors and P-N-P junction transistors operate with the emitter biased positively and the collector biased negatively with respect to the base. However, N-P-N junction transistors are biased with the emitter negative and the collector positive with respect to the base.

Sockets are required for many point-contact transistors. Connections should not be soldered or welded to the terminals of a transistor unless it is provided with long pigtail leads. Heat from a soldering iron or welding device can easily damage a germanium transistor. When soldering to transistors having pigtail leads, long-nose pliers should be employed to grip the pigtail tightly as close as possible to the body of the transistor until after the joint has completely cooled. The pliers will act as a heat sink to prevent the interior of the transistor from becoming hot. The soldering job should be done as quickly as possible, and the pigtail should be left as long as possible.

Large voltage surges must not be applied to transistors. A new circuit should be examined carefully for the possibility of surges before placing the transistor in the circuit. Steep signal waveforms, circuit switching, kickback from inductive components, sudden application of steady operating potentials, and similar causes may set up transients which will damage a transistor.

If, in addition to a theoretical consideration of transients, it is necessary to measure them experimentally in a circuit, one can do so by substituting an equivalent 3-terminal resistor network in place of the transistor.

Point-contact transistors normally need to be prevented from becoming d-c unstable and running to destruction. Figure 10.1 is an

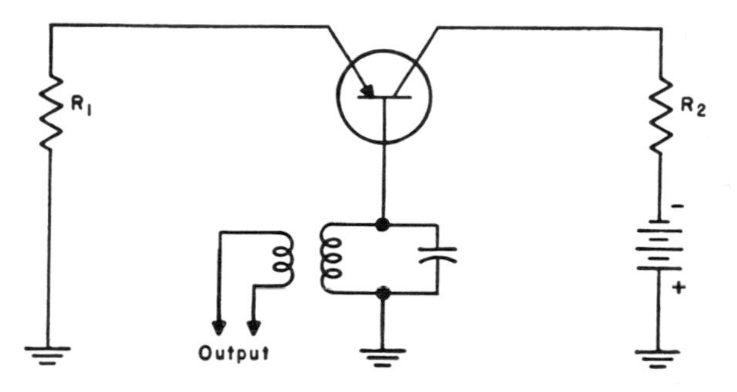

Fig. 10.1. Transistor oscillator with parallel-resonant circuit in the base lead.

example of an oscillator circuit which has a parallel resonant circuit connected between the transistor base and ground. Resistors R_1 and R_2 must be large enough to prevent the emitter and collector currents from exceeding their maximum rated values.

Many transistor amplifier circuits require current-limiting resistors, especially those employing coils or transformers instead of resistors in the input and output. Figure 10.2 shows such circuits, in which points A and B indicate where current limiting resistors should be inserted.

A point-contact transistor tends to become unstable when one connects external resistance between its base and ground. The employment of "cathode bias" in such a transistor circuit must be carefully considered. One should keep the bias resistance as small as possible to prevent excessive positive feedback. A point-contact transistor amplifier which is base-biased may oscillate unless we adequately by-pass the base resistor.

Excessive peak currents must be avoided in all transistor circuits. These are caused by large capacitances effectively in series with one of the electrodes of the transistor. We must provide current limiting resistors to reduce these peak currents.

Transistors should be derated when operated at high temperatures. You should keep transistors well away from hot chassis, tubes, resistors, and similar components.

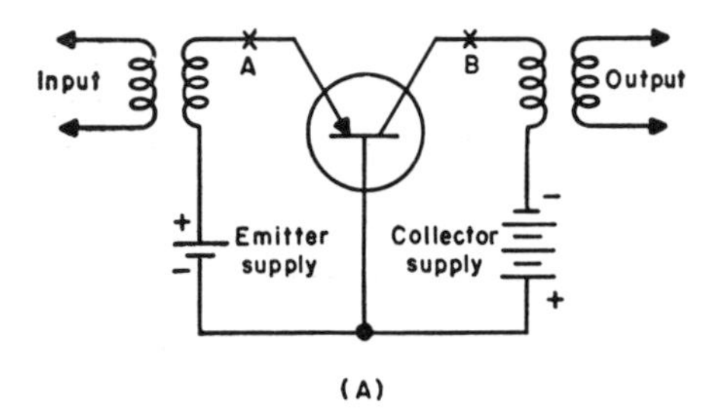

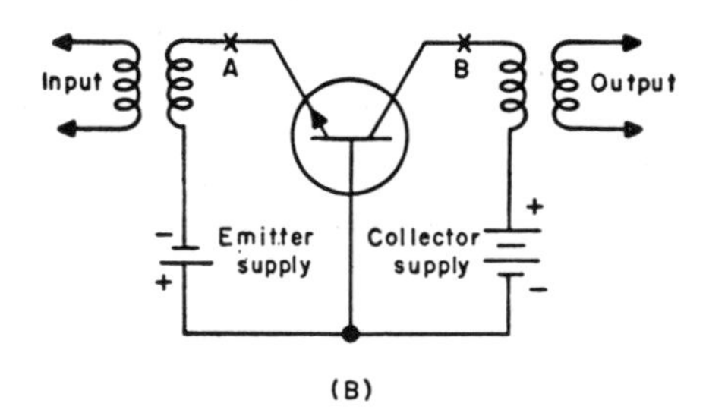

Fig. 10.2. Transformer coupled transistor amplifiers.

Although vibration and shock tests have shown that transistors are physically rugged, nevertheless they should be handled carefully. Transistors should not be tapped or hammered or dropped from great heights lest they be damaged. The mechanical mounting should not excessively pinch the transistor, otherwise possible internal deformations may result.

2. *Stabilization of operating points*[2]

The problem of supplying relatively constant current to the emitter and collector of a transistor is a major one. Operation of a junction transistor is practical at low voltages and currents, making high efficiency desirable.

However, the collector current at zero emitter current varies both among different transistors of the same type and with temperature in any one unit. A ten to one variation may occur with temperature, and cause the collector current to vary likewise in some circuits. The operating point in a resistance-coupled amplifier may shift and reduce the gain considerably. An increase in internal heating may result from such a shift in a power amplifier, and start a cumulative process which may permanently damage the transistor. By the proper circuit design, the operating point may be stabilized within limits with only a moderate increase in power dissipation.

Figure 10.3 shows a circuit for single-battery operation of a transistor, where E is the battery voltage, resistors R_1, R_2, and R_3 regulate the emitter, collector, and base currents, and R_L is the d-c load. Three assumptions are made: first, the collector-base voltage V_c has

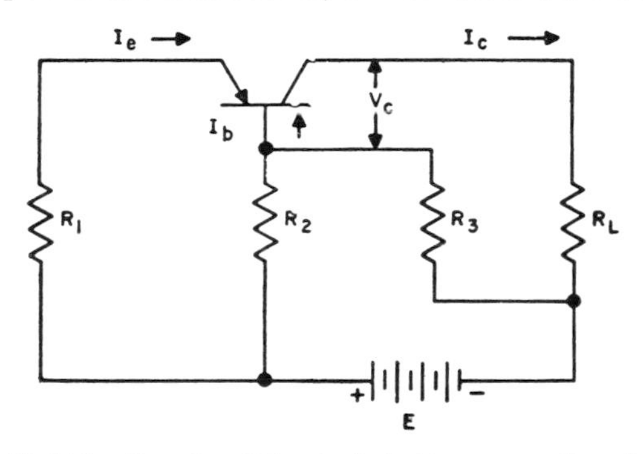

Fig. 10.3. Stabilization circuit for single battery operation of transistor.

negligible effects on the collector current; second, the current amplification factor α is constant over the operating range; and third, the emitter-base voltage V_e is zero. It is normally less than 0.1 v.

From the solution of the mesh equations for this circuit,

$$I_c = \frac{I_{c0}(1 + R_1/R_2 + R_1/R_3) + \alpha E/R_3}{1 - \alpha + R_1/R_2 + R_1/R_3} \tag{1}$$

$$I_e = \frac{I_c - I_{c0}}{\alpha} \tag{2}$$

$$I_b = \frac{I_{c0} - I_c(1 - \alpha)}{\alpha} \tag{3}$$

where I_{c0} is the collector current for $I_e = 0$.

A stability factor S may be derived by differentiating I_c with respect to I_{c0}.

$$S = \frac{1 + R_1/R_2 + R_1/R_3}{1 - \alpha + R_1/R_2 + R_1/R_3} \tag{4}$$

We desire S to be as small as possible for stable operation. However, the value of E and the power dissipated in the stabilizing resistors must be reasonable.

The value of I_c expressed in terms of S is

$$I_c = SI_{c0} + \frac{E}{R_3}(S - 1) \tag{5}$$

The desired operating point (V_c, I_c) is usually known. With these quantities and the battery voltage E, the size of the resistors can be calculated for any required value of S.

$$R_1 = \frac{\alpha(E - V_c - R_L I_c)}{I_c - I_{c0}} \tag{6}$$

$$R_2 = \frac{S - 1}{\dfrac{(1 - S + \alpha S)(I_c - I_{c0})}{\alpha(E - V_c - R_L I_c)} - \dfrac{(I_c - SI_{c0})}{E}} \tag{7}$$

$$R_3 = \frac{E(S - 1)}{I_c - SI_{c0}} \tag{8}$$

The total power supplied by the battery E is

$$P_{dc} = EI_c + \frac{(V_c + R_L I_c)(I_c - SI_{c0})}{S - 1} \tag{9}$$

In a practical example of a grounded-emitter circuit having a minimum permissible loading (net parallel resistance of R_2 and R_3) of 15,000 ohms, an S of 2 required a voltage E much larger than 10 v. Thus such a stability factor would waste considerable power. However, an S of 4 requires only 9.15 v for E, with $R_2 = 27$ kilohms, $R_3 = 34.5$ kilohms, $R_1 = 3000$ ohms, and $P_{dc} = 10.8$ mw. This total power dissipation consists of 5 mw in the transistor collector, 1 mw in the load resistance, and 4.8 mw in R_1, R_2, and R_3. Without the stabilization resistors the S factor is $1/(1 - \alpha)$, or for $\alpha = 0.9$, $S = 10$. Thus the stability factor has been improved 2.5 times.

Figure 10.4 gives a circuit requiring two batteries, or one tapped battery, and supplying a relatively constant emitter current.

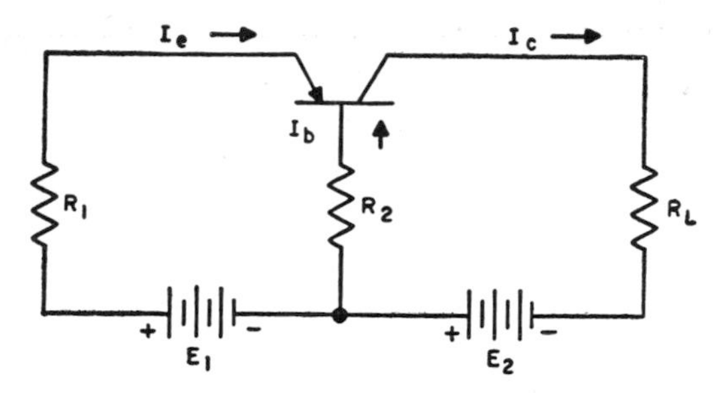

Fig. 10.4. Two battery circuit supplying relatively constant emitter current.

The equations for this circuit follow:

$$I_c = \frac{1}{R_1 + R_2(1 - \alpha)} [I_{c0}(R_1 + R_2) + \alpha E_1] \tag{10}$$

$$I_e = \frac{I_c - I_{c0}}{\alpha} \tag{11}$$

$$I_b = \frac{I_{c0} - I_c(1 - \alpha)}{\alpha} \tag{12}$$

$$S = \frac{R_1 + R_2}{R_1 + R_2(1 - \alpha)} \tag{13}$$

$$I_c = S\left(I_{c0} + \frac{\alpha E_1}{R_1 + R_2}\right) \tag{14}$$

$$R_1 = \frac{E_1[1 - S(1 - \alpha)]}{I_c - SI_{c0}} \tag{15}$$

$$R_2 = \frac{E_1(S - 1)}{I_c - SI_{c0}} \tag{16}$$

$$E_2 = V_c + R_L I_c - R_2 \left[\frac{I_c(1 - \alpha) - I_{c0}}{\alpha}\right] \tag{17}$$

$$P_{dc} = E_2 I_c + \frac{E_1(I_c - I_{c0})}{\alpha} \tag{18}$$

With the same operating conditions as for the previous example of the single battery circuit and for $S = 4$, the circuit values become $R_2 = 15{,}000$ ohms, $E_1 = 4.0$ v, $R_1 = 3000$ ohms, $E_2 = 5.17$ v, and $P_{dc} = 9.39$ mw.

Although the total battery voltage is the same as before, the power required is about 1.4 mw less. Hence either greater power dissipation or reduced stability is the price we must pay for the convenience of a single battery.

3. *Power supplies for transistors*[3]

When experimenting with transistor circuits, a variable-voltage power supply is desirable. With such a power supply it is easy to determine whether or not a given transistor circuit is critical as to voltage.

Figure 10.5 illustrates the circuit of a simple, compact, and inexpensive variable-voltage power supply for experimental transistor circuits. Potentiometer R_2 varies the alternating voltage applied to

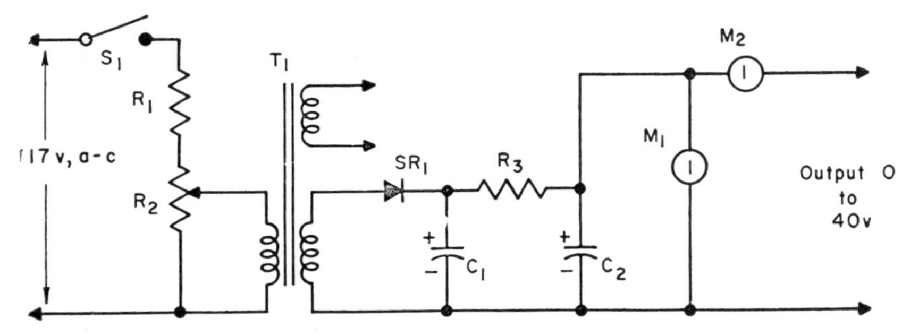

Fig. 10.5. A variable-voltage power supply for experimental transistor circuits. R_1 is 3300-ohm 2-w resistor; R_2 is 2000-ohm 2-w potentiometer; R_3 is 3300-ohm $\frac{1}{2}$-w resistor; C_1 and C_2 are 50-μf 50-v electrolytic capacitors; SR_1 is 25-ma selenium rectifier; T_1 is TV booster-type power transformer with 117-v secondary; M_1 is 0–50 voltmeter; M_2 is 0–5 ma meter; S_1 is S.P.S.T. switch.

the power transformer T_1, which has a 117 v secondary rated at about 20 ma. The supply is completed by a 25 ma selenium rectifier and a π type *RC* filter. The maximum output is 40 v at 5 ma with less than 2 mv ripple. Meters are included for both the output voltage and current.

When trying a new transistor circuit, it is a wise precaution to provide adequate resistance in series with the emitter to limit the current to the rated maximum for the transistor. The collector current should also be limited by a protective resistor in series with the collector supply. Such resistors should not be removed from the circuit until it is ascertained that excessive currents would not then flow.

The supply voltage should be turned down to zero before connecting it to the transistor circuits, and then gradually increased while watching the milliammeter.

Many junction transistor circuits require only one power supply. When a separate emitter battery is needed as in the grounded-base circuit, a flashlight cell may be employed along with this variable power supply.

Miniature transistor batteries have been developed which can last for reasonable periods, and are comparable in size with transistors and their circuit components.

4. *Circuit components for transistors*[4]

The advent of the transistor has challenged the designers of circuit components to produce parts comparable with the size of the transistor itself. Since the transistor requires low voltages and currents, very low-power resistors and very thin-dielectric capacitors are needed. Such capacitors may have breakdown voltages of about 10 to 50 v instead of the usual 150 to 750 v. Moreover, the transistor dissipates negligible heat compared with the average vacuum tube, a fact which further aids the development of tiny components. As a result, small fixed resistors, potentiometers, metallized paper capacitors, electrolytic capacitors, microminiature variable inductors, power transformers, audio transformers, and relays have been developed.

5. *Printed circuitry for transistors*[5]

The necessity of miniaturizing electronic equipment to reduce size and weight has risen out of the increasing utilization of electronics in military and industrial operations. An obvious way to miniaturize is to eliminate waste space and to reduce the space utilized for constructing and maintaining the apparatus. Although this method may be successful, it often creates other problems such as higher temperatures and expensive fabrication. The employment of high-temperature miniature components only makes matters worse. The advent of the transistor points the way to the solution of this increased temperature difficulty, since transistors generate low heat and operate at low energy levels with a reduction by several decades of the quantity of heat to be dissipated.

When transistors and comparably small components are utilized to miniaturize electronic equipment, it becomes extremely difficult to manipulate, wire, and solder them into the assembled unit. To do so by hand is tiresome, time consuming, and expensive, and results in a large rejection rate caused by errors in wiring, short circuits, etc.

A good approach to this problem is to break down a large assembly into small plug-in units. However, conventional hand wiring and soldering of components is still difficult in mass producing these smaller units. The answer to all these problems seems to be printed circuitry. The Signal Corps Engineering Laboratories has devised a treatment of printed circuits known as "auto-sembly"; this is a method of assembling small complex circuits consisting of miniature components without requiring manual dexterity or special training of assembly workers.

Auto-sembly employs a prefabricated (printed circuit) pattern prepared on an insulating base, which is perforated at points where component leads are to connect to the circuit. These perforations receive transistors and conventional JAN or special subminiature components from the blank side of the chassis. Finally, a "one-shot" mass soldering operation is accomplished by dipping the pattern side in a molten solder bath to connect each component lead to the circuit.

References

1. Rufus P. Turner, "Care of Transistors," *Radio and Television News*, Vol. XLIX, No. 2, Feb. 1953, pp. 40–41.
2. Richard F. Shea, "Transistor Operation: Stabilization of Operating Points," *Proc. IRE*, Vol. XL, No. 11, Nov. 1952, pp. 1435–1437.
3. Louis D. Carcano, "Transistor Power Supply," *Radio and Television News*, Vol. L, No. 4, Oct. 1953, p. 88.
4. G. W. A. Dummer, "Components for Transistors," *Wireless World*, Vol. LIX, No. 5, May 1953, pp. 196–199.
5. S. F. Danko and R. A. Gerhold, "Printed Circuitry for Transistors," *Proc. IRE*, Vol. XL, No. 11, Nov. 1952, pp. 1524–1528.

Chapter 11

NOISE AND TEMPERATURE EFFECTS IN TRANSISTORS

1. *Noise in transistor amplifiers*[1,2]

Noise in transistors differs from thermal and shot noise in that the transistor noise power per unit bandwidth varies approximately inversely with frequency. Figure 11.1 indicates the noise power per cycle bandwidth versus frequency. In this kind of noise spectrum each octave of frequency contains the same noise power.

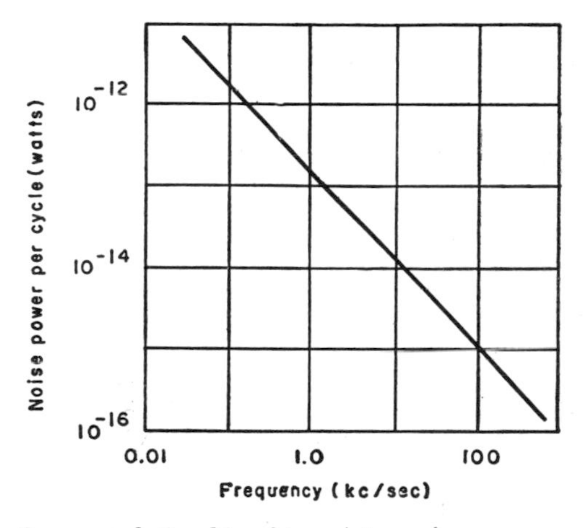

Fig. 11.1. Inverse relationship of transistor noise power per unit bandwidth with frequency.

Figure 11.2 shows a convenient way of representing transistor noise in the equivalent T network circuit by two noise-voltage generators having rms voltages E_{ne} and E_{nc} in the emitter and collector leads. We assume that none of the other elements of the equivalent circuit generates any noise.

Typical values are $E_{nc} = 100\ \mu\text{v}$ and $E_{ne} = 1\ \mu\text{v}$ for point-contact transistors measured at 1000 cps for a 1 cps bandwidth. For junction transistors corresponding voltages are $E_{nc} = 5\ \mu$v and $E_{ne} = 0.05\ \mu$v.

The noise figure of a transistor can more conveniently represent its noise properties in actual practice. We may define the noise figure F as the total noise power in the output divided by that portion of the output noise that results from thermal agitation in the source resistance R_g, neglecting thermal noise originating in the load impedance R_L. We normally express F in decibels. The noise figure is useful to compare the noise characteristics of different transistors.

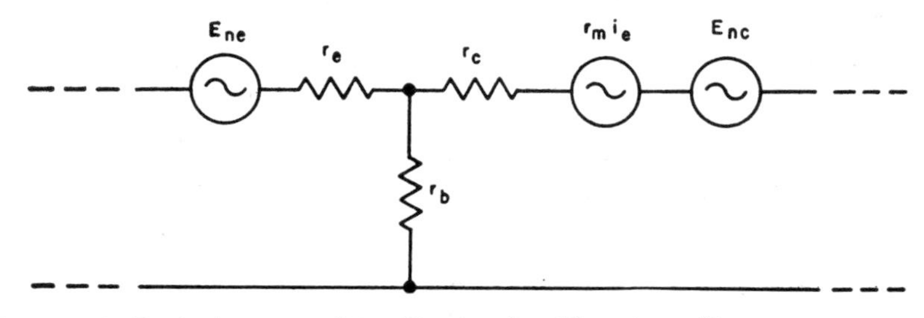

Fig. 11.2. Equivalent transistor T-network with noise voltage generators.

Point-contact transistors normally have noise figures at 1000 cps of 40 to 60 db, and junction transistors of 10 to 25 db.

We can express the noise figures for the grounded-base, grounded-emitter, and grounded-collector amplifier circuits in terms of open-circuit voltages and equivalent circuit parameters as follows:

grounded base

$$F = 1 + \frac{1}{4kTR_g(f_2 - f_1)}\left[E_{ne}{}^2 \oplus E_{nc}{}^2\left(\frac{R_g + r_e + r_b}{r_m + r_b}\right)^2\right] \quad (1)$$

grounded emitter

$$F = 1 + \frac{1}{4kTR_g(f_2 - f_1)}\left[E_{ne}{}^2\left(\frac{R_g + r_m + r_b}{r_m - r_e}\right)^2 \oplus E_{nc}{}^2\left(\frac{R_g + r_e + r_b}{r_m - r_c}\right)^2\right] \quad (2)$$

grounded collector

$$F = 1 + \frac{1}{4kTR_g(f_2 - f_1)}\left[E_{ne}{}^2\left(\frac{R_g + r_c + r_b}{r_c}\right)^2 \oplus E_{nc}{}^2\left(\frac{R_g + r_b}{r_c}\right)^2\right] \quad (3)$$

where k is Boltzmann's constant $= 1.347 \times 10^{-23}$ watt sec/degree K, and T is the absolute temperature in degrees K, and $f_2 - f_1$ is the frequency band, and $\oplus$ means addition with attention to any correlation between E_{ne} and E_{nc}. We can replace this operation by simple addition when there is no correlation. These equations indicate that the noise figures are independent of R_L.

Average noise figures for the CK727 P-N-P junction transistor in the common-base, common-emitter, and common-collector circuits are given in Figs. 11.3, 11.4, and 11.5, respectively.[3] The Type CK727 is intended for low-level audio applications where low noise factor is of prime importance.

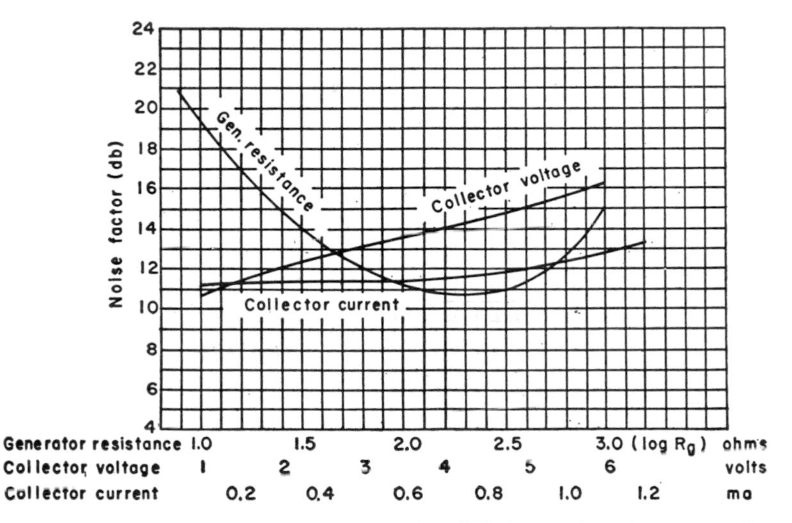

Fig. 11.3. Average noise characteristics for CK727 transistor in common-base circuit. Conditions:

Collector voltage (V_c): R_g is 100 ohms, I_c is -0.5 ma.
Collector current (I_c): R_g is 100 ohms, V_c is -1.5 v.
Generator resistance (R_g): V_c is -1.5 v, I_c is -0.5 ma.
Load resistance is 200,000 ohms.

These curves demonstrate that the noise figure of a transistor depends on the operating point. For example, Figs. 11.3 and 11.4 show that the noise factor increases greatly as the collector voltage rises, and is less dependent upon the collector current.

Figures 11.3 and 11.4 also indicate that there is a value of the gen-

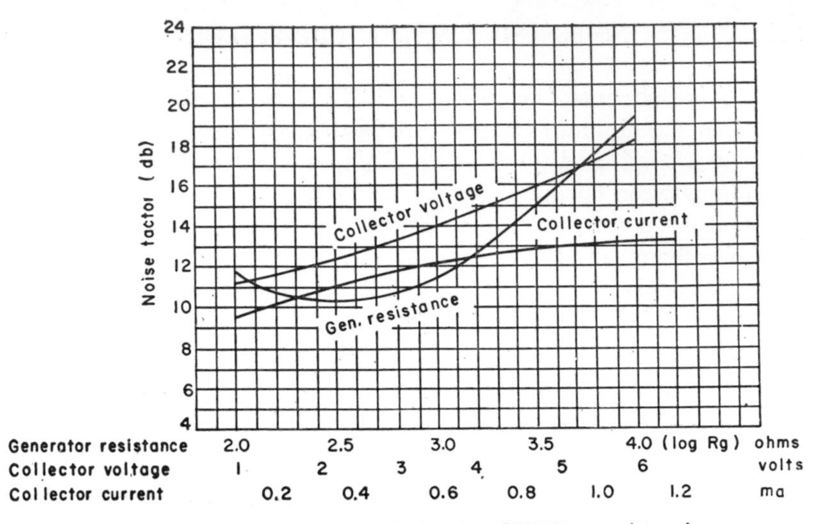

Fig. 11.4. Average noise characteristics for CK727 transistor in common-emitter circuit. Conditions:

Collector voltage (V_c): R_g is 1000 ohms, I_c is -0.5 ma.
Collector current (I_c): R_g is 1000 ohms, V_c is -1.5 v.
Generator resistance (R_g): V_c is -1.5 v, I_c is -0.5 ma.
Load resistance is 20,000 ohms.

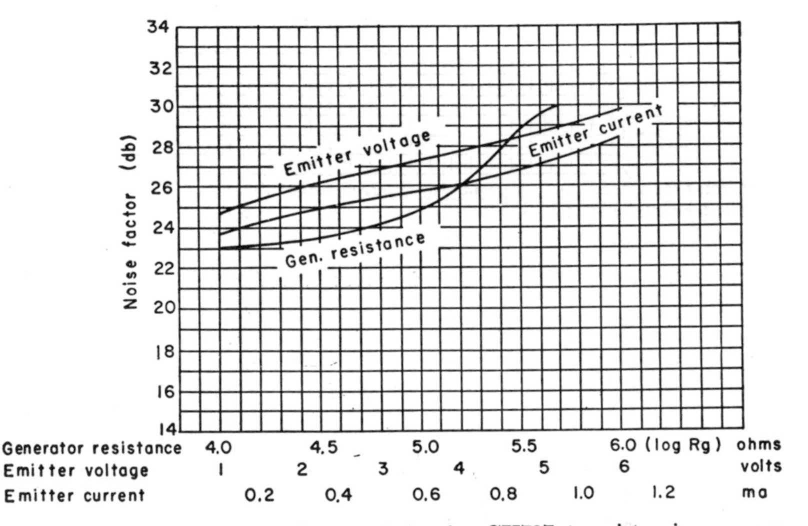

Fig. 11.5. Average noise characteristics for CK727 transistor in common-collector circuit. Conditions:

Emitter voltage (V_e): R_g is 100,000 ohms, I_c is -0.5 ma.
Emitter current (I_e): R_g is 100,000 ohms, V_c is -1.5 v.
Generator resistance (R_g): V_c is -1.5 v, I_c is -0.5 ma.
Load resistance is 10,000 ohms.

erator resistance R_g for which the noise factor is minimum. However, these curves demonstrate that the noise figure does not depend critically on the values of R_g. The values of R_g for which these minimums occur are given by the following equations:[1,2]

grounded base and grounded emitter

$$R_g \cong \left[(r_e + r_b)^2 \oplus \frac{E_{ne}^2}{E_{nc}^2} (r_m + r_b)^2 \right]^{1/2} \tag{4}$$

grounded collector

$$R_g \cong \left(r_b^2 \oplus \frac{E_{ne}^2}{E_{nc}^2} r_c^2 \right)^{1/2} \tag{5}$$

We may employ somewhat larger or smaller values of R_g without an appreciable increase in amplifier noise. For example, with the grounded-base connection it can be shown theoretically that if we increase or decrease the value of R_g four times, we change the noise figure at most 2.12 times or 3.2 db. In actual practice this figure is normally much less. Therefore we cannot improve the signal-to-noise ratio by adding a resistance in series with R_g or in parallel with the input of the transistor amplifier.

Figure 11.5 shows that the common-collector circuit has a considerably larger noise factor than the other two configurations.[3]

Transistor noise power per cycle bandwidth varies approximately inversely with frequency.[1,2]

$$P_n \cong k/f \tag{6}$$

The total noise power in a frequency band extending from frequency f_2 to f_1 will be

$$P_n = k(\ln f_2 - \ln f_1) = k \ln \frac{f_2}{f_1} \tag{7}$$

The corresponding equation for the thermal noise power due to R_g is

$$P_n = k'(f_2 - f_1) \tag{8}$$

The noise figure for the bandwidth limited by the frequencies f_2 and f_1 is

$$F = 1000F_0 \frac{\ln f_2/f_1}{f_2 - f_1} \tag{9}$$

where f_0 is the noise figure at 1000 cps for a bandwidth of 1 cycle.

If $f_2/f_1 \cong 1$, then

$$\ln f_2/f_1 \cong (f_2 - f_1)/f_1$$

and

$$F \cong F_0(1000/f_1) \tag{10}$$

Therefore we can regard the noise figure as relatively independent of bandwidth provided that the bandwidth is comparatively small.

For some applications we would like to express the noise of a transistor amplifier by an equivalent noise generator of voltage E_n in series with R_g. The available power (the power transferred to a matched load) at the input due to E_n can be shown to be

$$P_0 = E_n^2/4R_g = 0.9 \times 10^{-17} \times F_0 \times \log (f_2/f_1) \quad \text{w} \tag{11}$$

Figure 11.6 shows a plot of this equation. An approximate expression for Eq. (11) is

$$P_0 \cong 0.9 \times 10^{-17} \times F_0 \times \log (1 + \Delta f/f) \quad \text{w} \tag{12}$$

where Δf is the bandwidth and f is the center frequency.

Equation (11) indicates that the noise power is a function of the ratio of the frequencies f_2 and f_1 and not of their magnitudes. Equation (12) demonstrates that with a constant bandwidth the noise power decreases with an increase of the center frequency.

For many amplifiers the noise in the output is largely determined by the noise of the first stage. The signal-to-noise ratio at the output

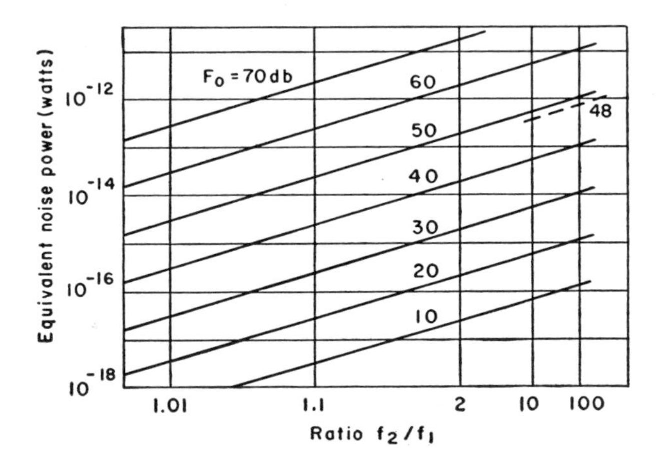

Fig. 11.6. Available equivalent noise power.

of a transistor amplifier then equals the ratio of the available signal power in the input to the available equivalent noise power P_0 of Eq. (11), or

$$\frac{S}{N} = \frac{V_g^2}{4R_gP_0} = \frac{V_g^2}{3.6 \times 10^{-17} \times R_g \times F_0 \times \log f_2/f_1} \tag{13}$$

where V_g is the rms signal voltage.

With this equation we can determine the maximum permissible noise figure of a transistor for the first stage of an amplifier. For example, if the available signal power is 10^{-8} w in a band from 50 cps to 5 kc/sec and the signal-to-noise ratio is 40 db or 10^4, then P_0 must be 10^{-12} w or less. From Fig. 11.6 for $f_2/f_1 = 100$ the maximum permissible noise figure is 48 db.

The measurement of noise figures is described in Chapter 6.

According to Eqs. (1) and (2) the noise figures for grounded-base and grounded-emitter amplifiers are approximately equal. The average difference was only 1 db for a large number of transistors. Hence we may utilize either of the above configurations for measuring the noise figure.

Figure 11.7 indicates the variation of the noise figures with frequency for two junction transistors. The agreement of these curves with Eq. (9) is quite good.

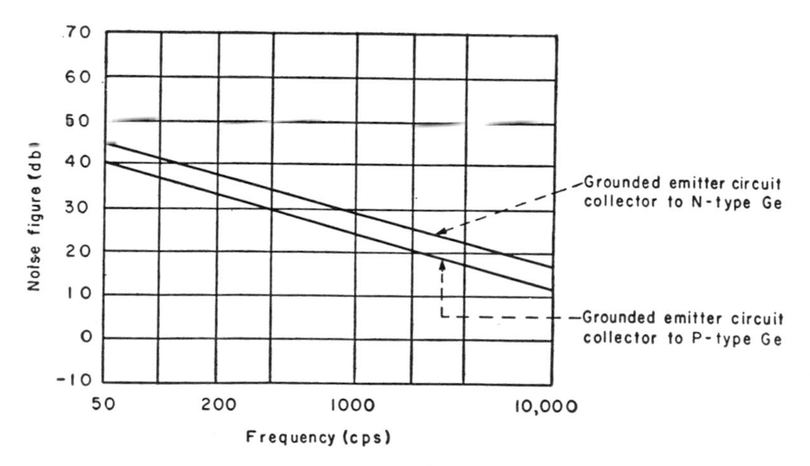

Fig. 11.7. Transistor noise figure versus frequency, for two different types of junction transistors.

Normally, in multistage transistor amplifiers the first stage causes the largest part of the noise figure. However, if the equivalent source impedance of the second stage differs greatly from the value of R_g given by Eqs. (4) and (5), we must also consider the noise contributed by the second stage.

The noise figure of a two-stage amplifier is

$$F = F_1 + (F_2 - 1)/G_1 \tag{14}$$

where F_1 and F_2 are the noise figures of the first and second stages, respectively, and G_1 is the available power gain of the first stage. The equations giving this available power gain for the three configurations are as follows:

grounded base

$$G_1 = \frac{\alpha^2 r_c R_g}{(r_e + r_b + R_g)\,[r_e + r_b(1 - \alpha) + R_g]} \tag{15}$$

grounded emitter

$$G_1 = \frac{\alpha^2 r_c R_g}{(r_e + r_b + R_g)} \times \frac{1}{[r_e + r_b(1 - \alpha) + R_g(1 - \alpha)]} \tag{16}$$

grounded collector

$$G_1 = \frac{r_c R_g}{(r_c + r_b + R_g)} \times \frac{1}{[r_e + r_b(1 - \alpha) + R_g(1 - \alpha)]} \tag{17}$$

The noise figure of the second stage is determined by the operating point of the second transistor and the first stage output resistance. We can change this output resistance by transformer coupling the two stages. This coupling will not affect G_1. We can reduce the effect of the second stage by adjusting the transformer turns ratio so that the apparent source impedance of the second stage is that given by Eqs. (4) and (5).

If transformer coupling is not used between the two stages, it can be shown that the noise figure of a two-stage grounded-emitter amplifier is approximately

$$F = F_1 + \frac{E_{nc2}^2}{4KT(f_2 - f_1)} \times \frac{[r_{e1} + r_{b1}(1 - \alpha_1) + R_g(1 - \alpha_1)]^2}{\alpha_2^2 r_{c2}^2 \alpha_1^2 R_g} \tag{18}$$

With this equation we can calculate the contribution of the second stage to the total noise figure for direct or RC coupled amplifiers.

Noise in transistor amplifiers is like contact noise in its strong dependence on frequency. Total noise power depends on the ratio of the frequencies limiting it instead of being proportional to amplifier bandwidth.

Figure 11.8 shows the variation of noise factor with emitter current for a typical N-P-N alloy junction transistor, whereas Fig. 11.9 gives the variation of noise factor with collector potential.[4] These curves indicate that, in general, an increase in potential or current raises the

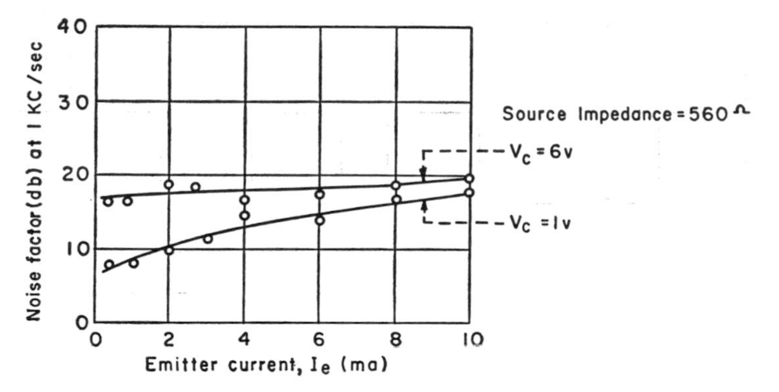

Fig. 11.8. Variation of noise factor with emitter current, for a typical N-P-N alloy junction transistor.

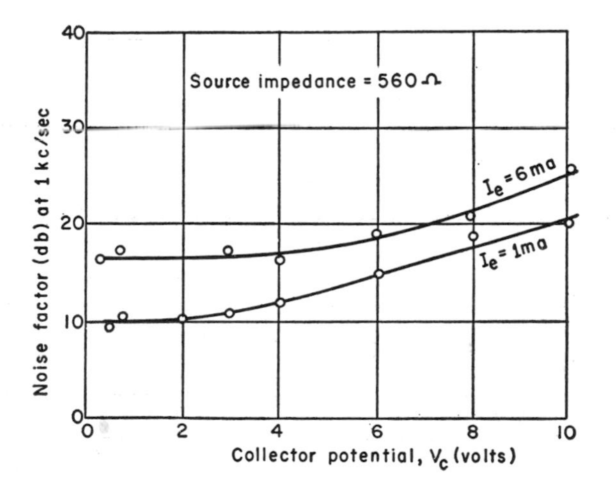

Fig. 11.9. Variation of noise factor with collector potential, for a typical N-P-N alloy junction transistor.

noise, and a minimum noise factor is reached at about 1 v collector potential and 1 ma emitter current for this type of transistor.

2. *Variation of transistor parameters with temperature*

To obtain data regarding temperature effects in Western Electric transistors, Types 1698 and 1768, parameter measurements were

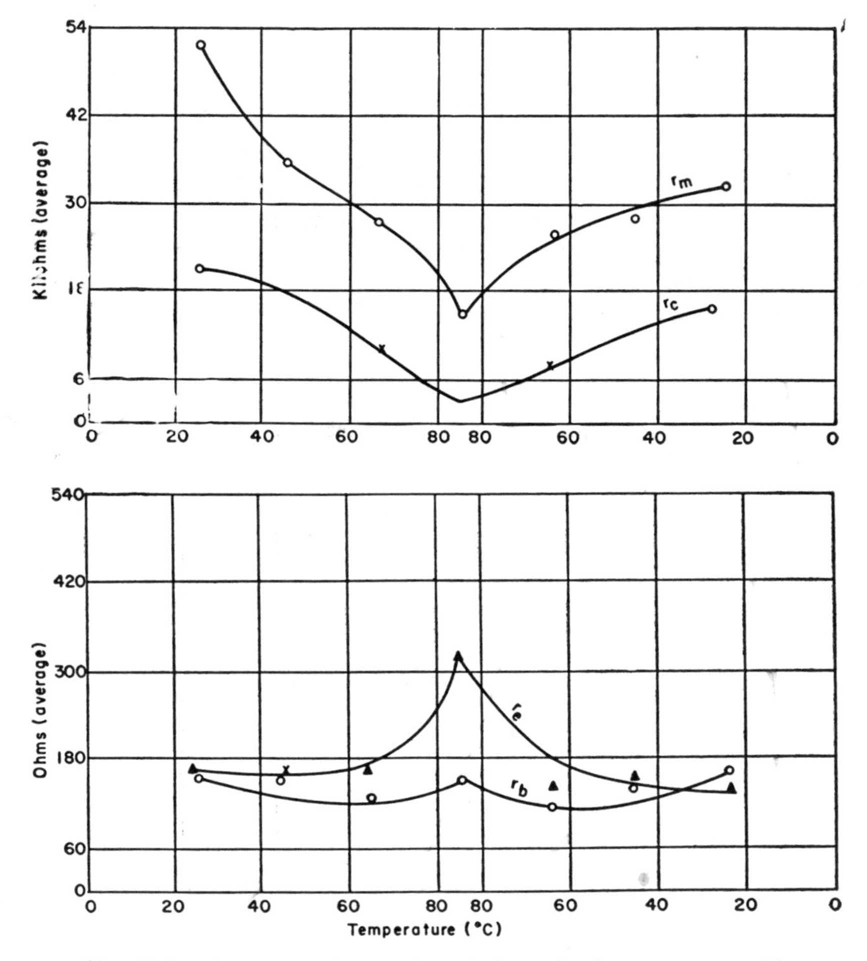

Fig. 11.10. Average variation of equivalent circuit parameters with temperature, for Type 1698 transistors.

made[5] on 20 Type 1698 and 30 Type 1768 transistors for temperatures from 25° to 85°C. It should be noted that 85°C operation of these transistors exceeds the maximum temperature ratings specified by the manufacturer. Destructive testing was considered necessary to determine the absolute limits of operation for these types of transistors.

The Type 1698 is a point-contact transistor triode in cartridge form. It is designed for switching circuits where the large-signal parameters of the active device are of primary interest. The maximum-rated ambient temperature is 55°C.

Figure 11.10 represents the average variation of the equivalent circuit parameters with temperature for 20 Type 1698 transistors. These measurements were made with $V_c = -30$ v and $I_e = 1$ ma. The temperature cycle began at room temperature, rose to 85°C, and then decreased to room temperature. Although the transistors were held at the elevated temperatures only long enough to obtain thermal equilibrium and make electrical measurements, r_m and r_c suffered definite permanent changes indicating that excessive temperatures had been applied. Moreover, certain transistors oscillated at the elevated

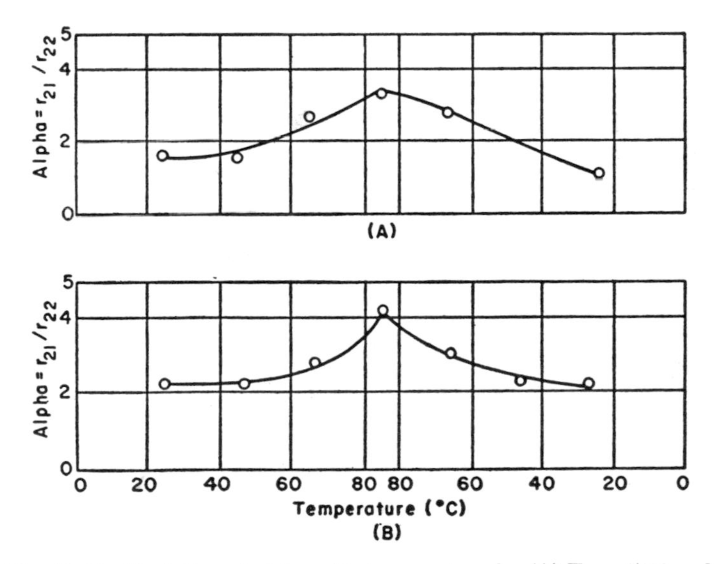

Fig. 11.11. Variation of alpha with temperature for (A) Type 1768 and (B) Type 1698.

temperatures and were unstable when returned to room temperature. Some of these units could be made stable by reducing the bias.

The lower curve of Fig. 11.11 indicates the variation of current gain, alpha, with temperature for Type 1698 transistors.

Figure 11.12 presents the variation of I_{c0}, the collector current for zero emitter current and 40 v collector potential, and V_{c1}, the collector voltage for the transistor when in the low resistance or saturation condition, with temperature for Type 1698 transistors. The value of V_{c1} is measured with 1 ma emitter current and 2 ma collector current.

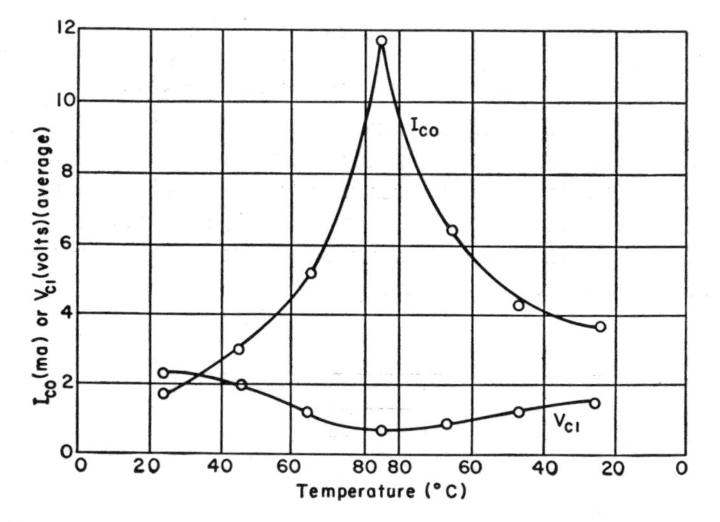

Fig. 11.12. Variation of I_{c0} and V_{c1} with temperature, for Type 1698.

For switching applications the collector resistance must be adequate when the transistor is in the cutoff or high-resistance condition. The measurement of I_{c0} at room temperature should indicate that the Type 1698 units have a resistance of 20,000 ohms or more.

The Type 1768 is a point-contact transistor triode developed for low-voltage, low-power drain, high-efficiency oscillator and amplifier applications. Maximum ratings are 50°C ambient temperature and 120 mw collector dissipation.

The upper curve of Fig. 11.11 shows alpha as a function of temperature for 30 Type 1768 transistors.

Although the small signal characteristics changed markedly at the elevated temperatures, it is notable that the transistors gave considerable gain at 85°C. For example, average 1698 units in a linear class A grounded-base circuit gave a maximum available gain of 16.2 db at 85°C compared with 22.4 db at 25°C. The maximum available gain was calculated neglecting the positive feedback due to r_b. The operating gain was with $R_G = 300$ ohms and $R_L = 15{,}000$ ohms.

Although both 1698 and 1768 transistors could deliver useful gain at 85°C, thermal and electrical instability prevent reliable operation and cause not only temporary but permanent deterioration of characteristics.

Type 1698 and Type 1768 units operate satisfactorily up to about 60°C in many small signal applications. The decrease in gain in this temperature range is only about 2 db. The gain remains essentially constant because the decrease of r_c with temperature is largely offset by the increase in alpha.

The temperature dependence of the electrical characteristics of Type 1698 transistors seriously limits their application to switching circuits which must operate reliably at high ambient temperatures. Many direct-coupled switching circuits will not operate satisfactorily with Type 1698 transistors beyond the temperature range of 40° to 50°C. Stabilization of the transistor's direct-current operating point with a suitable auxiliary circuit may increase this range. Alternating-current coupling should also be helpful to extend the temperature range. Even with alternating-current coupling, as the maximum dissipation ratings are approached at elevated temperatures, the temperature dependence of I_{c0}, as demonstrated in Fig. 11.12, results in sufficient internal heat to induce thermal instability.

Figure 11.13 shows the variation of alpha with temperature for three junction transistors of different collector resistivity.[6] These curves only indicate the general trend since there were other variables present. The density of minority carriers in the collector region increases with temperature, but can be kept low by utilizing very low-resistivity germanium in the collector region. The diffused impurity junction automatically meets this low-resistivity requirement. For fused-contact transistors, alpha remains nearly constant up to 120°C and decreases at higher temperatures. These units permit stable grounded-emitter circuits at high temperatures. This is in contrast to junction transistors having high-resistivity collector regions, for which at high temperatures alpha often rises above unity causing

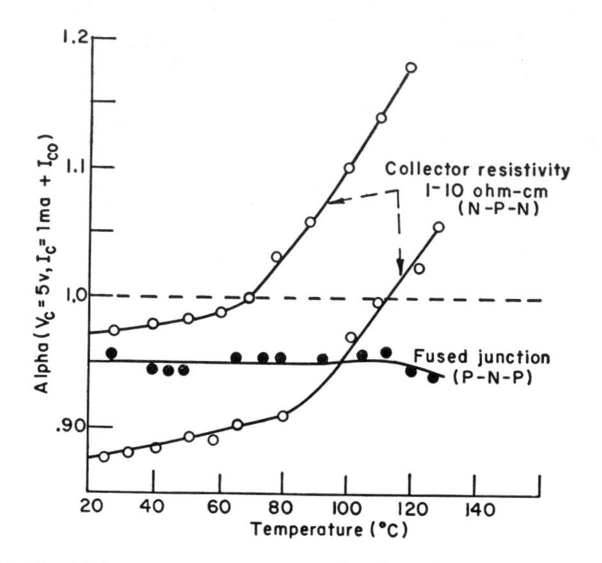

Fig. 11.13. Alpha versus temperature, for three junction transistors of different collector resistivity.

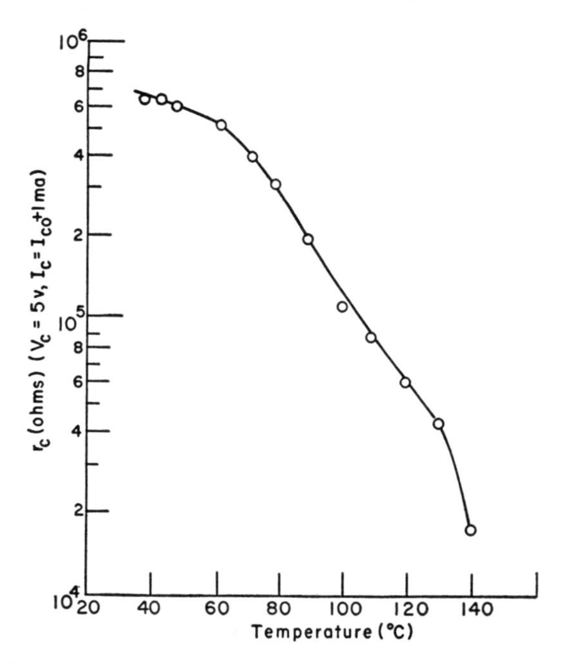

Fig. 11.14. Collector resistance versus temperature for a fused-impurity P-N-P junction transistor.

circuit instability. Fused-contact P-N-P junction transistors have successfully operated above 140°C in circuits requiring alpha less than unity.

Figure 11.14 gives the collector resistance r_c versus temperature for a fused-impurity P-N-P junction transistor. This curve indicates that the collector resistance decreases at high temperatures, but may be usably high even above 130°C.

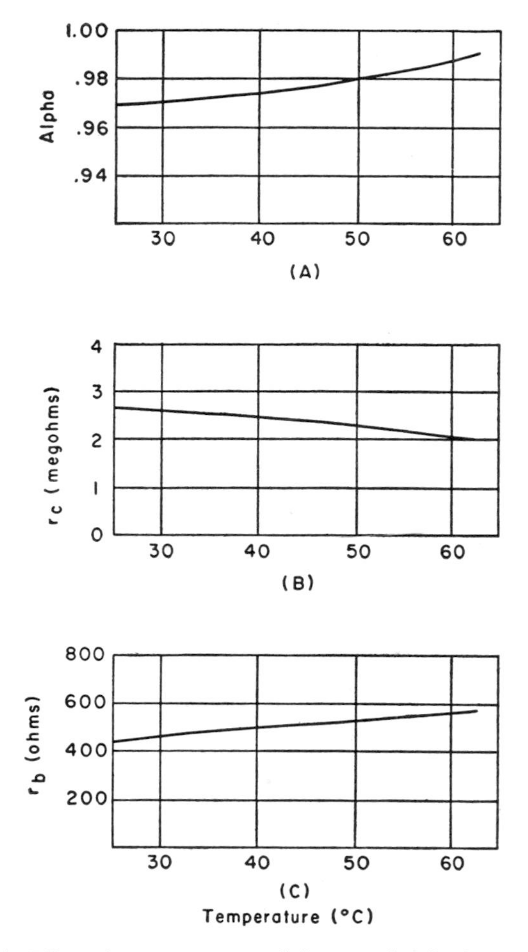

Fig. 11.15. Effect of temperature on alpha, r_c and r_b, for fourteen M1752 junction transistors.

There are several ways in which the operating temperature of the transistor affects its characteristics. The minimum collector current I_{c0}, the saturation inverse current of the collector junction, increases exponentially with temperature. At room temperature I_{c0} may be less than 10 μa, but rises to several milliamperes at 100°C. Increasing the temperature thus causes larger dissipative losses which lower the efficiency of the transistor and make low-level operation less attractive. Also, there is more heat to remove and less of the allowable dissipation can be useful. Finally the decrease in r_c lowers the power gain, although sizable power gain can be obtained above 140°C in the grounded-emitter connection, which is possible at these temperatures with fused-junction transistors because alpha remains less than unity.

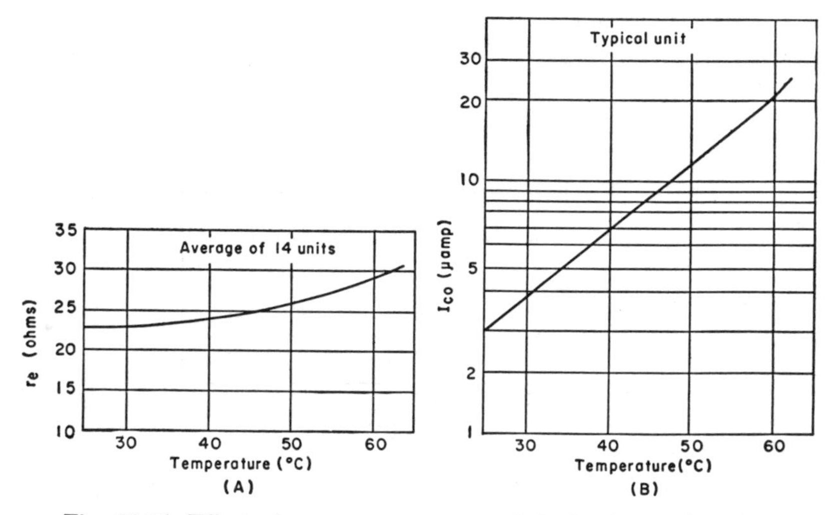

Fig. 11.16. Effect of temperature on r_e and I_{c0} for M1752 junction transistors.

Figures 11.15 and 11.16 show the effect of temperature on α, r_c, r_b, and r_e for fourteen M1752 grown junction transistors over a limited temperature range.[7] The effect of temperature on I_{c0} is also given for a typical unit. The saturation current I_{c0} varies much more widely than the other parameters, its measured temperature coefficient averaging about 7 per cent per degree C.

Although the other characteristics are much less temperature sensitive than the saturation current, the limitations caused by temperature effects are still important. As the temperature is raised, r_c decreases, r_b and r_e increase, and α increases slightly. The reduction in r_c is usually the most serious effect, limiting the useful working temperature to about 70°C for these germanium junction transistors.

Figure 11.17 indicates the effect of temperatures on transistor parameters for Types CK721 and CK722 junction transistors.[8] Alpha remains relatively constant with rise in temperature, r_c decreases, and

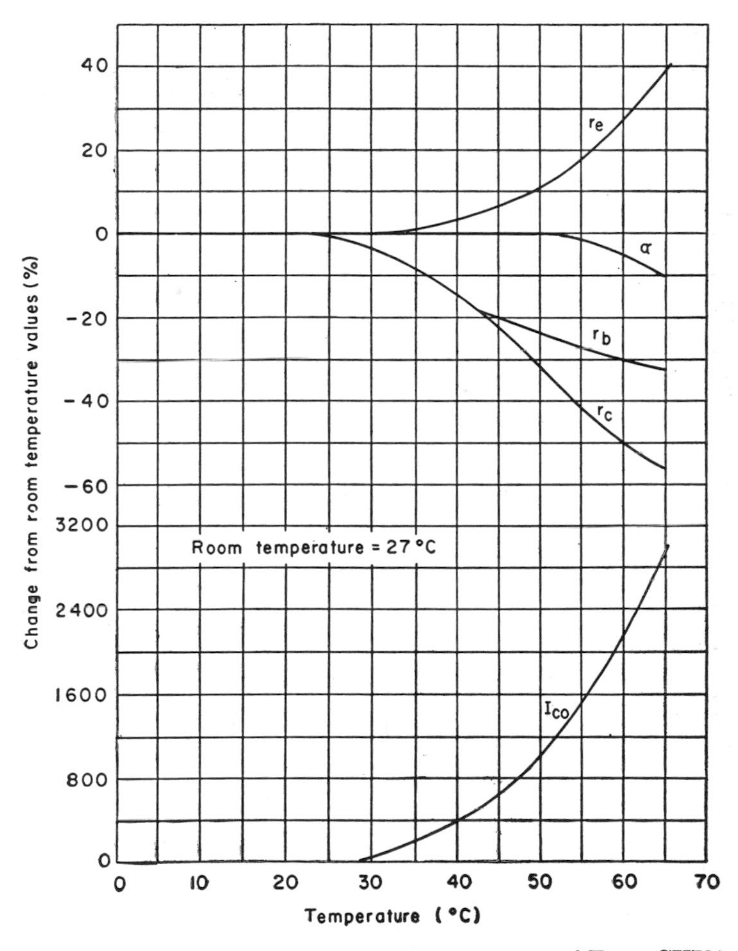

Fig. 11.17. Effect of temperature on the parameters of Types CK721 and CK722 junction transistors.

r_e increases. Although r_b is shown as decreasing, it also decreases in the low temperature range. Thus it tends to be maximum at normal temperatures. The curve for I_{c0} demonstrates the enormous extent that temperature affects the saturation current.

References

1. Reprinted with permission from R. F. Shea, *Principles of Transistor Circuits*, 1953, John Wiley & Sons, Inc., New York, pp. 438–448.

2. E. Keonjian and J. S. Schaffner, "An Experimental Investigation of Transistor Noise," *Proc. IRE*, Vol. XL, No. 11, Nov. 1952, pp. 1456–1460.

3. *Tentative Data for Type CK727 Germanium Transistor*, Receiving Tube Division, Raytheon Manufacturing Co., Newton, Mass., July 1, 1954.

4. Dietrich A. Jenny, "A Germanium N-P-N Alloy Junction Transistor," *Proc. IRE*, Vol. XLI, No. 12, Dec. 1953, pp. 1728–1734.

5. Abraham Coblenz and Harry L. Owens, "Variation of Transistor Parameters with Temperature," *Proc. IRE*, Vol. XL, No. 11, Nov. 1952, pp. 1472–1476.

6. John S. Saby, "Fused Impurity P-N-P Junction Transistors," *Proc. IRE*, Vol. XL, No. 11, Nov. 1952, pp. 1358–1360.

7. K. D. Smith, "Properties of Junction Transistors," *Tele-Tech and Electronic Industries*, Vol. XII, No. 1, Jan. 1953, pp. 76–77.

8. F. M. Dukat, *Characteristics of the Raytheon P-N-P Junction Transistors*, Receiving Tube Division, Raytheon Manufacturing Co., Newton, Mass.

Chapter 12

TRANSISTOR AUDIO FREQUENCY AMPLIFIERS AND POWER AMPLIFIERS

1. *Introduction*

The junction transistor lends itself particularly well to audio frequency applications. Here its advantages over the point-contact type are readily apparent. The junction transistor exhibits lower noise, higher power gain, greater collector circuit efficiency (approaching 50 per cent for class A operation), lower harmonic distortion, and greater circuit stability. It is short-circuit stable. Also, its cost is lower. Audio frequencies are normally well within the frequency response of the junction transistor, so that its lower frequency range of operation is no handicap.

2. *Microphone preamplifiers*[1]

A microphone preamplifier circuit suitable for a carbon microphone is shown in Fig. 12.1. By choosing the grounded-emitter configura-

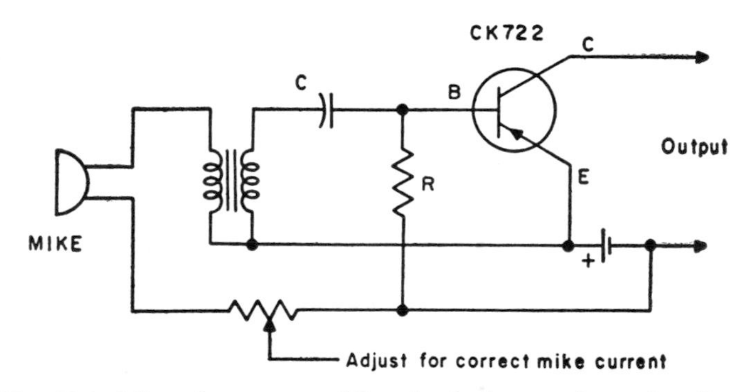

Fig. 12.1. Microphone preamplifier circuit for a carbon microphone.

tion, only one battery is required. This battery also supplies current for the carbon microphone. For this reason when low battery drain is desired, another type of microphone should be substituted for the carbon microphone.

Several circuits for dynamic microphones are illustrated in Fig. 12.2. Figure 12.2(A) presents the circuit of a dynamic microphone directly coupled to the amplifier. Dynamic microphones of from 100

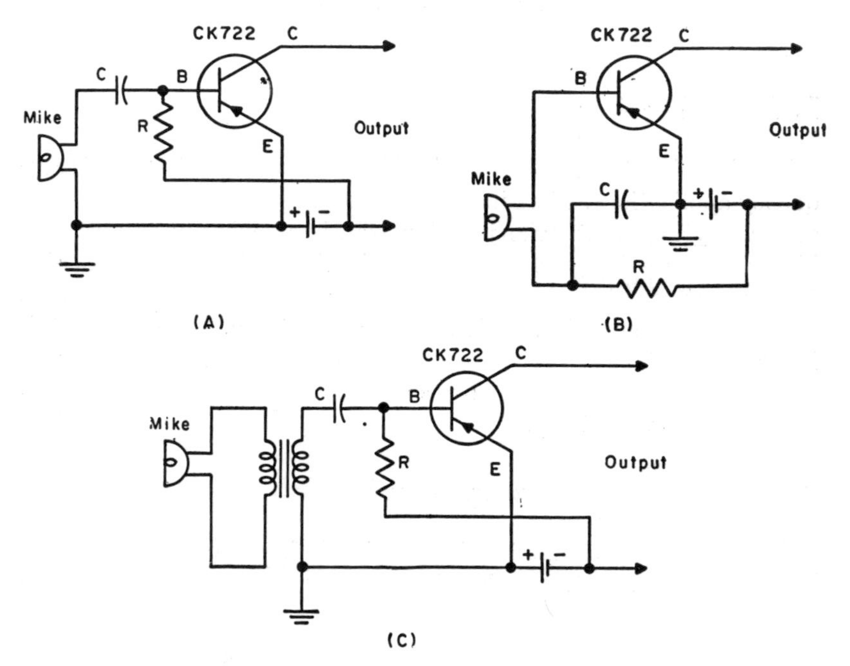

Fig. 12.2. (A) Dynamic microphone input circuit, (B) variation of circuit (A), and (C) transformer-coupled dynamic microphone input.

to 1000 ohms impedance may be so connected without too great an impedance mismatch. Capacitor C should be large enough to pass, without excessive loss, the lowest frequency to be reproduced. Resistor R is normally at least 100,000 ohms for the CK722 transistor, and is chosen to limit the collector current to a maximum of 0.5 ma with the greatest gain and the lowest noise.

Figure 12.2(B) is an alternative arrangement to Fig. 12.2(A).

Figure 12.2(C) shows transformer coupling of the microphone to the amplifier. This circuit can match dynamic or magnetic microphones, having impedances larger than 1000 ohms, to the input of the amplifier. This connection will also serve for high-impedance crystal microphones. For this purpose, an intercom voice coil-to-input grid transformer may be connected in reverse as an impedance step-down transformer.

3. *Output stage connections*[1]

Figure 12.3(A) gives the circuit for directly coupling, to the output stage, magnetic phones of a few thousand ohms impedance for 2 or 3 mw output. For either low impedance phones or high impedance

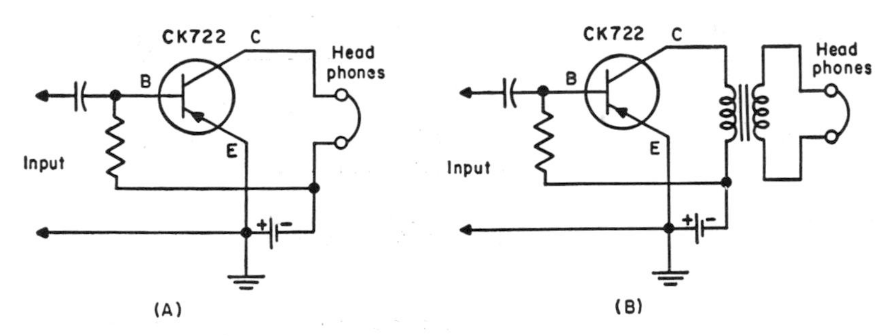

Fig. 12.3. (A) Direct-coupled output and (B) transformer-coupled output.

crystal phones, a matching transformer is required. This connection is shown in Fig. 12.3(B). To find the approximate load impedance to match the output transistor, divide the collector direct voltage by the collector direct current.

4. *Volume control circuits*[1]

Figure 12.4(A) illustrates a satisfactory volume control for resistance coupled circuits. A potentiometer is connected as the collector load resistor, with the arm feeding the signal to the input of the following stage.

Figure 12.4(B) is a good circuit for controlling the volume of transformer coupled stages. To have negligible shunting effect on the signal in the full volume position, the potentiometer should have a resistance at least ten times the rated ohmic load value of the secondary of the input transformer.

Each of the above volume control circuits has the advantage of attenuating the a-c signal without disturbing the d-c operating point of the transistor. A good place for a volume control is in the first stage of a multistage amplifier; this prevents a large signal from overloading the following stages.

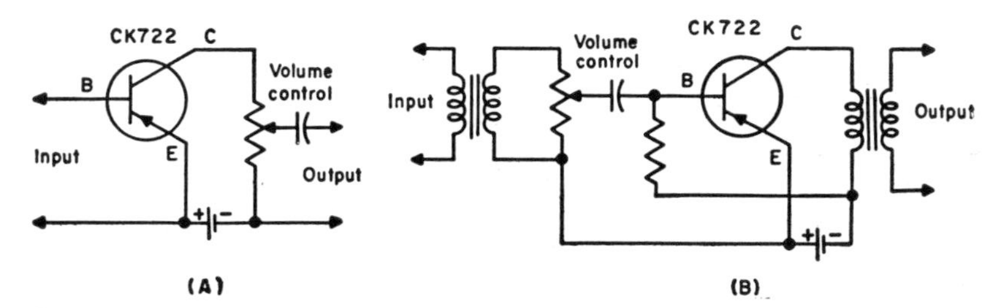

Fig. 12.4. (A) Volume control for resistance coupling and (B) volume control for transformer coupling.

5. *A two-stage N-P-N transistor audio amplifier*[2,3]

The circuit of a two-stage grounded-emitter amplifier is given in Fig. 12.5. This transformer-coupled amplifier employs two M-1752 junction transistors, has a pass band from 100 to 20,000 cps, and a power gain of approximately 90 db. For a collector voltage range of 1 to 20 v, the gain is relatively independent of the collector voltage. As this voltage is increased, only the available undistorted power output increases. For a collector voltage of 1.5 v, the collector current

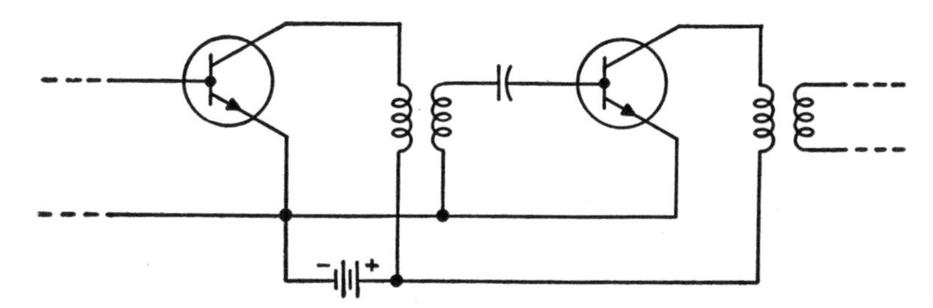

Fig. 12.5. Two-stage N-P-N transistor audio amplifier.

is approximately 0.5 ma per stage, giving a total power drain of 1.5 mw. Under these conditions, the amplifier will deliver about 0.7 mw of class A power output. The noise figure of this amplifier lies in the range of 10 to 15 db at 1000 cps, depending upon the collector voltage.

6. *An improved two-stage N-P-N transistor amplifier*[4]

Figure 12.6 shows an improved two-stage N-P-N transistor amplifier with a number of interesting features. Each stage is connected as a grounded-emitter amplifier for audio frequencies, and biased as a grounded-base circuit for direct current. This form of biasing holds

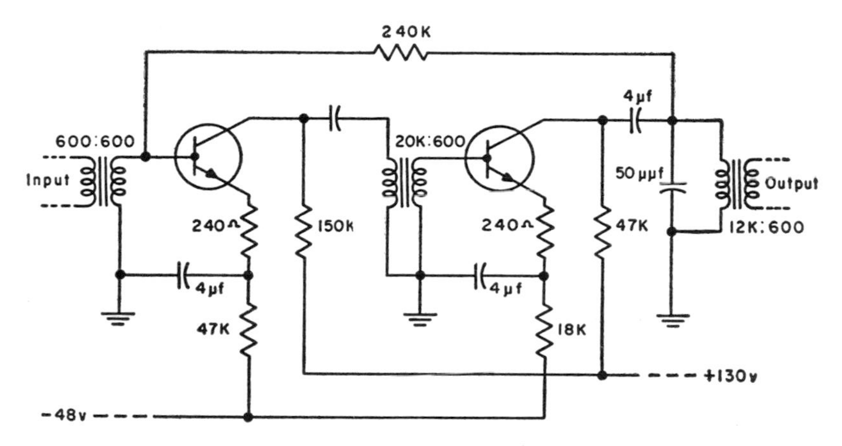

Fig. 12.6. An improved two-stage N-P-N transistor amplifier.

Battery Power:

First stage	0.14 w
Second stage	0.33 w
Total	0.47 w

Output:

12.5 mw (+11 dbm)

the emitter current constant, resulting in a more uniform collector operating point. The output stage collector is resistance shunt fed, so that a subminiature transformer can match the transistor to a line impedance. The output transistor operates with high efficiency. It is biased at an operating point of 22.5 v at 2.2 ma, or at 50 mw. The maximum sine-wave output is +11.1 dbm (db above 1 mw). With the output transformer loss of 1.6 db and the shunt loss of 1.1 db, the transistor delivers +13.8 dbm, only 0.2 db short of the theoretical maximum for 50 per cent class A efficiency, or +14 dbm.

Without feedback, the over-all gain of the two stage N-P-N amplifier is about 55 db. At least 15 db of negative feedback is achieved by local series feedback from unby-passed emitter resistance and by over-all shunt feedback from coupling the output collector to the input base. The performance characteristics of this amplifier are given in Fig. 12.7. As shown there, the maximum square wave output is +13 dbm. It is worth noting that the second-harmonic distor-

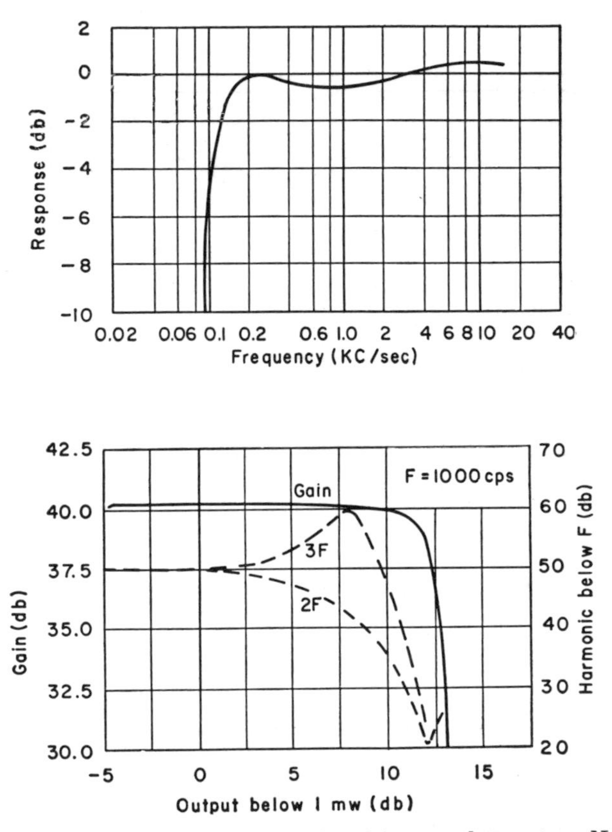

Fig. 12.7. Performance characteristics of improved two-stage N-P-N transistor amplifier.

tion is down 35 db at +10 dbm, only 3 db back from maximum output. The 40 db of over-all gain with negative feedback is constant within a few tenths of a db at ordinary laboratory temperatures. The frequency response is flat for voice frequencies, and is excellent for high audio frequencies.

7. *A temperature-compensated d-c amplifier*[5]

Figure 12.8 illustrates a two-stage d-c amplifier using a junction diode as a temperature-stabilized element. This amplifier has a dy-

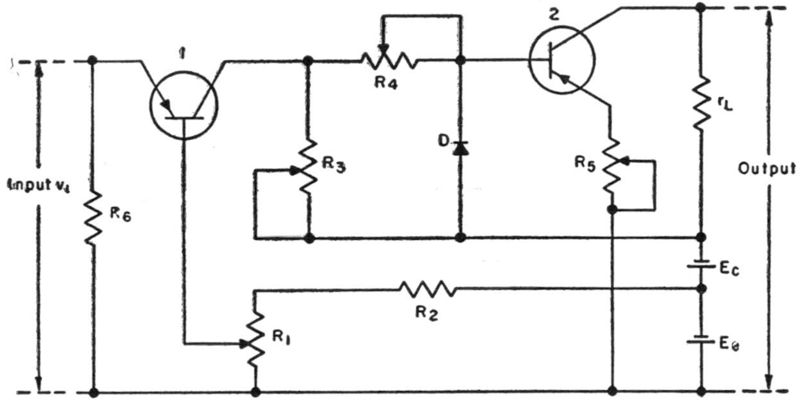

Fig. 12.8. A temperature-compensated d-c amplifier.

Table of Characteristics

1.	No. 1, No. 2	G.E., P-N-P junction transistors
2.	Diode D	G.E., junction diode
3.	E_c	12 v
4.	E_e	1.5 v
5.	I_{c1}	0.43 ma
6.	I_{c2}	2 ma
7.	R_1	100 ohms
8.	R_4	1000 ohms
9.	R_2	1000 ohms
10.	R_3	15,000 ohms
11.	R_5	500 ohms
12.	R_6	100 ohms
13.	$\Delta V_{1\,min}$	0.5 mv
14.	$V_{1\,max}$	50 mv

namic range of 100 to 1, or 40 db, and an over-all power gain of 23 db for an output load resistance of 1000 ohms. The input resistance of the amplifier is 50 ohms.

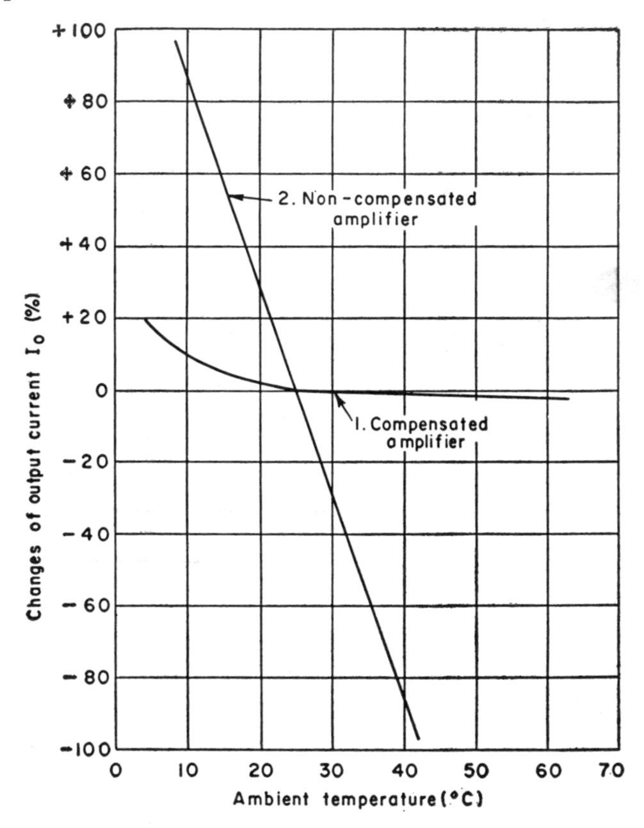

Fig. 12.9. Temperature characteristics of amplifier shown in Fig. 12.8.

The temperature characteristics of this amplifier are shown in Fig. 12.9. Curve 1 is for the compensated amplifier, whereas curve 2 is for the noncompensated amplifier with diode *D* removed and the values of the resistors changed to restore I_0 to its original value.

8. *Push-pull N-P-N transistor amplifiers*[4]

Figure 12.10 gives two possible circuits for push-pull N-P-N transistors. In the upper diagram, constant emitter current bias is employed for each transistor. Although two batteries are shown, a single battery could be used. With the proper bias conditions and load line for class A operation, a maximum power output of almost 50 mw, or half the total allowable collector dissipation of the two transistors, could be obtained. If the two transistor collector currents are well balanced, a center-tapped transformer of subminiature size would be practical. The overload characteristics of this amplifier could be im-

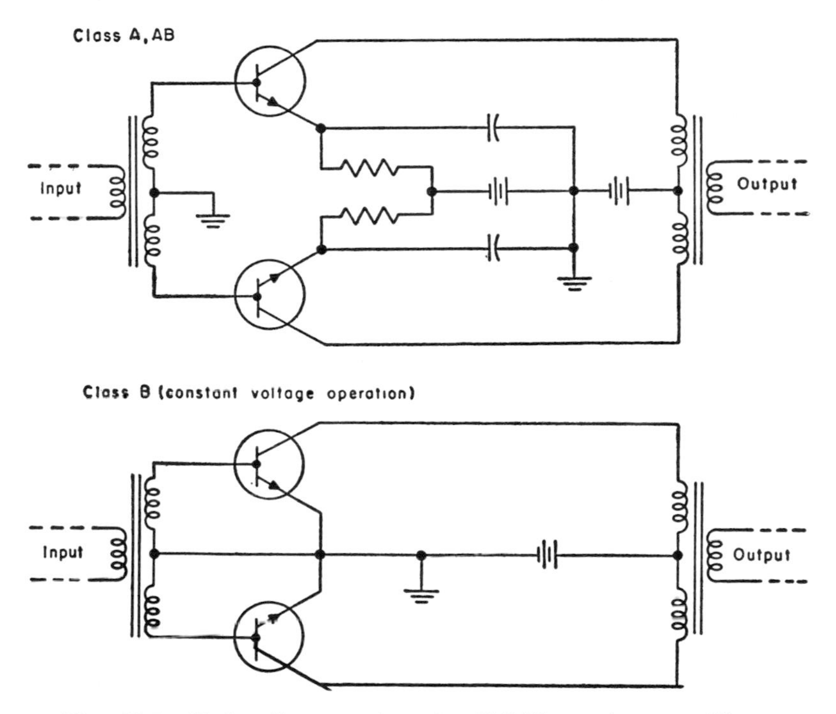

Fig. 12.10. Push-pull connections for N-P-N transistor amplifiers.

proved by adjusting the load and bias for class AB operation. Then the emitter by-pass capacitors must be sufficiently large to maintain the quiescent operating point, since rectification takes place when the maximum class A signal is exceeded.

In the lower diagram of Fig. 12.10 a circuit for class B operation is shown. The transistors are biased at almost zero collector current with full battery voltage. The advantage of this is that little power is required during the idle condition.

For the circuits described above, an additional driver stage, not shown in the figures, would be required. Thus, although the amplifier would require three transistors, the reduction in size and power drain would make this type of circuit attractive.

9. *Phonograph amplifier*[6]

A transistor phonograph amplifier is illustrated in Fig. 12.11. This circuit employs one 2N36 and two 2N37 P-N-P junction transistors. The simplicity of the circuit does not detract from its operational quality. Remarkably faithful audio reproduction is achieved with a moderately good signal-to-noise ratio.

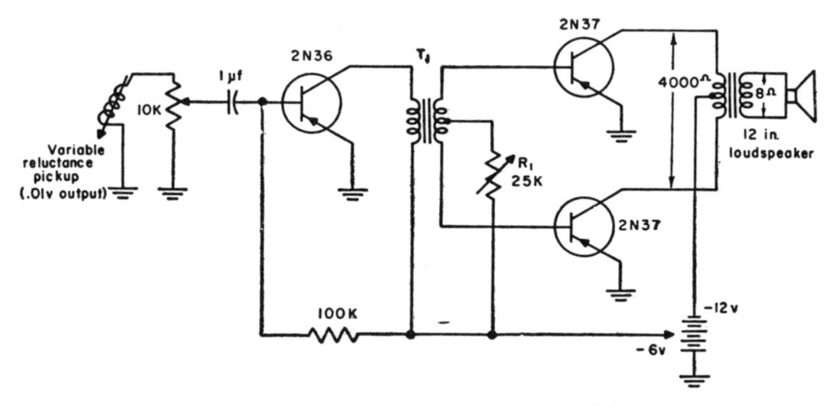

Fig. 12.11. Transistor phonograph amplifier.

In practice the resistance R_1 is adjusted for a total collector current of 8 ma. The transformer T_1 is used primarily for phase inversion. In the circuit shown, the power output is approximately 50 mw.

10. *Transistor amplifier suitable for intercom systems*[7]

Figure 12.12 shows a single-ended transistor amplifier with the last two transistors, T_3 and T_4, connected in tandem to minimize the loss of power in the resistors that keep the emitter current constant. The emitter of T_4 is connected directly to the collector of T_3. Transistor T_3 is stabilized with a 1500 ohm resistor in the emitter lead and a voltage divider supplying the base voltage. Transistor T_3 supplies a constant current to the emitter of the last transistor to stabilize it against drift or other temperature changes.

The amplifier has an output of about 150 mw, an over-all power gain of 70 db, and requires a total battery consumption of 570 mw. Such an amplifier can provide economical audio output for intercommunicating systems.

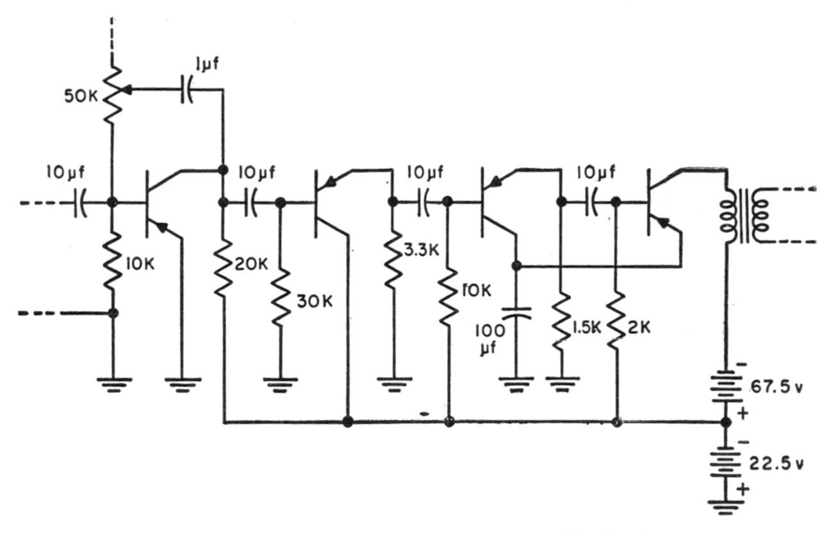

Fig. 12.12. Single-ended transistor amplifier suitable for intercom systems.

11. *Push-pull class-A transistor amplifier*[5]

Figure 12.13 gives a push-pull P-N-P transistor amplifier producing 300 mw class A for 1400 mw of power consumption. Voltage and current stability with time and temperature are excellent.

12. *Push-pull class-B amplifier for speech application*[7]

Figure 12.14 illustrates a push-pull class B amplifier for speech application where higher distortion is permissible in exchange for the improved efficiency and insignificant standby power. This is the cir-

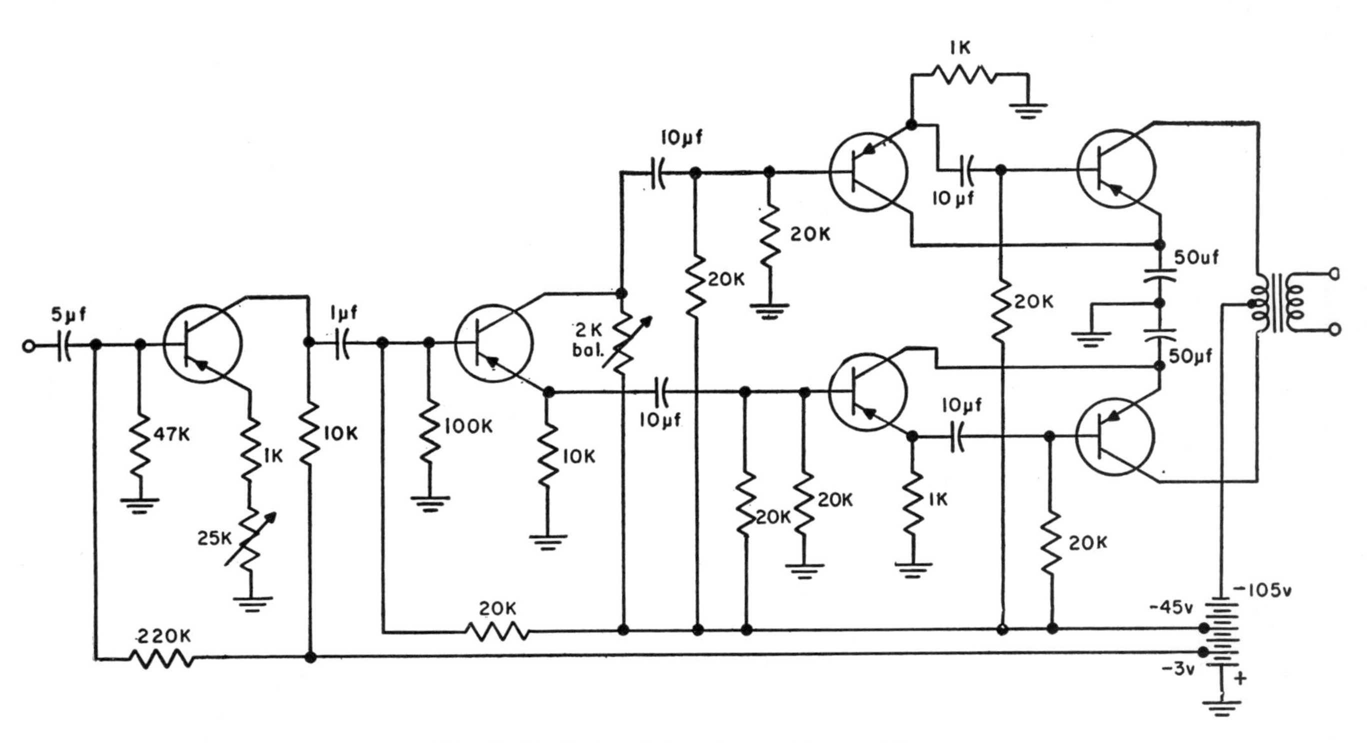

Fig. 12.13. Push-pull class-A transistor amplifier.

cuit of a completely self-contained electronic megaphone. The unit has about 850 mw of audio power, yet at low levels consumes only 100 mw of power including about 50 mw for the carbon microphone. The efficiency is approximately 65 per cent. Power is obtained from one Minimax battery.

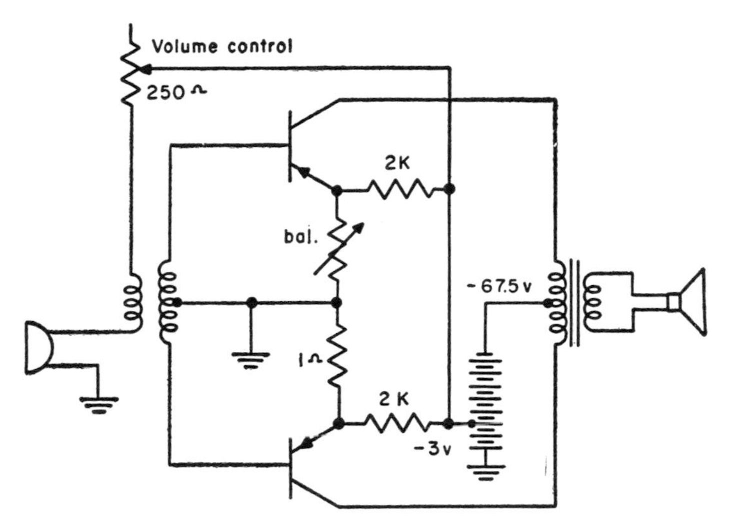

Fig. 12.14. A push-pull class-B amplifier for speech use.

13. *Complementary symmetry amplifiers*[8]

Complementary symmetry amplifiers are unique in transistor electronics in that no counterparts exist in vacuum tube circuits. Such amplifiers depend upon the symmetrical properties of P-N-P and N-P-N junction transistors. While the vacuum tube conducts by negative charges, or electrons, somewhat like the N-P-N transistor, there is no vacuum tube which conducts by positive charges, or holes, like the P-N-P transistor.

A push-pull transistor amplifier with complementary symmetry is shown in Fig. 12.15. This circuit operates without a transformer or phase inverter. Although the amplifier has push-pull action, both the input and the output are single-ended. With no input signal there is no direct current in the 10,000 ohm load resistor for a matched pair of P-N-P and N-P-N transistors; the collector current of one unit

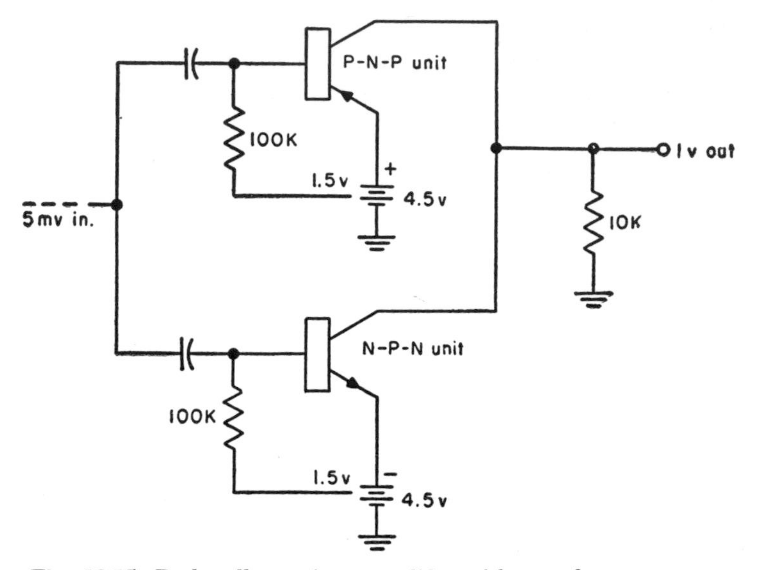

Fig. 12.15. Push-pull transistor amplifier with complementary symmetry.

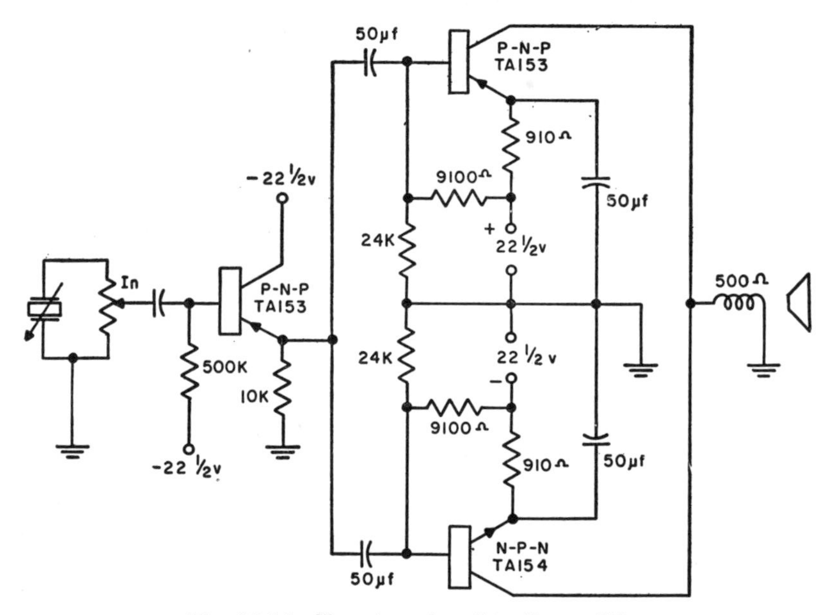

Fig. 12.16. Class-A push-pull audio amplifier.

cancels that of the other. A positive input signal increases the collector current of the N-P-N transistor and decreases the collector current of the P-N-P transistor. This causes a large output current to flow in the 10,000 ohm load resistor. A negative input signal produces a similar output current in the reverse direction.

Figure 12.16 gives the circuit of a class A audio amplifier with two P-N-P transistors and one N-P-N transistor, providing 100 mw of audio output directly into a 500 ohm voice-coil speaker. This amplifier employs two $22\frac{1}{2}$ v hearing-aid batteries. Since there is no direct current flowing through the load, the voice coil is balanced.

References

1. Charles W. Martel, "Transistorize Your Audio Amplifiers," *Radio and Television News*, Vol. XLIX, No. 3, March 1953, pp. 40–41.
2. R. L. Wallace, Jr. and W. J. Pietenpol, "Some Circuit Properties and Applications of N-P-N Transistors," *Proc. IRE*, Vol. XXXIX, No. 7, July 1951, p. 762.
3. J. A. Morton, "Present Status of Transistor Development," *Bell System Tech. J.*, Vol. XXXI, No. 3, May 1952, pp. 411–442.
4. R. S. Caruthers, *Some System Applications of Transistor Amplifiers*, Bell Telephone Laboratories, Inc., 1951.
5. Reprinted with permission from Richard F. Shea, *Principles of Transistor Circuits*, John Wiley & Sons, Inc., New York, 1953, pp. 120–121, 179–181.
6. *CBS-Hytron Transistor Manual, An Introduction to Transistor Theory, Data, and Applications, Bulletin E 212*, CBS-Hytron, a Division of Columbia Broadcasting System, Inc., Danvers, Mass.
7. R. F. Shea, "Transistor Power Amplifiers," *Proceedings of Symposium, Progress in Quality Electronic Components*, Washington, D. C., May 1952, pp. 144–149.
8. George Clifford Sziklai, "Symmetrical Properties of Transistors and Their Applications," *Proc. IRE*, Vol. XLI, No. 6, June 1953, pp. 717–724.

Chapter 13

TRANSISTOR RADIO-FREQUENCY AMPLIFIERS

1. *455 kc i-f amplifiers*

Figure 13.1 shows a practical 455 kc intermediate frequency amplifier employing point-contact transistors.[1] The two intermediate coils and tuning capcitors are in separate shield cans, with capacitive coupling between the two tuned circuits to give a bandpass characteristic.

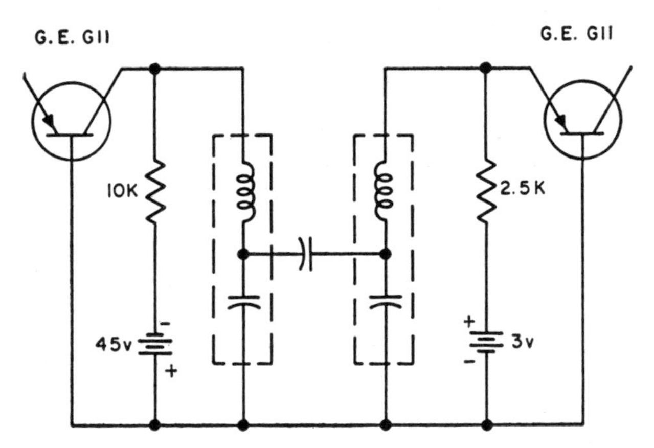

Fig. 13.1. A practical 455-kc/sec i-f amplifier employing point-contact transistors.

Figure 13.2 is the circuit for measuring the gain of alloy P-N-P junction transistors in a grounded-base 450 kc intermediate frequency amplifier.[2] The collector tap on the coil is at about one-third of the winding. The tuning capacitor connects to the emitter of the following transistor. The collector circuit of the second transistor was tuned to the same frequency as that of the first transistor to minimize reaction in tuning. The Q of the second stage was made about the same as that of the first stage. A few measurements permit the gain to be calculated. Alpha is about 0.9 at 450 kc. With the collector connected, the impedance of the coil is approximately 20 ohms. From a measurement of the Q of the coil, the resistance of the emitter was found to be about 19 ohms. The emitter input sees a Q of 43.8. The collector voltage was 36 per cent of the total coil voltage. The collector output resistance was 12,800 ohms. The coil impedance was 52,500 ohms, with a tap at 6600 ohms for the value in series with the collector. Therefore the gain $= 0.9 \times 0.36 \times 43.8 \times 12{,}800/19{,}400 = 10.5$ times. This compares with the measured gain of 10.9 times.

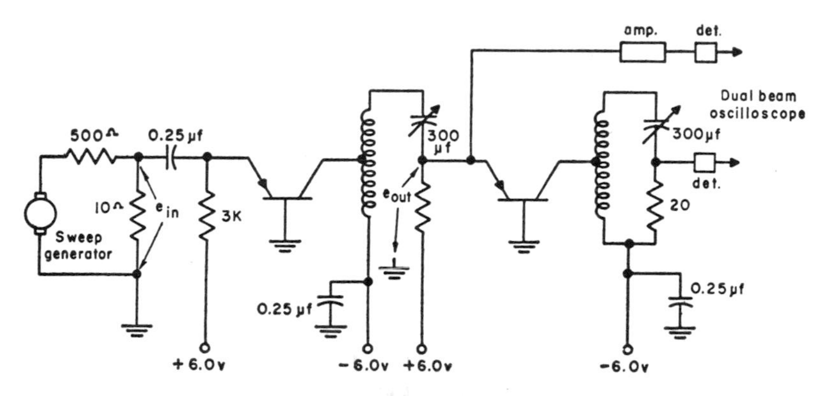

Fig. 13.2. Circuit for measuring gain of 450-kc/sec i-f amplifier utilizing alloy P-N-P junction transistors in grounded-base configuration.

Figure 13.3 indicates the circuit for a grounded-emitter intermediate frequency amplifier.[2] This differs from the preceding grounded-base circuit mainly in that only 0.6 of the tuning capacitor is in series with the following base input. This connection has a larger emitter input resistance than the grounded-base configuration. The tuned circuit reactance is only about 700 ohms. The second base input sees a Q of 24.6, which is roughly one-half that of the grounded-base circuit. The transistor output impedance is approximately 6300 ohms. The tuned circuit impedance is about 17,200 ohms with the collector tapped at 2100 ohms. The current gain $\alpha/(1 - \alpha)$ for the transistor is 4.6 times. The collector tap is located at one-third of the coil. The calculated gain $= 4.6 \times \frac{1}{3} \times 24.6 \times 0.6 \times \frac{6300}{8400} = 16.95$ times. This compares with the measured gain of 16.1 times.

The choice of the second transistor in the two preceding circuits could alter the results considerably. In the grounded-emitter configuration care must be exercised to avoid overloading the transistor. The base current is the differential current; if the alternating current becomes too large, the transistor input impedance begins to vary rapidly and causes bad distortion. With 2 ma emitter current the maximum input voltage should not exceed about 25 mv. When larger inputs are required, the grounded-base circuit or a larger emitter current may be employed.

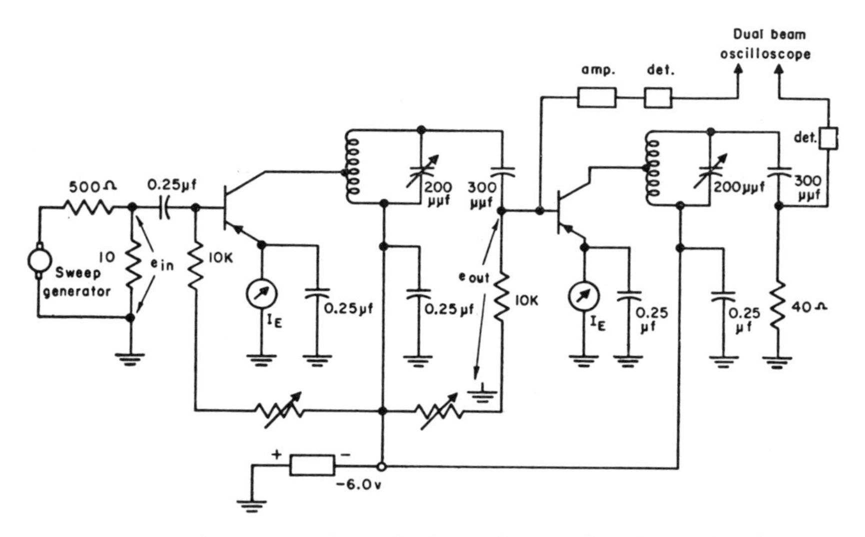

Fig. 13.3. Grounded-emitter circuit employing alloy P-N-P junction transistors in a 450-kc/sec i-f amplifier.

When point-contact transistors were first applied to high-frequency amplifiers, they usually employed the grounded-base circuit. The principle of duality determined that the single-tuned vacuum tube amplifier corresponded to a transistor amplifier with a series resonant circuit for the interstage network. The necessary condition for this is that the output short-circuit current amplification must be larger than unity. For the point-contact transistor this occurs in either the grounded-base or the grounded-emitter configuration. For the junction transistor only the grounded-emitter connection meets this requirement.

Figure 13.4 shows a point-contact transistor amplifier having a series-resonant circuit as the interstage coupling network.[3] The load of the first stage is the input impedance z_i of the second stage, which is in series with the tuned circuit. The effective Q of this amplifier stage is modified by z_i, because it is in series with the resonant circuit. The power gain per stage is approximately α^2.

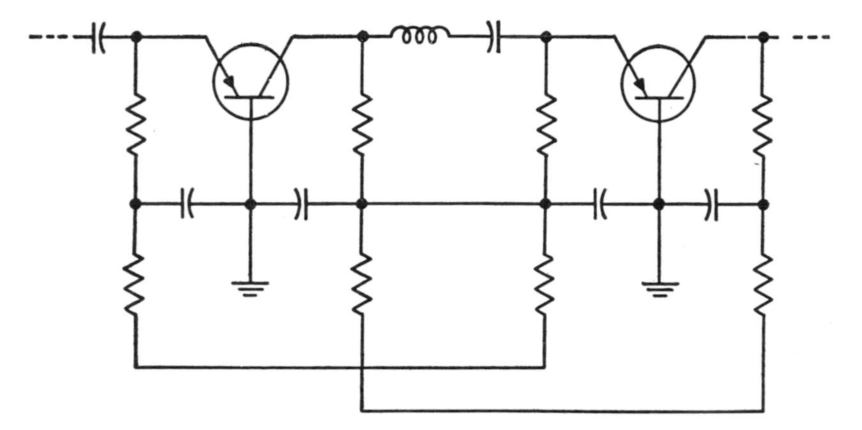

Fig. 13.4. Point-contact transistor amplifier with series-resonant circuit as interstage coupling network.

The parallel-resonant circuit can also be utilized for interstage coupling. A parallel-tuned coupling network normally causes point-contact transistors to become short-circuit unstable. Adequate positive resistances must be inserted in the circuit to overcome the negative resistance component of the input impedance, or oscillation will occur. When parallel-resonant coupling circuits are employed with point-contact transistors, the latter are generally of the short-circuit stable variety. A stable amplifier with point-contact transistors can generally be achieved by properly controlling the operating point. Another way to obtain a stable point-contact transistor amplifier is to insert a resistance in series with the emitter in the grounded-base circuit. This results in the loss of about 3 to 6 db of gain.

Figure 13.5 gives several simplified circuits for coupling transistor stages with parallel-resonant circuits.[3] In Fig. 13.5(A) the second transistor connects directly into the parallel-resonant circuit, either in series with the inductance or in series with the capacitance. In Fig.

13.5(B) the second amplifier connects to the junction of capacitors C_1 and C_2. These capacitors act as an impedance-reducing device in addition to forming part of the parallel-resonant circuit. In Fig. 13.5(C) the second transistor is inductively coupled to the resonant

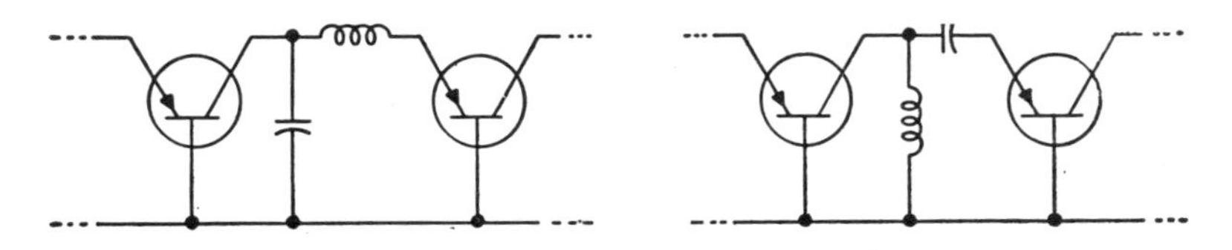

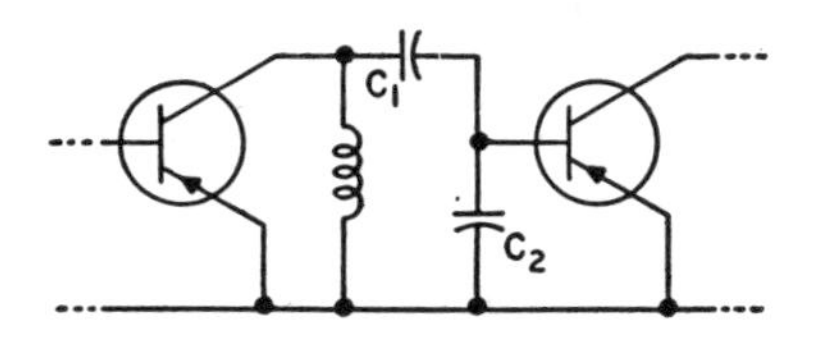

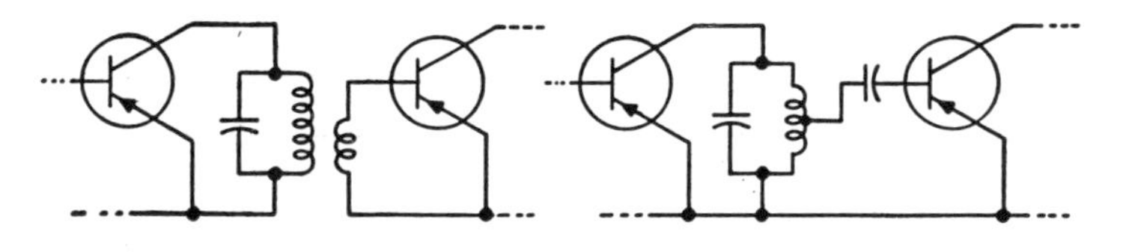

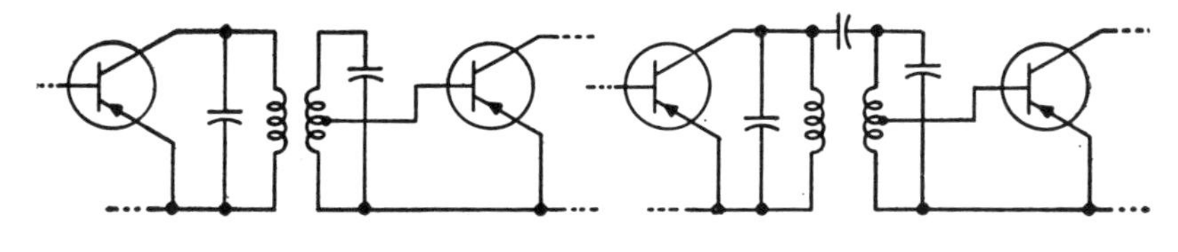

Fig. 13.5. Practical arrangements for coupling transistor stages with parallel-resonant circuits.

circuit and the secondary is untuned. The input impedance of the following amplifier is matched by an impedance step-down. In Fig. 13.5(D) double-tuned circuits with either inductive coupling or capacitive coupling are shown. Impedance step-down is indicated to match the low input impedance of the second transistor.

When designing an interstage coupling network consisting of a parallel-resonant circuit, we must consider the input and output impedances of each amplifier stage since these impedances in effect are in parallel with the resonant circuit. The output impedance of the preceding transistor will appear as the source impedance of the following stage, and the input impedance of the following transistor will appear as the load of the preceding stage. In a multistage amplifier these impedance values are calculated on the assumption that all the transistors are practically identical.

Figure 13.6(A) [3] indicates a parallel-resonant *RCL* circuit shunted by the effective output impedance z_o' and the effective input impedance z_i'. These two effective impedances are the output impedance z_o and the input impedance z_i after the required impedance transfor-

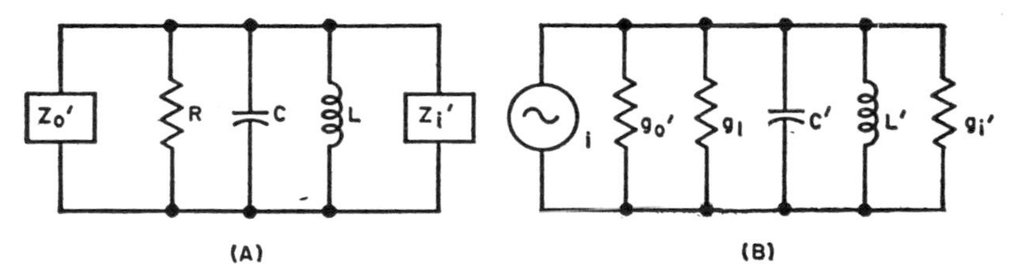

Fig. 13.6. High-frequency equivalent circuits of a parallel-resonant *RCL* interstage coupling network.

mations. Figure 13.6(B) shows the equivalent circuit when the reactive components of z_o' and z_i' are combined with the reactive elements of the parallel-resonant circuit. At resonant frequency maximum power will be transferred from the preceding transistor through the interstage coupling network of the following stage when

$$g_i' = gl + g_o' \tag{1}$$

where gl represents the loss in the interstage coupling network. Let the power loss factor F_p be defined as the ratio of available power minus the loss in the coupling network to the available power. Then

$$F_p = \frac{g_o'}{g_o' + gl} = \frac{1}{1 + gl/g_o'} \tag{2}$$

The total conductance and the inductance or the capacitance will determine the effective Q of such an amplifier stage. At resonant frequency ω_o equals $2\pi f_o$,

$$Q = \frac{\omega_o C'}{g_o' + gl + g_i'} = \frac{\omega_o}{\Delta\omega} \tag{3}$$

where $\Delta\omega$ is the bandwidth at the half-power points on the selectivity curve of this amplifier stage. If Q_o is the original unloaded Q of the parallel-tuned circuit,

$$Q_o = \frac{\omega_o C}{gl} = \frac{\omega_o}{\Delta\omega_o} \cong \frac{\omega_o C'}{gl} \tag{4}$$

where $\Delta\omega_o$ is the bandwidth. We obtain the required impedance-matching conditions in terms of the required bandwidth by combining Eqs. (1), (3), and (4) to get

$$\Delta\omega = 2\left(\frac{g_o'}{C'} + \Delta\omega_o\right) \tag{5}$$

solving for g_o',

$$g_o' = \left(\frac{\Delta\omega}{2} - \Delta\omega_o\right) C' \tag{6}$$

and

$$g_i' = \frac{\Delta\omega}{2} C' \tag{7}$$

For a given resonant circuit unloaded Q and the desired effective Q of the amplifier stage, the required impedance transformation ratios can be found from Eqs. (6) and (7). To satisfy narrow band requirements, normally both the output impedance of the preceding transistor and the input impedance of the following stage must be stepped up.

Figure 13.7 is the circuit[3] of a 455 kc/sec intermediate frequency amplifier which was designed according to the foregoing principles. It has 58 db power gain, 14 kc/sec bandwidth, and a battery current of only 3.5 ma. This circuit was developed around experimental N-P-N rate-grown junction transistors having the following average characteristics; $\alpha = 0.9$, $r_e = 30$ ohms, $r_b =$ about 100 ohms, $r_c = 1$ megohm, and $f_{\alpha o} =$ about 1 mc for $I_e = 1$ ma and $V_c = 5$ v. At 455 kc the grounded-emitter connection gives an average available power gain of 18 db per stage. The average input impedance of each

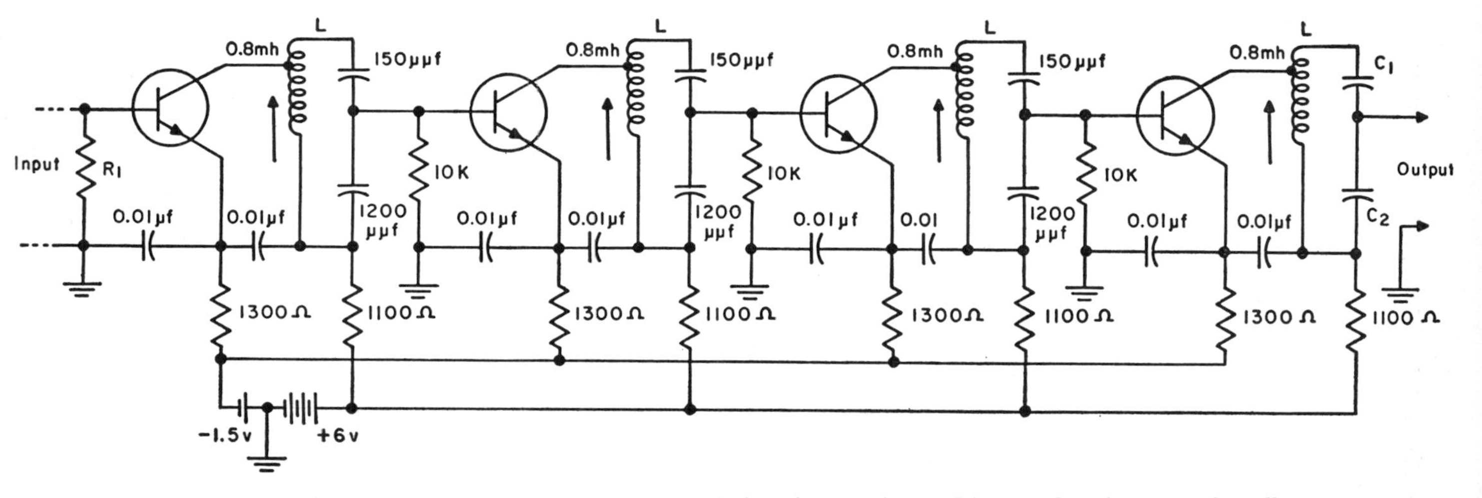

Fig. 13.7. Four-stage 455-kc/sec i-f amplifier utilizing rate-grown N-P-N junction transistors. L is tapped at 37 per cent for collector connection.

stage is

$$z_i = \frac{1}{\frac{1}{200} + j\omega 1600 \times 10^{-12}} \quad \text{ohms} \tag{8}$$

The average output impedance is

$$z_o = \frac{1}{10^{-4} + j\omega 25 \times 10^{-12}} \quad \text{ohms} \tag{9}$$

If the desired over-all effective Q of the four-stage amplifier is about 30, an inductance of about 0.8 mh and a Q_o of about 90 require a capacitance C' of about 150 $\mu\mu$f. Each stage, then, must have an effective Q of about 15. The input impedance transformation ratios are found from equations (6) and (7) to be

$$g_o/g_o' = 7.3 \tag{10}$$

and

$$g_i/g_i' = 350 \tag{11}$$

Equation (2) gives the power loss in the coupling circuit as approximately 1.74 db per stage.

If we reduce the inductance to 300 μh and maintain Q at 90, C' becomes approximately 400 $\mu\mu$f. The output and input impedance transformation ratios for the same amplifier effective Q are $g_o/g_o' = 2.74$ and $g_i/g_i' = 132$.

If we substitute 300 μh inductances in the circuit of Fig. 13.7, we will need a 60 per cent tap on each inductance and must increase each 1200 $\mu\mu$f capacitance to 2990 $\mu\mu$f. The power loss in the coupling circuit will be about the same as before. Nonuniformity of the experimental transistors and mismatch in the actual circuit cause a loss of 2 to 3 db per stage in a practical amplifier.

2. *Radio-frequency amplifiers*

Figure 13.8 shows a high-frequency amplifier employing 2N32 point-contact transistors.* Since point-contact transistors have current amplification factors larger than unity, negative resistances generated in the input circuit may cause oscillation. This is especially true of transistors like the 2N32 which are not short-circuit stable.

* The material in this paragraph is based on *Application Considerations for RCA Commercial Transistors*, by R. M. Cohen, Publication No. St-817, 1953, Tube Division, Radio Corporation of America, Harrison, N. J.

Adequate circuit resistance must be inserted in series with either the emitter or the collector, or both in combination; otherwise the transistor amplifier stages will oscillate, and the transistor current may increase sufficiently to damage the transistor. The circuit of Fig. 13.8 provides effective short-circuit stability and also matches the high output impedance of the first transistor to the low input impedance of the second transistor. The inductance L_1 and tuning capacitor C_1

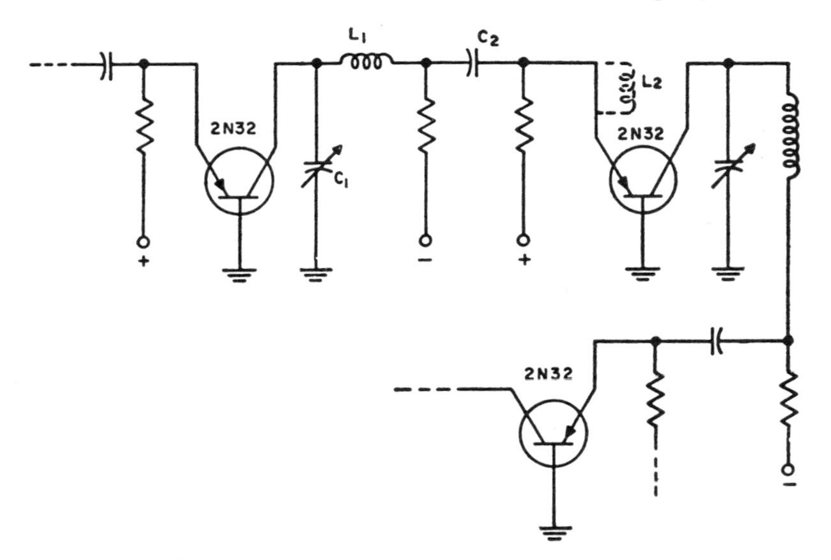

Fig. 13.8. Coupling method for 2N32 point-contact transistors, providing stability and impedance matching.

form a parallel-resonant circuit. If R represents the effective series resistance, we should select values of L_1 and C_1 for the tuned circuit such that the parallel resistance L/CR equals the output impedance of the first transistor, and naturally, so that L_1 and C_1 resonate at the required frequency. We can obtain greater selectivity by inserting a coil L_2 in series with the emitter of the second transistor and resonating this inductance with coupling capacitor C_2.

3. *High-frequency amplifiers*

Figures 13.9 and 13.10 give the circuits and frequency response of single-tuned and double-tuned 22 mc/sec intermediate frequency am-

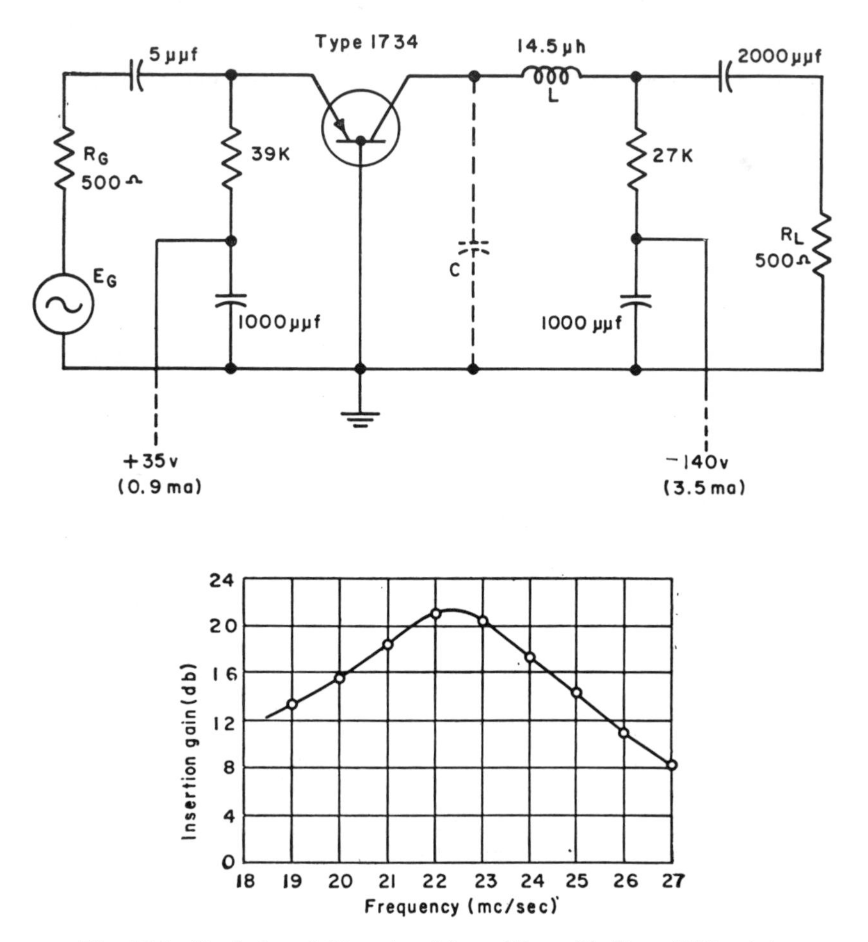

Fig. 13.9. Single-tuned 22-mc/sec i-f amplifier with Type 1734 point-contact transistor.

plifiers with Type 1734 point-contact transistors.[4] In each circuit the external collector inductances resonate with the internal and stray collector-to-base capacitance. In the double-tuned circuit overcoupling gives the double-peaked curve.

Point-contact transistors normally can operate at higher frequencies than junction transistors.

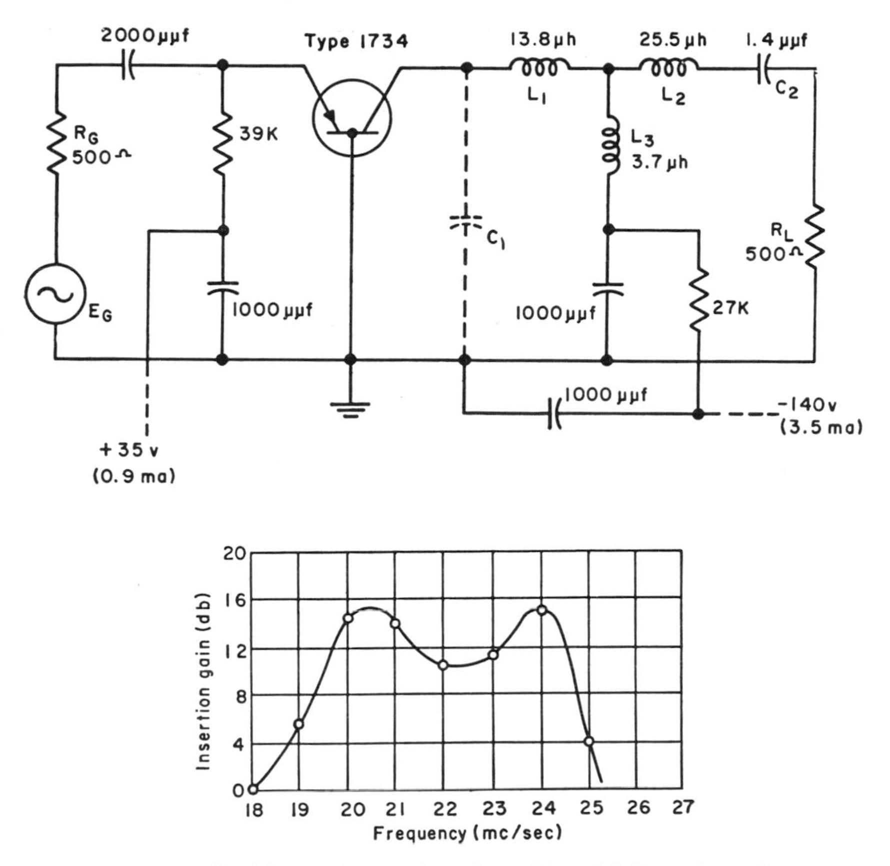

Fig. 13.10. Double-tuned 22-mc/sec i-f amplifier with Type 1734 point-contact transistor.

4. *Bandpass amplifiers with surface-barrier transistors*[5]

In high-frequency bandpass amplifiers with transistors we must avoid regeneration caused by inherent feedback within the transistor. A neutralizing circuit can prevent such regeneration. Figure 13.11 is the simplified circuit of a neutralized grounded-base amplifier for a transistor having such large collector resistance that it may be neglected in the gain calculations. For clearness the 0.5 ma emitter supply and the 3 v collector battery are left out of Fig. 13.11. The input is isolated from the output by the bridge consisting of the circuit elements r_N and C_N, along with the internal base resistance and collector capacitance of the transistor. Figure 13.12 represents the equivalent circuit of this amplifier, where r_b is the small-signal equivalent base resistance, r_b' is the spreading resistance or effective high-

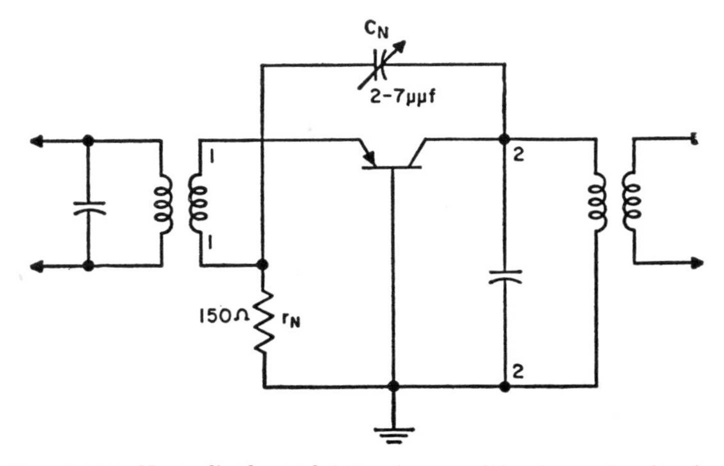

Fig. 13.11. Neutralized-tuned 30-mc/sec amplifier for surface-barrier transistor.

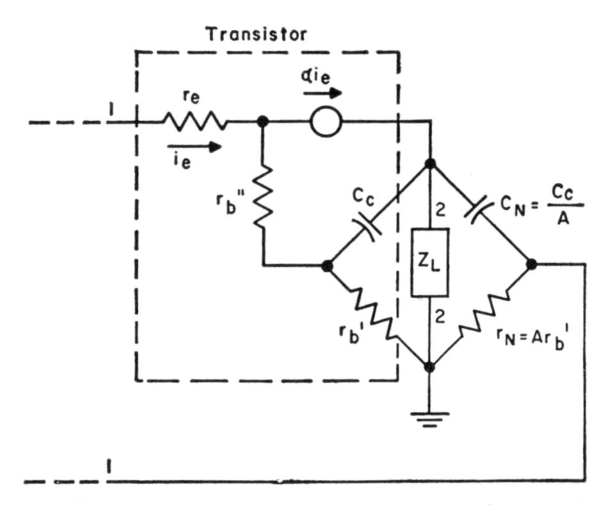

Fig. 13.12. Equivalent circuit of neutralized 30-mc/sec amplifier for surface-barrier transistor.

frequency base resistance, r_b'' is the difference between r_b and r_b', C_c is the collector capacitance, and A is the impedance ratio in the neutralizing bridge circuit, or C_c/C_N.

If, as usual, the ratio is approximately unity, and $1 - \alpha$ is much less than unity, the maximum available power gain G_p from a neutralized stage with a transistor having negligibly high collector resistance can be shown to be approximately

$$G_p \cong \frac{\alpha^2}{8(2\pi f r_b' C_c)^2} \tag{12}$$

This approximation holds true to within 1 or 2 db for most surface barrier transistors. The fundamental parameter $r_b'C_c$ controls the gain. Surface-barrier transistors have a low collector capacitance and are therefore well suited for high-frequency bandpass amplifiers.

The circuit of Fig. 13.11 achieved an over-all nonregenerative circuit insertion gain of 13 db at 30 mc/sec including coil losses of 5 db with a surface-barrier transistor having an alpha cutoff frequency of about 50 mc/sec.

References

1. John A. Doremus, "Point-Contact and Junction Transistors," *Radio-Electronic Engineering Section, Radio and Television News*, April 1952.
2. J. R. Nelson, "Transistor I-F Amplifiers," *Tele-Tech and Electronic Industries*, Vol. XII, No. 12, Dec. 1953, pp. 68–69.
3. R. F. Shea, *High Frequency Applications of Point-Contact Transistors*, 1953 Transistor Short Course Proceedings, June 8–19, Penn. State College, pp. XI–8–15.
4. R. S. Caruthers, *Some System Applications of Transistor Amplifiers*, Bell Telephone Laboratories, Inc., New York, 1951.
5. J. B. Angell and F. P. Keiper, "The Surface Barrier Transistor, Part III—Circuit Applications of Surface Barrier Transistors," *Proc. IRE*, Vol. XLI, No. 12, Dec. 1953, pp. 1709–1712.

Chapter 14

TRANSISTOR AUDIO-FREQUENCY OSCILLATORS

1. *Theory of sine-wave oscillators*

Figure 14.1 shows one of many possible point-contact transistor oscillator circuits.[1] The following equation specifies the conditions necessary for a transistor circuit to oscillate:

$$\alpha_{cr} - 1 \geqq \frac{r_e + Z_e}{r_b + Z_b} \tag{1}$$

where α_{cr} is the current gain of the circuit, r_e is the transistor emitter resistance, and r_b is the transistor base resistance. In practice, α_{cr} depends upon the external collector impedance Z_c.

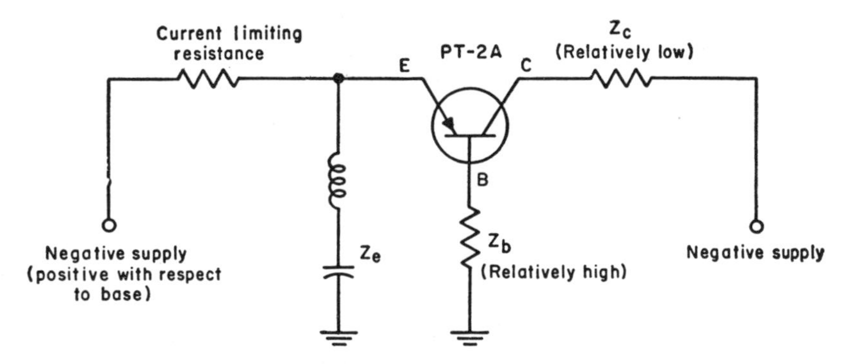

Fig. 14.1. Sine-wave oscillator utilizing a point-contact transistor.

For a given transistor, we must adjust the external impedances Z_e, Z_b, and Z_c to satisfy the above equation. We can produce oscillation by making Z_e small, Z_b large, and Z_c small (so that α_{cr} will be large).

A resonant circuit tuned to the desired frequency controls the frequency of oscillation. In Fig. 14.1 a series-resonant circuit connected between emitter and ground furnishes the required low emitter impedance at the resonant frequency. A series-resonant circuit connected to the collector or a parallel-resonant circuit in the base lead would also satisfy the equation.

The point-contact transistor makes possible simple oscillator circuits because with suitable external resistances it can produce a negative resistance.[2] For example, assume that a typical transistor operating at low currents has the parameters $r_e = 200$ ohms, $r_b = 200$ ohms, $r_c = 10{,}000$ ohms, and $r_m = 30{,}000$ ohms. For maximum power from our oscillator, let us make the load resistance $R_L = 10{,}000$ ohms to match the collector resistance. If we employ the grounded-base circuit to obtain a negative input resistance at the emitter, the input resistance will be

$$R_{11} = r_e + r_b - \frac{r_b(r_b + r_m)}{R_L + r_c + r_b} \tag{2}$$

Substituting the values for the transistor parameters and the load resistance gives

$$R_{11} = 400 - \frac{200(30{,}200)}{20{,}200} = \text{about } 100 \text{ ohms}$$

This does not give us the desired negative resistance, so we insert an 800-ohm resistor in series with the base, effectively making $r_b = 1000$ ohms. Now

$$R_{11} = 1200 - \frac{1000(31{,}000)}{21{,}000} = \text{about } -300 \text{ ohms}$$

We can readily design a circuit which equals 300 ohms at one frequency, and has a larger impedance at all other frequencies. We can employ a series-resonant circuit consisting of a capacitor and a coil having a resistance of 300 ohms. Assuming that our coil has a Q of about 30, the equation $\omega L = QR$ gives us an inductive reactance of nearly 10,000 ohms. For a frequency of 798 cps, we will require a 2 henry inductance. With the resistors to supply the emitter and collector biases, the circuit[2] becomes that of Fig. 14.2.

Next consider the transistor oscillator circuit with a series-resonant circuit connected between the collector and ground.[2] The output impedance of the grounded-base circuit is

$$R_{22} = r_c + r_b - \frac{r_b(r_b + r_m)}{R_G + r_e + r_b} \tag{3}$$

where R_G is the input generator resistance. If $R_G = 0$ and r_b is made

1000 ohms by inserting an 800 ohm resistor in the base lead, then

$$R_{22} = 11{,}000 - \frac{1000(31{,}000)}{1200} = -15{,}000 \quad \text{ohms}$$

A negative resistance this large may find application in crystal oscillator circuits, but is not suitable for ordinary *LC* circuits. Also it is difficult to find a place to connect a load circuit, except in series with the controlling *LC* circuit; this is undesirable since it lowers the system *Q* and decreases the frequency stability.

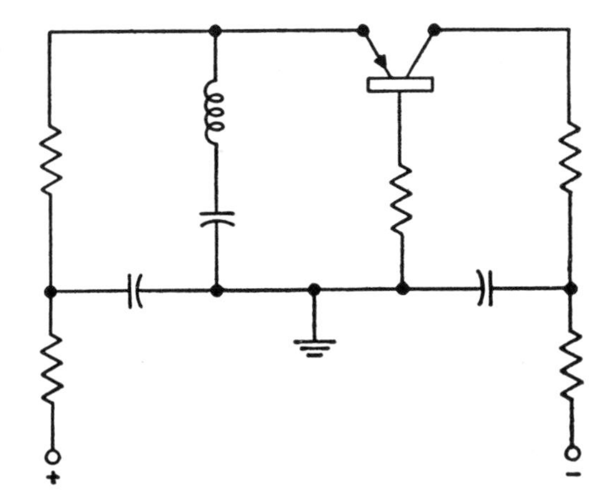

Fig. 14.2. Oscillator circuit utilizing negative emitter impedance obtained with external base resistor.

Let us now turn to the transistor oscillator with a parallel-resonant circuit in the base lead.[2] The equation for the input impedance of the grounded-emitter circuit is

$$R_{11} = r_b + r_e + \frac{r_e(r_m - r_e)}{R_L + r_e + r_c - r_m} \tag{4}$$

Substituting our values we have

$$R_{11} = 200 + 200 + \frac{200(30{,}000 - 200)}{20{,}200 - 30{,}000}$$

$$\cong 200 + 200 - 600 = -200 \quad \text{ohms}$$

If we connect in the base lead a circuit which has an impedance of 200 ohms at only one frequency, the system will oscillate. We could employ a parallel-resonant circuit with an impedance of about 250 ohms. But if we wish a Q of 50 to control the oscillator frequency, we would have an inductance and a capacitance with a reactance of only 5 ohms at the resonant frequency. This specifies a tiny inductance and a huge capacitance. The solution of the problem is to insert about 5000 ohms between the emitter and ground. The effective value of r_e becomes 5200 ohms, and this increases the base input impedance to almost $-25{,}000$ ohms. With this impedance magnitude we can utilize

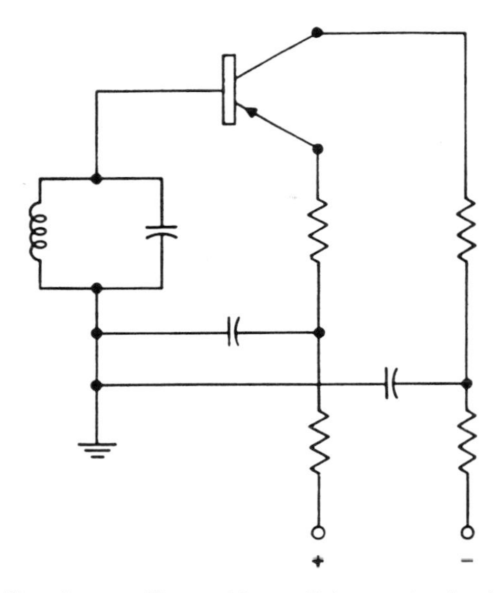

Fig. 14.3. Transistor oscillator with parallel-resonant circuit in the base lead.

ordinary tuned circuits having good Q. Figure 14.3 shows such a circuit[2] which oscillates nicely at 800 cps with a coil of 100 mh inductance and a Q of 50, a good transistor, and bias currents supplied through suitable resistors.

Another type of transistor oscillator[2] operates with a series-resonant circuit connected between the emitter and the collector. The output impedance of a grounded-emitter circuit is

$$R_{22} = r_c + r_e - r_m + \frac{r_e(r_m - r_e)}{R_G + r_b + r_e} \tag{5}$$

With $R_G = 0$, this becomes

$$R_{22} = 10{,}000 + 200 - 30{,}000 + \frac{200(29{,}800)}{400}$$
$$= \text{about } -5000 \text{ ohms}$$

Figure 14.4(A) indicates this circuit, which will oscillate if the resistance of the series-resonant circuit is less than 5000 ohms at resonance. This is an impedance of crystal magnitude, and there is no place to load the circuit. However, we can rearrange the circuit as shown in

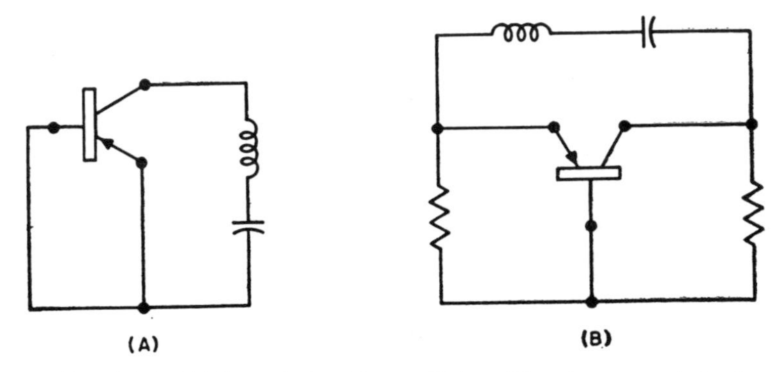

Fig. 14.4. (A) Grounded-emitter oscillator with series-resonant circuit in the collector lead. (B) The circuit of (A) rearranged as a grounded-base amplifier with feedback from collector to emitter.

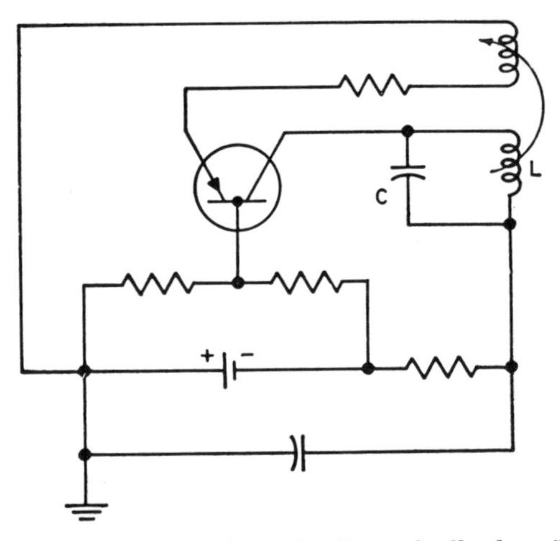

Fig. 14.5. Basic circuit of tuned-collector feedback oscillator.

Fig. 14.4(B). Then we have a satisfactory grounded-base amplifier with positive feedback from collector to emitter. The grounded-base circuit produces no phase shift from the emitter input to the collector output, and the series-resonant circuit will feed back energy from the collector which will be in phase with the emitter current at only one frequency.

We can employ transistors in various forms of the feedback type of oscillator. We should place the tuned circuit in an electrode lead which has a resistance comparable with the shunt resistance of the resonant circuit. Figure 14.5 is the basic circuit of a tuned-collector feedback oscillator.[3]

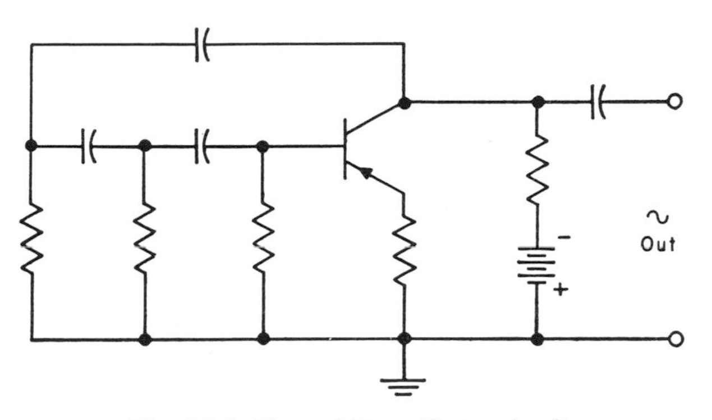

Fig. 14.6. Phase-shift oscillator circuit.

Figure 14.6 gives the circuit [4] of a phase shift oscillator. It will operate with either point-contact or junction transistors. The common emitter circuit causes the input signal at the base to undergo a 180° phase shift at the collector output. For oscillation, the feedback circuit, consisting of the three *CR* sections of the network, must produce an additional 180° phase shift at the working frequency. Since the three *CR* sections are normally alike, each must give a 60° phase shift at the frequency of oscillation.

2. *Practical 800 cps transistor oscillators*[5]

Figure 14.7 shows two practical 800 cps oscillators utilizing point-contact transistors. The circuit of Fig. 14.7(A) has a parallel-resonant circuit in the base lead. The inductance of the tuned circuit is the primary of a transformer, from the secondary of which the output is taken. The circuit of Fig. 14.7(B) has a series-resonant circuit for feedback from the collector to the emitter. The output is taken from the collector through the 0.01 μf capacitor to isolate the output from the collector direct voltage.

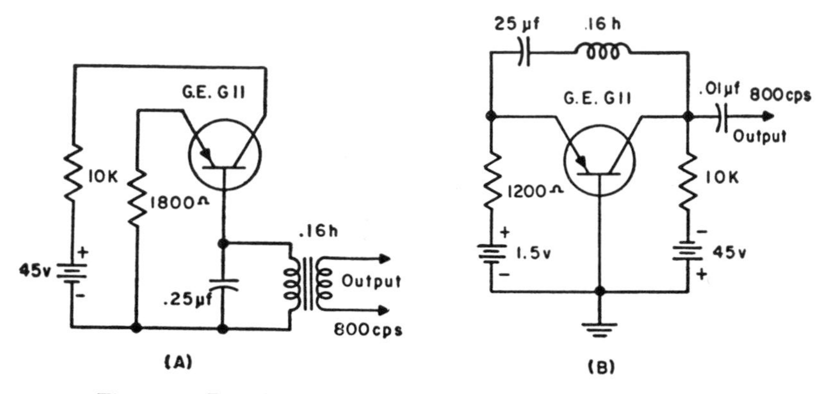

Fig. 14.7. Practical 800-cps point-contact transistor oscillators.

3. *Several applications of transistor audio oscillators*[6]

Figure 14.8 describes the circuit of an audio frequency oscillator employing a point-contact transistor. This device has mainly been utilized for demonstration purposes, but has possibilities for electronic musical instruments such as organs, etc. A transformer, whose collector winding is tuned, provides feedback from collector to emitter. A single battery supplies all biases. A resistor in the base lead furnishes the emitter bias in both the oscillator and the amplifier.

Figure 14.9 gives the circuit of an audio frequency oscillator in a lineman's test set for maintaining the repeaters of a carrier telephone system. This oscillator provides a 1600 cps ringing tone. Although the oscillator could be powered by batteries, battery failure would prevent the linesman from calling the test board. Therefore a rectifier composed of four germanium varistors produces the 20 to 30 v direct voltage necessary for operating the oscillator. A hand-cranked magneto generator, which the linesman normally employs for ringing on voice frequency lines, energizes the rectifier. The nominal frequency of this magneto generator is 16 cps but this may vary from 12 to 36 cps depending on the speed of cranking, and the signal often has a poor wave shape.

In Fig. 14.9 a transformer having a tuned collector winding provides feedback from collector to emitter. The 100 ohm resistor in series with the base of the transistor gives additional feedback. The 1200 ohm resistor in series with the emitter protects the transistor

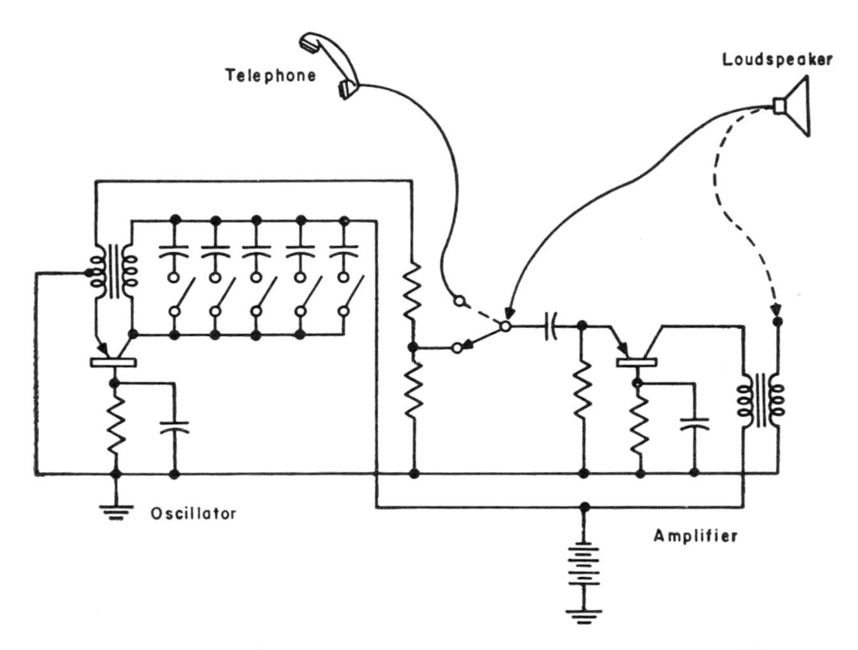

Fig. 14.8. An early audio-frequency transistor oscillator and amplifier with point-contact transistors.

from surges originating in the set and on the telephone line under test. Any Type A1723 transistor will operate in this circuit without readjustment.

This test set oscillator provides about 1 mw into a 600 ohm load at a nominal frequency of 1600 cps. The frequency variation is well within the ±20 cps tolerance for all conditions of temperature, humidity, changes in transistors, and different supply voltages caused by variation in speed of cranking the magneto generator. The wave shape is essentially sinusoidal with the harmonic distortion about 40 db below the fundamental output.

This test set is designed to operate between −67°F and +150°F. As Fig. 14.9(B) indicates, the change in output over this temperature range is between 1 and 2 db. The frequency varies only about 2 or 3 cps between these temperature extremes.

Figure 14.10 represents the circuit of an 80 cps high-efficiency oscillator. This oscillator operates from a single 6 v power supply, has low power drain, and provides constant output with a wide range of transistor characteristics. The drop in an impedance in the base lead supplies emitter bias. The power available is so small that the drain through bleeders has to be limited. Two $\frac{3}{16}$ in. disk copper oxide

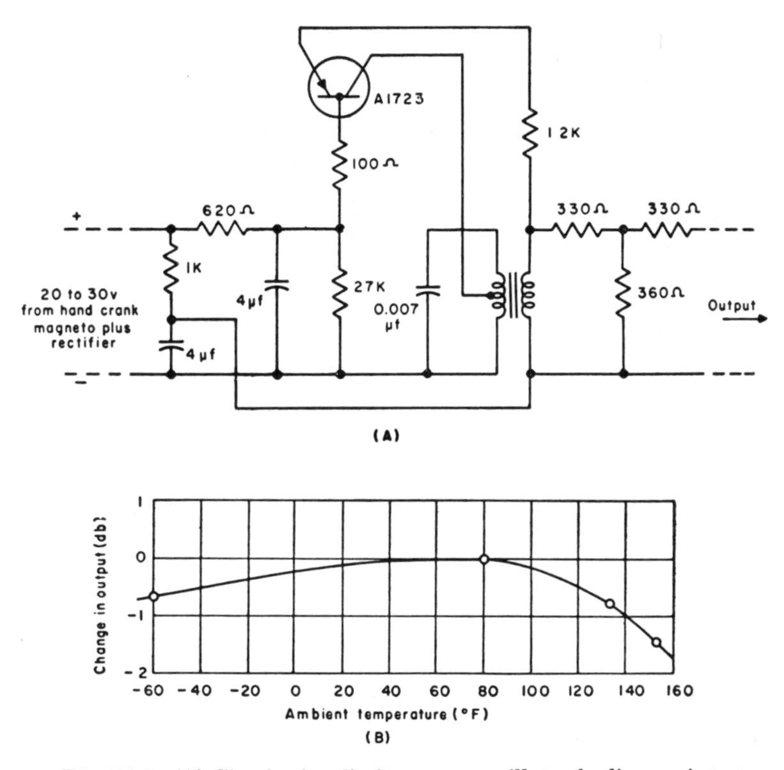

Fig. 14.9. (A) Circuit of audio-frequency oscillator for lineman's test set. (B) Output change with temperature for lineman's audio-frequency oscillator.

varistors in the base connection provide a high d-c resistance at the instant power is applied. The d-c resistance of these varistors decreases when additional collector current flows through them as oscillations build up.

An automatic volume control circuit maintains constant output. A diode rectifies part of the output, and the emitter receives an additional bias of about $\frac{1}{4}$ v across the 250 ohm resistor between the center tap of the output transformer and ground. The automatic volume control voltage is of a polarity to oppose the emitter bias caused by

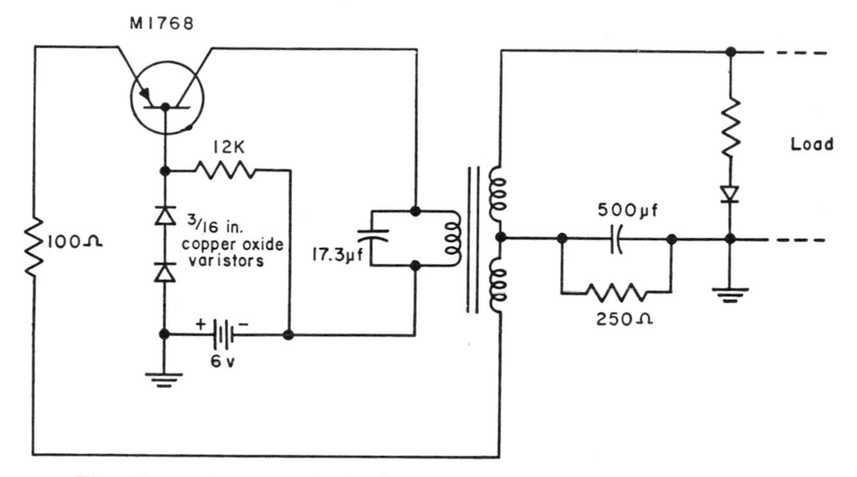

Fig. 14.10. An 80-cps, high efficiency oscillator employing an M1768 point-contact transistor.

the varistors in the base circuit, and produces a net negative emitter bias. Variation of this effective bias changes the operating angle and hence controls the output. Class C operation results, raising the output efficiency.

This oscillator produces an output power of 10 mw for an input of 28.9 mw from a 6 v battery. An over-all efficiency of 34 per cent is thus achieved. The actual efficiency of the collector circuit is about 60 per cent, with the remaining power dissipated in bleeder current, transformer losses, etc. The harmonic distortion is about 21 db below the fundamental at the above output.

This oscillator exhibits an exceptional degree of uniformity in output with transistors of various characteristics. When 61 Type M1768 transistors of manufacturing specification were tested in this oscillator, 90 per cent of these units gave an output which varied less than 0.4 db from the mean output power.

4. *Low-drain transistor audio oscillator*[7]

Figure 14.11 shows the circuit of a low-drain transistor audio oscillator designed to provide carrier power to a magnetic amplifier. This oscillator employs a Western Electric A1768 point-contact transistor.

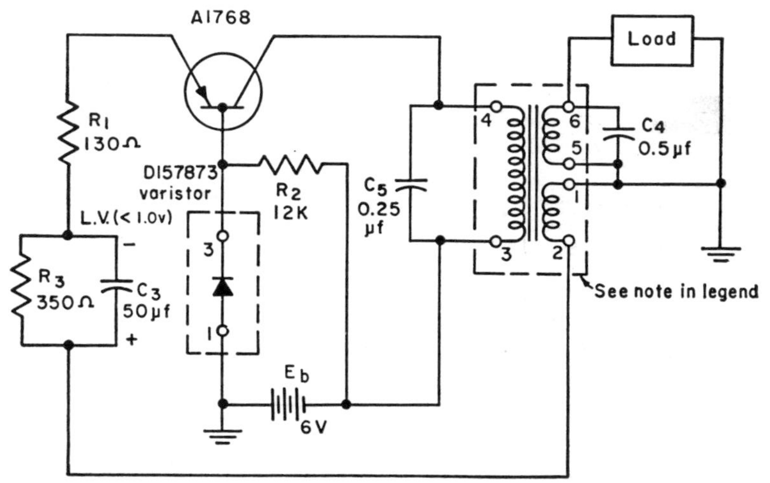

Fig. 14.11. Circuit of low-drain transistor audio oscillator. Note: the three-winding transformer turns ratio equals 1 (1–2) to 2.8 (3–4) to 9.6 (5–6). L (5–6) equals 3.2 henrys, and Q (5–6) nonloaded equals 13.5 at 120 cps.

The design requirements are a nominal battery supply voltage of 6 v with a range of +6 per cent to −15 per cent, a maximum power drain of 35 mw from the battery, a single fixed frequency of 130 cps, a frequency drift of ±17 per cent over total life, an output voltage of 8.5 rms at nominal battery voltage with 20 per cent permissible distortion across an 11,000 ohm resistance, and a variation of rms output voltage of the same percentage as the battery voltage.

The circuit operates class C with an operating angle of about 150°. Transformer feedback was utilized for several reasons. Since the load impedance is much larger than the best collector load impedance for maximum collector conversion efficiency, a step-up output transformer is required. A parallel-resonant circuit is needed so that the oscillator will present the lowest possible impedance to the load at all harmonics. A transformer can most efficiently transfer from the collector the emitter power required to maintain oscillations. The transformer feedback winding was placed in the emitter circuit instead of the base circuit to minimize parasitic oscillations. The oscillator must operate from a single battery and be self-starting. In a vacuum tube plate current initially flows with no bias on the grid and the cathode resistance biases the grid negatively to the desired operating point. However, we must bias the emitter of a transistor in the forward direction before appreciable collector current flows. Although in a single-battery circuit the base potential, resulting from I_{co} flowing through the internal base resistance of the transistor, develops some forward bias, this current is normally kept as low as possible. Therefore when we connect the collector battery to the circuit, oscillation may not begin unless we provide sufficient initial positive emitter current to produce the necessary transistor gain to start oscillation. Once we start oscillation, a self-biasing resistor in the emitter circuit reduces the operating angle and increases the efficiency much like the tube cathode resistor.

A varistor in the base circuit solves this problem. The varistor has a negative slope d-c resistance-versus-current characteristic, which is practically identical with that of the emitter. Thus the varistor provides the proper kind of base resistance to enable the maximum emitter current to flow for a given bleeder starting current. This starting current divides about equally between the emitter and base circuits. As the collector current increases and the base current rises correspondingly, the varistor resistance falls from its initially large value to a comparatively small value and the circuit becomes d-c stable. Also this practically eliminates the enlargement of the normal collector current variation of different transistors because of d-c positive base feedback, since a rise of varistor current causes the voltage drop across the varistor to increase slowly.

The emitter circuit components R_3 and C_3 provide negative bias resulting from rectified emitter current flowing in R_3. This negative bias is necessary to overcome the positive bias on the emitter under steady-state conditions due to the varistor in the base circuit. A net negative emitter bias is necessary to bias the transistor beyond cutoff, get collector current conduction over less than half the operating cycle, and obtain class C operation with increased collector conversion efficiency.

Elements R_3 and C_3 serve another purpose. They prevent a large change in the oscillator output when transistors having different parameters are substituted in the oscillator, and when transistor characteristics change with temperature. The bias across R_3 is proportional to oscillator output and varies the operating angle, causing automatic volume control. The battery voltage serves as the reference potential for this automatic volume control action.

The varistor in the base lead causes the slope of the emitter input d-c EI characteristic at collector potentials above 3 v to be negative over a wide range of emitter current. The emitter current can rise rapidly so that the collector current becomes saturated as in transistor switching circuits. Under initial starting conditions sine-wave oscillations may never begin because the transistor may either lock up in a conducting state or operate as a blocking oscillator. Resistance R_1 is placed in the emitter circuit to give a positive but small net resistance for all Type 1768 transistors. This permits the emitter current to rise rapidly enough and still maintains a d-c stable circuit so that the desired a-c oscillations can build up to a stable state. With $R_1 = 130$ ohms, the input voltage current characteristic at 6.0 v collector voltage has a positive slope, and only a few tenths of a volt change in feedback voltage is required to produce 6 or 7 ma emitter current. This is sufficient to cause collector current saturation.

Capacitor C_5 by-passes the harmonics of the collector current pulse around the collector winding leakage reactance to obtain a short collector current rise time.

The oscillator transformer load winding has a nonloaded Q of 13.5 at 120 cps; the loaded Q is 5.2.

Neglecting the high core losses of the transformer which resulted from emphasis on space reduction, the transistor achieves a net efficiency of 34 per cent in converting d-c power to a-c power. The collector circuit efficiency is nearly 60 per cent as compared with the theoretical maximum efficiency of 74 per cent for a class C, square wave current, sine-wave voltage oscillator with a 150° operating angle. Several useful losses account for the difference between the 60 per cent collector efficiency and the 34 per cent net efficiency. These consist of the power dissipated in the bias circuit and the emitter circuit series resistance, bleeder power for self-starting, power dissipated in the base circuit, and emitter power to maintain oscillation. The net efficiency of 34 per cent is considered quite satisfactory because most of the above power dissipation aids in constant and reliable circuit operation.

5. *1000 cps transistor oscillator*[8]

Figure 14.12 shows the circuit of a 1000 cps transistor oscillator operating class C and having an excellent waveform. Resistor R_1 determines the emitter current, and therefore the collector current as well. If we heavily load the oscillator output, we will have to make R_1 lower than the specified value. However, if we lightly load the oscillator, we can make the value of R_1 higher.

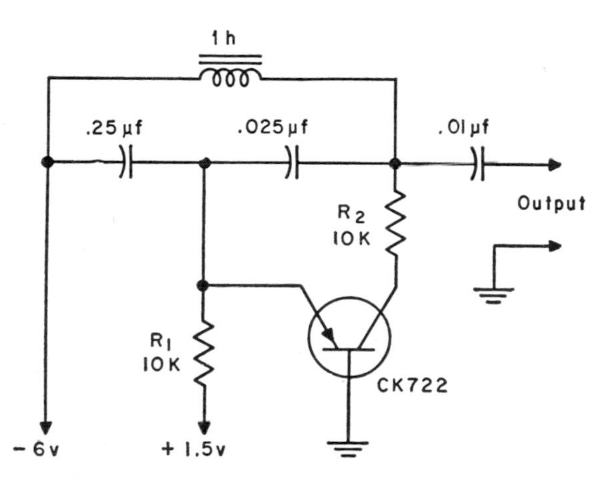

Fig. 14.12. One-thousand cycle/sec transistor oscillator employing standard circuit components.

Resistor R_2 limits the reverse collector current when the collector end of the tuned circuit swings positive. Too low a valuc flattens the positive peak of the wave. Too high a value stops oscillation. Large values produce a better waveform. The load and the Q of the coil determine the value of R_2. With a high Q toroid coil, values from 10,000 to 20,000 ohms are suitable. With a low Q choke, we can employ from 0 to 1000 ohms.

The battery voltage is not critical. The current drain is approximately 0.1 ma for the circuit values given. The peak output voltage nearly equals the collector battery voltage.

We can replace R_2 with a crystal diode having its anode connected to the collector. However its performance is about the same as that of the resistor.

6. *Amplitude stabilized transistor oscillator*[9]

Figure 14.13 describes the circuit of an amplitude stabilized transistor audio frequency oscillator. Two junction transistors operate class C in a push-pull common-emitter connection. The circuit achieves an over-all efficiency up to 75 per cent, low distortion, over 100 db signal-to-noise ratio, and high amplitude stability. Large changes in supply voltage, output loading, and temperature cause only about 1 per cent variation in amplitude. To accomplish this

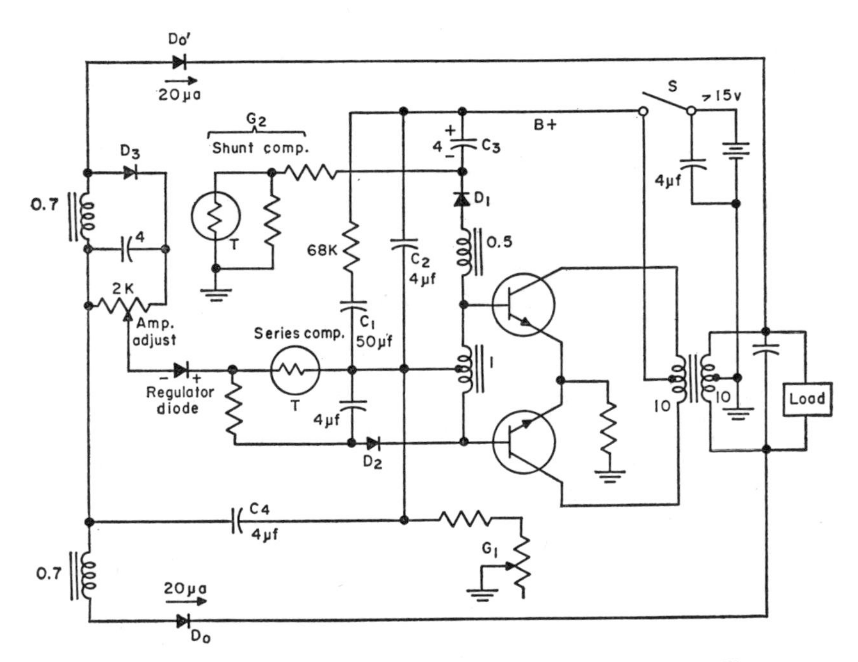

Fig. 14.13. Circuit of amplitude-stabilized transistor oscillator. Note: all windings are on a common core; adjacent figures indicate the relative number of turns.

stabilization the output amplitude is compared with a reference voltage which the Zener effect produces in a silicon P-N junction diode.

A silicon junction diode normally has extremely high incremental resistance (thousands of megohms) in the reverse direction up to a certain voltage determined by the thickness of the junction and the conductivity of the semiconductor. At this voltage, known as the Zener or breakdown voltage, the incremental resistance suddenly drops to a few hundred ohms or less. Therefore, like a gas-tube glow discharge, the voltage can not rise higher unless comparatively large currents flow. Figure 14.14 shows the voltage-current characteristic

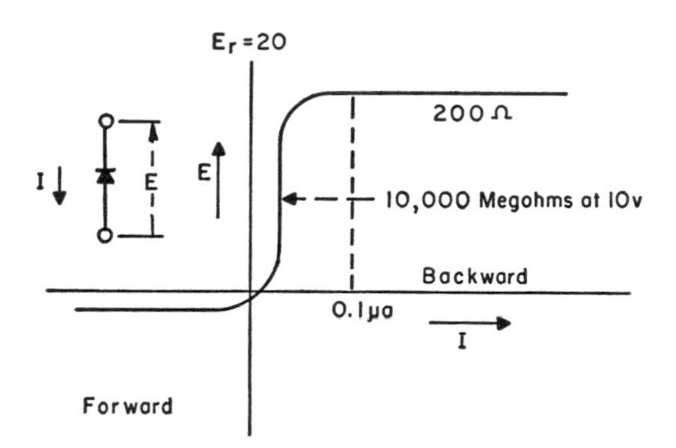

Fig. 14.14. Typical silicon junction diode characteristic, showing breakdown effect.

of a typical silicon junction diode. When any appreciable back current flows through the diode, its voltage stays at the break-down potential of 20 v. For example, raising the current from 10 μa to 100 μa, increases the voltage by about 20 mv or 0.1 per cent. A junction diode can act as a reference battery. This junction diode will be called the regulator diode hereafter. Since we require a current to establish amplitude stabilization, this current can also maintain breakdown voltage in the regulator diode.

In the circuit of Fig. 14.13, all the windings are part of a common transformer; the adjacent numbers indicate their turns ratios. The base winding provides the feedback alternating voltage, a positive direct voltage through diode D_1 for shunt compensation, and a negative direct voltage through D_2 for series compensation.

The series compensation obtains its rectified voltage from one-half of the base winding. In series with the regulator diode we insert the alternating voltage from which a rectified voltage is obtained by the two balanced windings marked 0.7. This maximizes the adjustment range while minimizing the associated power dissipation. By making the two balanced windings and the diode D_3 reversible, by a four-position switching connection, and by adjusting the potentiometer, we can obtain a continuous voltage change equal to four times the peak alternating voltage of either of the two windings. If the peak voltage is 1 v, the total adjustment range is 4 v, making the output range 14 ± 2 v peak.

When the battery switch S is first closed, C_1 and the 68,000 ohm resistor supply a surge of current into the base winding. This is necessary to start oscillations, since zero bias is "cutoff," unlike the vacuum tube where cutoff is normally caused by a negative bias. Capacitor C_2 and rectifier filter capacitor C_3 connect to $B+$ instead of ground for the same reason. Capacitor C_2 prevents sudden changes in the average base voltage.

Single by-pass or filter capacitors are adequate for all the circuit capacitors except the tuning capacitor and starting unit C_1. The lowest operating frequency determines their minimum required values. In the upper audio range, 4 μf is sufficient. Tantalum units are especially suitable because of their small size and extremely small leakage.

Capacitor C_4 by-passes the regulator diode and the amplitude adjustment and compensating voltages in series with it. This causes I_r, the regulating direct current obtained from the base circuit, to flow as smooth direct current instead of short pulses, and minimizes the effective resistance of the regulating path. However, if the regulator diode is a soft-breakdown diode in which the current must exceed about 100 μa or more to establish the required low incremental resistance, this diode should be left unby-passed so that the relatively high current peaks of I_r (1 ma peak for 40 μa average) drive the diode into true breakdown saturation.

With typical values of circuit parameters, the output impedance from either side to ground is calculated roughly as 200 ohms, which direct measurements confirm. A 20,000 ohm resistance connected from one side to ground reduces the output voltage about 1 per cent. This increases the loading by 5 mw, or 25 per cent.

The efficiency and amplitude stability of this transistor oscillator are exceptional. It has achieved an over-all efficiency as high as 75 per cent. Such efficiencies are attainable if the supply battery voltage just barely exceeds the peak collector swing. Doubling the battery voltage would halve the efficiency; the extra power goes into collector dissipation. There are three main power losses: the transformer loss is normally about 10 per cent of the output; the power losses in various bleeder and compensator resistances and in the regulator diode usually do not exceed 1 or 2 mw; and the collector dissipation in the two transistors is the chief power loss.

The output voltage stability is remarkable. A 50 per cent change in battery voltage varies the output by only a fraction of 1 per cent. This assumes that the battery voltage exceeds the regulating voltage and the transistors maintain their typically high collector resistance over the entire voltage range.

When different typical transistors are plugged into the circuit, the amplitude remains similarly constant. The oscillator operates uniformly with an amplitude loss of 2 or 3 per cent when only one transistor is left in the circuit.

Adequate compensation can hold the amplitude variations caused by temperature changes to 1 or 2 per cent over a range of 40°C. An increase of loading from 20 to 25 mw may cause the output to fall about 1 per cent.

This oscillator, feeding a junction diode rectifier, can form a highly efficient regulated d-c power supply. With a 10 v battery, 200 v at 20 to 200 μa has been obtained at an over-all efficiency of 60 per cent. This 200 v output may have a superimposed noise voltage of about 2 mv peak-to-peak, for a ratio of rectified voltage to peak-to-peak noise voltage equal to 10^5 or roughly 100 db. In actual practice the noisiest transistors have given a ratio of 70 db, whereas the quietest units showed a value of 120 db. The 1 kc/sec noise figures of these transistors ranged from about 20 db to 60 db.

With an output Q of about 15, second-harmonic distortion is 60 to 70 db below the fundamental with push-pull operation, or 30 to 40 db with only one transistor. Third harmonic distortion is about -40 db with either push-pull or single transistor operation.

This oscillator circuit can supply approximately 10 to 100 mw of power at efficiencies higher than 50 per cent and with amplitude stability of about 1 per cent. The oscillator can not only serve as a compact battery powered source of alternating current, but can provide stable d-c outputs over a wide range of voltages.

References

1. *CBS-Hytron Transistor Manual, An Introduction to Transistor Theory, Data, and Applications, Bulletin E 212*, CBS-Hytron, A Division of Columbia Broadcasting System, Inc., Danvers, Mass.

2. Thomas Roddam, "Transistor, 3-Earthed-Emitter and Earthed-Collector Circuits as Amplifiers and Oscillators," *Wireless World*, Vol. LIX, No. 4, April 1953, pp. 175–178.

3. Herbert J. Reich, "Transistors and Transistor Circuits," *Electrical Manufacturing*, Part I, Vol. L, No. 5, Nov. 1952, pp. 106–112; Part II, Vol. L, No. 6, Dec. 1952, pp. 102–105. Copyright 1952, by the Gage Publishing Co.

4. *Data Sheet, Transistors by Hydro-Aire, Inc.*, Hydro-Aire Inc., Burbank, Calif.

5. John A. Doremus, "Point-Contact and Junction Transistors," *Radio-Electronic Engineering Section, Radio and Television News*, April 1952.

6. R. S. Caruthers, *Some Experimental and Practical Applications of Transistor Oscillators*, Bell Telephone Laboratories, Inc., 1951.

7. D. E. Thomas, "Low-Drain Transistor Audio Oscillator," *Proc. IRE*, Vol. XL, No. 11, Nov. 1952, pp. 1385–1394.

8. Louis Carcano, "Transistor Oscillator," *Radio and Television News*, Vol. L, No. 5, Nov. 1953, p. 166.

9. E. R. Kretzmer, "An Amplitude Stabilized Transistor Oscillator," *Proc. IRE*, Vol. XLII, No. 2, Feb. 1954, pp. 391–401.

Chapter 15

TRANSISTOR RADIO FREQUENCY OSCILLATORS

1. *Basic radio frequency oscillators*

The Hartley circuit is the simplest vacuum tube oscillator.[1] A part of the tank coil feeds back sufficient voltage to the grid to maintain oscillations. Figure 15.1(A) indicates a typical Hartley vacuum tube oscillator. The grounded-cathode circuit gives a 180° phase shift between grid and plate voltages, and therefore the coil must attenuate the plate voltage and produce an additional 180° phase shift. This is accomplished by crossing the two lower connections between tube and coil.

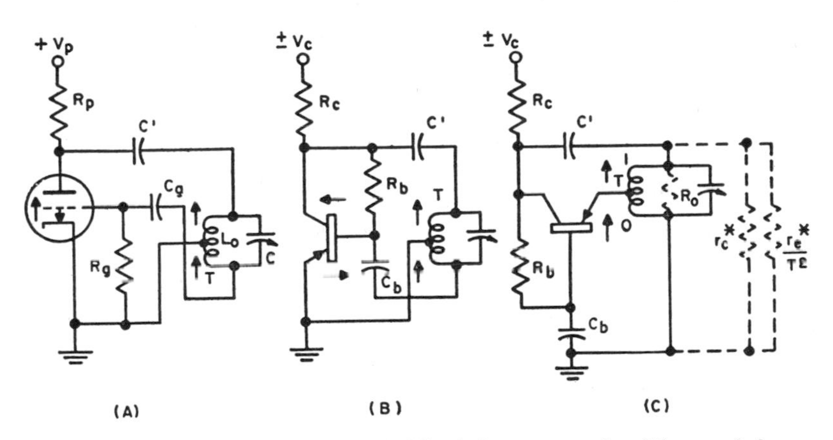

Fig. 15.1. Hartley oscillator with (A) triode vacuum tube, (B) grounded-emitter transistor, and (C) grounded-base transistor.

A transistor in the grounded-emitter connection is analogous to a grounded-cathode vacuum-tube circuit according to the principle of duality. We obtain the Hartley transistor oscillator[1] of Fig. 15.1(B) by substituting a grounded-emitter transistor for the tube in circuit

(A). The grounded-base, grounded-emitter, and grounded-collector circuits are all alike as long as we have the same closed loop. We can redraw circuit (B) in the grounded-base configuration of Fig. 15.1(C). This circuit produces no phase reversal so that the autotransformer must give a positive attenuation V_e/V_c from the turns ratio or tap T. Drawn in this fashion, the leads no longer cross over.

In all three circuits, suitable radio frequency chokes or resistors R_p and R_c feed the supply voltages, whereas the blocking capacitors C' pass the radio frequency energy. In the tube circuit the grid leak R_g adjusts the grid potential, but the base leaks R_b of the transistors keep the base potential at an appropriate level.

The condition of self-excitation in a transistor differs from that in a vacuum tube oscillator because the emitter constant-voltage impedance r_e^* loads the autotransformer.[1] Assuming that the emitter impedance is large compared with the coil inductive reactance ωL_o, we can describe the tank circuit in terms of three equivalent resistors. These consist of the equivalent parallel resistance R_o of the free tank circuit proportional to the quality factor $Q = R_o/\omega L_o$, the emitter resistance r_e^* transformed by the autotransformer windings into r_e^*/T^2, and the collector impedance r_c^*. We can combine these three resistances by adding their conductances:

$$Y_T = \frac{1}{R_o} + \frac{1}{r_c^*} + \frac{T^2}{r_e^*} \tag{1}$$

Self-excitation occurs when this sum becomes zero, and one of the terms must be negative to fulfill this requirement. We know from vacuum tube oscillators that the plate resistance must be negative, and hence so must the collector resistance in a transistor. Furthermore, it can be shown[1] that if alpha is very close to unity, a Hartley transistor oscillator will operate at high efficiency with a center-tapped coil.

The emitter voltage and the collector impedance have an inductive phase which is compensated by a capacitive phase of the tank circuit. Thus the oscillator frequency is always lower than the resonant frequency f_o of the free tank circuit.

In practical applications tapped coils, or tapped capacitors as in the Colpitts circuit, are inconvenient. An external voltage division is the simplest way to avoid tapping the tank in single-transistor oscillators. Figure 15.2 illustrates three such circuits.[1] Each tank circuit consists of a two-terminal coil L_o in parallel with a capacitor C_o. These circuits are formed by loading the transistor between each pair of its three terminals in turn with the tank circuit, and connecting the choke (*ch*) or an equivalent resistor as a feedback attenuator in series with the remaining transistor impedance. According to a circular exchange, the feedback in circuit (A) runs counterclockwise from the

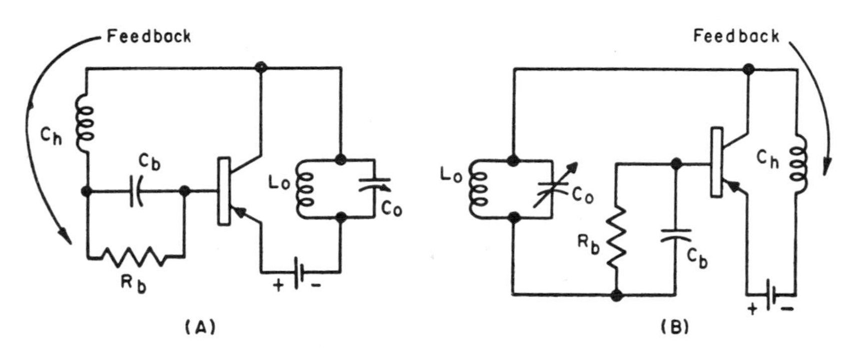

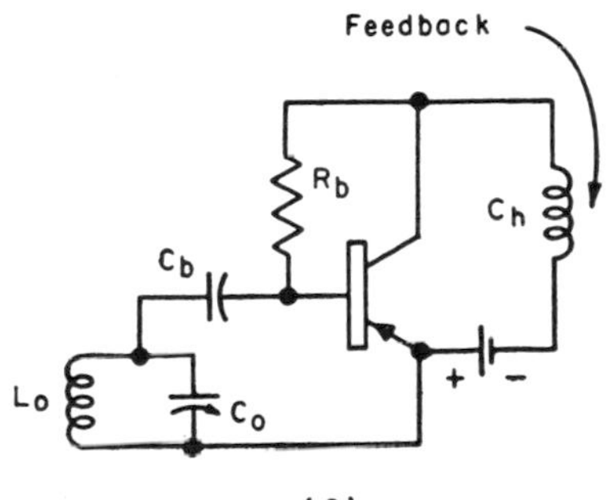

Fig. 15.2. Transistor oscillator circuits with negative output impedances.

collector to the base, in circuit (B) clockwise from collector to emitter, and in circuit (C) counterclockwise from emitter to collector. Base capacitors C_b block the direct potentials, and leak resistors R_b improve the transistor efficiency.

The regenerative feedback causes negative output resistances between any selected pair of the transistor elements. Circuit (C) is the simplest example; it produces a negative base resistance if alpha is larger than unity and the choke impedance is less than a critical value (ch_{cr}). Similar principles apply to the other two oscillators except that alpha must be about unity, and circuit (B) requires that (ch) be greater than (ch_{cr}) because the feedback current flows in the opposite direction. Also, circuit (A) oscillates with (ch) less than (ch_{cr}).

The imaginary components of the feedback channels cause out-of-phase conditions such that in (A) the oscillator frequency is above and in (B) is below the frequency f_o of the free tank circuit.

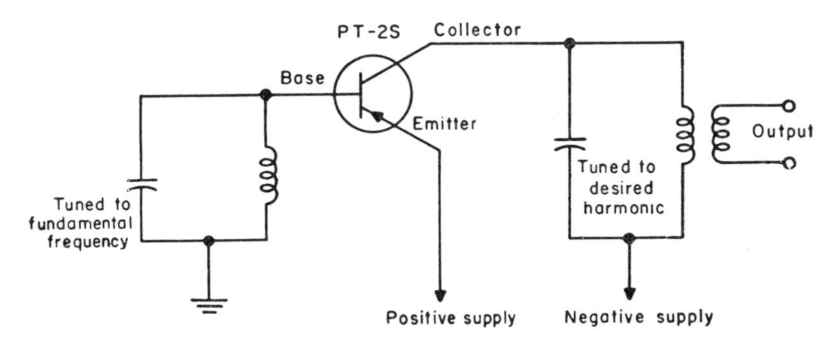

Fig. 15.3. Frequency multiplier circuit employing a point-contact transistor.

Figure 15.3 shows a frequency-multiplier circuit utilizing a point-contact transistor.[2] For oscillation Z_e should be low, Z_b high, and Z_c low. A parallel-resonant circuit gives the desired high external base impedance, and also determines the frequency of oscillation. The external emitter impedance Z_e is a comparatively low resistance. A parallel-resonant circuit in the collector lead is tuned to the desired harmonic of the oscillation frequency. This resonant circuit provides the necessary low external collector impedance at the frequency of oscillation.

2. *Oscillators for superheterodyne broadcast receivers*

Figure 15.4 gives two circuits for the local oscillator of experimental broadcast-band superheterodyne receivers.[3] In Fig. 15.4(A) inductive coupling provides the feedback. This oscillator requires only one power supply, since a resistor in the base circuit furnishes the emitter

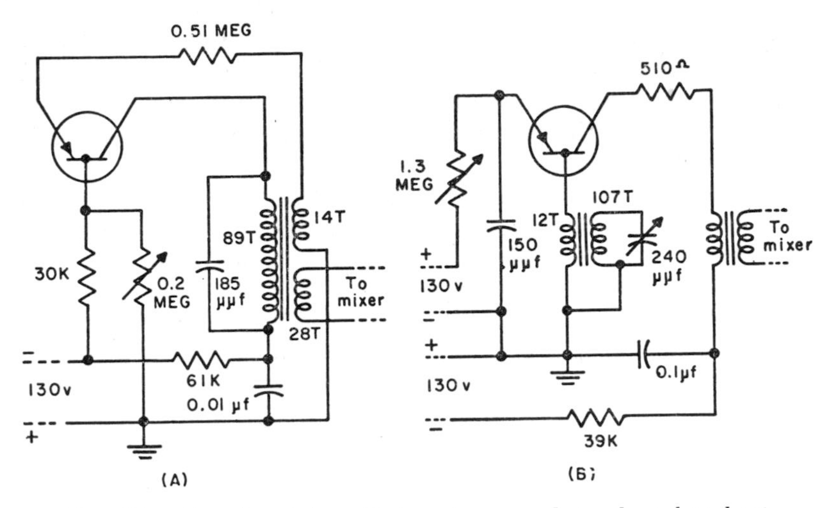

Fig. 15.4. Experimental oscillators for super-heterodyne broadcast receivers.

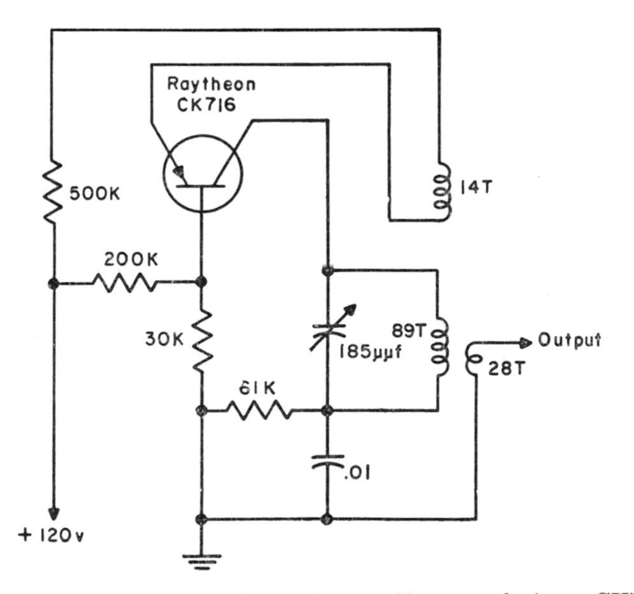

Fig. 15.5. Broadcast super-heterodyne oscillator employing a CK716 point-contact transistor.

bias. This bias is also adjustable by a variable bleeder resistance.

In Fig. 15.4(B) a tuned circuit in the base lead acts as a common impedance between the collector and emitter circuits to produce the necessary feedback. The second voltage supply provides the emitter bias.

A frequency range of both oscillators in Fig. 15.4 is about 1000 to 2000 kc/sec. For this experimental equipment the transistors were selected point-contact units without any attempt to achieve interchangeability of the transistors.

Figure 15.5 describes the circuit of a broadcast superheterodyne oscillator employing a CK716 point-contact transistor.[4]

3. *UHF and VHF transistor oscillators*

A 50 mc/sec oscillator circuit utilizing a Type 2N33 point-contact transistor[5] is shown in Fig. 15.6. Typical operation at 25°C requires a collector supply voltage of −8 v and a collector current of −3.3 ma d-c. The emitter direct current is 0.3 ma. The useful power output is about 1.0 mw.

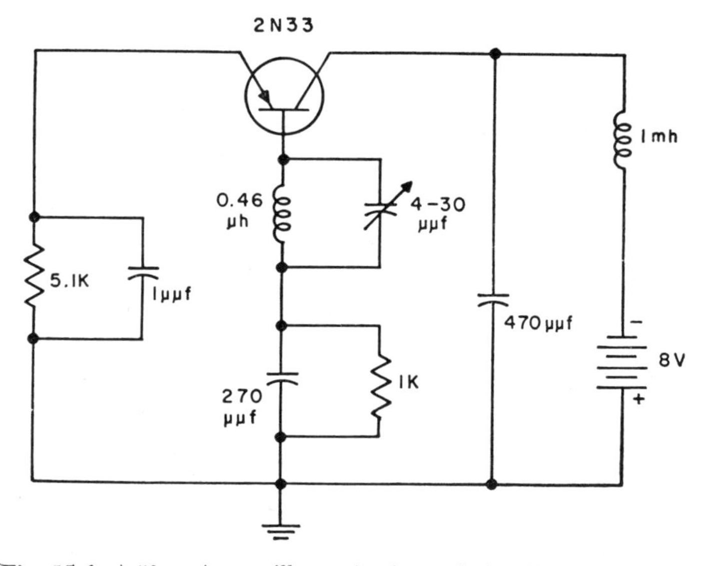

Fig. 15.6. A 50-mc/sec oscillator circuit employing Type 2N33 point-contact transistor.

A number of P-type point-contact oscillator transistors* have been made with the same point-contact spacings and germanium resistivities as some earlier N-type point-contact oscillator transistors.[6] Because of the superior rectification properties of N-type germanium, the N-type transistor has a larger reverse collector resistance than the P-type unit. The average collector resistance for 40 N-type oscillator transistors was 10,000 ohms, whereas that for 40 P-type transistors was only 6400 ohms. The N-type transistor had a somewhat larger current amplification factor than the P-type transistor. The average current amplification factor of the N-type transistors was 2.8 as compared with 2.0 for the P-type transistors.

The feedback resistance of the N-type transistors is greater than that of the P-type devices. The 40 N-type transistors had an average feedback resistance of 400 ohms; that of the 40 P-type transistors was 250 ohms. Although the emitter of the N-type transistor is biased positively, the high feedback characteristic causes the emitter voltage to decrease and become negative over the main operating range of the transistor. Likewise, the high feedback characteristic of the P-type transistor causes the negatively biased emitter to become positive over the main operating range of the transistor.

P-type transistors have achieved oscillation frequencies as high as 425 mc/sec. Figure 15.7 gives the circuit of this point-contact transistor oscillator. The self-biasing resistor in the emitter lead and the by-passed resistance in the base circuit supply emitter bias. The feedback path for oscillation is provided by the internal capacitance between collector and emitter. An oscillation range from 5 to 425 mc/sec may be covered by varying the inductance and capacitance of the parallel-resonant circuit in the collector lead. N-type point-contact oscillator transistors were also tested in this circuit by reversing the polarity of the battery voltage. For 40 units of each type the median value, or point at which 50 per cent of the devices fall above and 50 per cent below, was 112 mc/sec for N-type oscillator transistors and 149 mc/sec for the P-type units.

In the realm of transistors, self-oscillations of the charge carriers, the holes or electrons, are unknown and improbable because of diffusion, etc. However, in point-contact transistors, Hollmann[7] has ob-

* This material has been taken from F. L. Hunter and B. N. Slade, "High-Frequency Operation of p-Type Point-Contact Transistors," *RCA Review*, Vol. XV, No. 1, March 1954, pp. 121–134.

served internal oscillations which somewhat resemble the free-electron oscillations discovered by Barkhausen and Kurz. These transistor oscillations occur without any external resonator, and their frequency is related to the operating conditions by a formula similar to the Barkhausen-relation $\lambda^2 V_g = K$ or $f_o^2/V_g = K'$, where V_g is the positive grid potential.

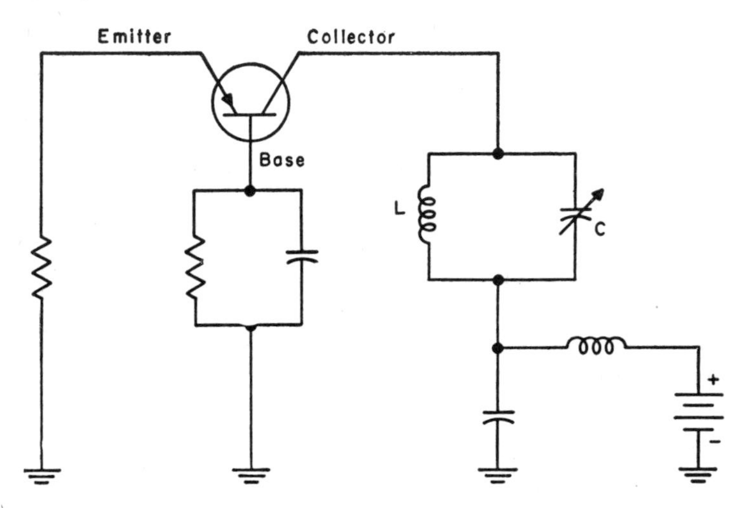

Fig. 15.7. Oscillator circuit for P-type point-contact transistors. *Courtesy of RCA.*

We can understand the mechanism of internal transistor oscillations by referring to the equivalent circuit[7] of Fig. 15.8. This indicates the transistor in the grounded-base connection surrounded by its "cold" electrode and socket capacitances C_E, C_{EC}, and C_C. Also, the barrier-layer capacitance C_c is in parallel with the collector resistance r_c.

The input impedance of the grounded-base transistor is approximately[8]

$$Z_{in} \cong r_e + r_b(1 - \alpha_o) \tag{2}$$

In the neighborhood of the alpha cutoff value f_c, the short-circuit current gain α_o is complex and may be calculated from the empirical formula[9]

$$\alpha = \frac{\alpha_o}{1 + jf/f_c} = \alpha_o \frac{1 - jf/f_c}{1 + (f/f_c)^2} \tag{3}$$

Substituting Eq. (3) into Eq. (2) gives the input impedance[9]

$$Z_{in} \cong r_e + r_b\left(1 - \frac{\alpha_o}{1 + (f/f_c)^2}\right) + j\alpha_o r_b \frac{f/f_c}{1 + (f/f_c)^2} \tag{4}$$

which consists of the resistance

$$R_s \cong r_e + r_b \frac{1 + (f/f_c)^2 - \alpha_o}{1 + (f/f_c)^2} \tag{5}$$

in series with the inductance L_s, whose reactance is

$$\omega L_s = \alpha_o r_b \frac{f/f_c}{1 + (f/f_c)^2} \tag{6}$$

in accordance with the positive sign of the imaginary term of Eq. (4).

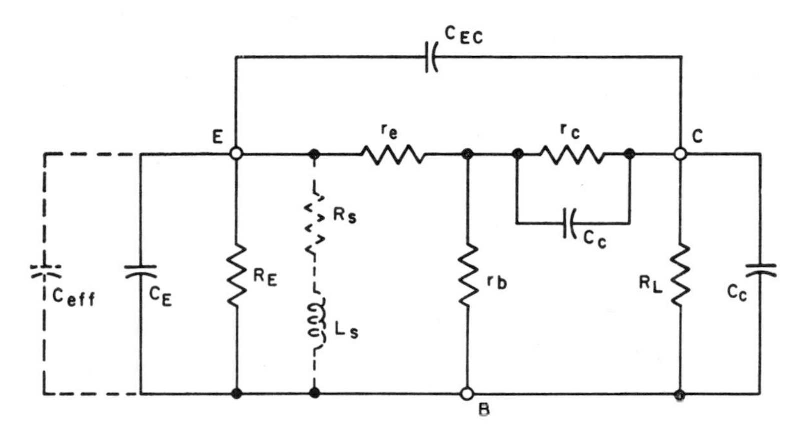

Fig. 15.8. Equivalent circuit of point-contact transistor surrounded by its "cold" capacities.

If the collector capacitance and the external capacitances are considered to be lumped together in an effective capacitor C_{eff} between emitter and base, this capacitance and the induced inductance L_s comprise a series-resonant circuit whose frequency is

$$f_o = f_c(2\pi f_c \alpha_o r_b C_{eff} - 1)^{-1/2} \tag{7}$$

When the series resistance $R_s \gtreqless 0$, self-excitation occurs, leading to a critical current gain

$$\alpha_c = \left(1 + \frac{r_e}{r_b}\right)\left[1 + \left(\frac{f_o}{f_c}\right)^2\right]$$

$$= 1 + \frac{r_e}{r_b} + \frac{1}{2\pi f_c r_b C_{eff}} \qquad (8)$$

If a transistor has a sufficiently large α_o it can excite its internal resonator at a frequency which to a first-order approximation is proportional to the square root of the cutoff frequency f_c.

For example,[7] assume that a radio frequency transistor has the characteristics $r_e = 300$ ohms, $r_b = 200$ ohms, $\alpha_o = 10$, $f_c = 40$ mc/sec and $C_{eff} = 4$ $\mu\mu$f. Substituting these values, the term $2\pi f_c r_b C_{eff} = 2/\alpha_o$, and Eq. (8) gives $\alpha_c = 7.5 < \alpha_o$, so that we can expect internal oscillations with the frequency $f_o \cong f_c = 40$ mc/sec.

It is interesting to compare these internal transistor oscillations with the electron oscillations in a positive grid tube.[7] In the latter, the "dancing" electrons themselves form the only resonant system, and their displacement current results in a negative resistance. In transistors, the emitter circuit has the collector capacitance reflected into it with the opposite phase, or as an induced inductance which forms a resonant circuit with the normal transistor capacitances.

An analogy may help us to understand the induced emitter inductance. In a vacuum tube triode, the Miller effect causes the grid capacitance to increase considerably because the grid and plate voltages are 180° out of phase; hence the displacement current is directly proportional to the voltage amplification. In the grounded-base transistor circuit, we have the reverse situation since the emitter and collector voltages are in phase.

With unity voltage amplification, no voltage difference exists between the collector and the emitter, and only the collector current charges the collector capacitance C_c. For a voltage gain larger than unity, the collector voltage surpasses the input voltage causing the emitter to "see" the collector capacitance with opposite phase, or as an inductance. Hence we may attribute the induced emitter inductance to a "dual Miller effect."

Transistors with a sufficiently large α_o, such as Type 2N33, generate internal oscillations whose frequency depends on α_o, r_b, and C_{eff}. Such a transistor with 10,000 ohm resistors in the emitter and collector circuits produced internal oscillations powerful enough for a grid dip meter to measure them in close vicinity to the oscillating transistor.

Figure 15.9 gives the variation of f_o^2 with the collector current.[7] This is a straight line giving the transistor-oscillation formula, $f_o^2/I_c = K$, which is the dual of the Barkhausen relation. For collector currents from 2 to 8 ma, the frequency of the internal oscillations increases from 25 to 75 mc/sec depending on the characteristics of individual transistors.

To stabilize the frequency we may insert an external resonator such as a tank circuit into the collector lead. Then the free oscillations lock in like electron oscillations in a Barkhausen tube.

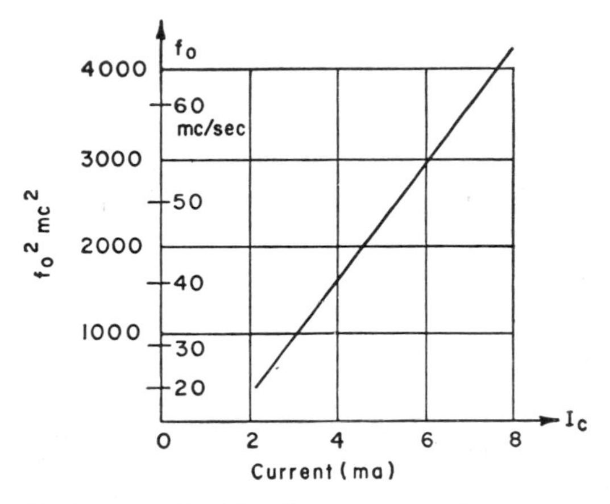

Fig. 15.9. Variation of f_0^2 with collector current, for an internally oscillating Type 2N33 point-contact transistor.

The large nonlinearity of transistors not only causes distortion but also makes the resonators nonharmonic. Both effects result in an efficient frequency multiplication known as a "circular frequency multiplication"[1] because it occurs only within the transistor and its attached resonators. We may visualize a circular frequency multiplier as a linear multiplier cascade wound around a single active element.

Therefore we can place a tank circuit resonating at a high harmonic in the collector lead to form a simple oscillator circuit. With an ordinary *LC* tank operating at the second or third harmonic, frequencies of about 100 mc/sec may easily be produced. However, with a cavity resonator, frequencies as high as 600 mc/sec have been observed on a microwave absorption meter.

4. *Crystal-controlled transistor oscillators*

Figure 15.10 shows a piezoelectric transistor oscillator[3] which was studied as a possible substitute for a vacuum tube oscillator which supplied the carrier to a modulator in a carrier telephone system. This oscillator drove a grounded-base point-contact transistor amplifier which delivered 30 mw at 184 kc/sec. Although less than the 200 mw which the present electron-coupled vacuum tube oscillator generates, this was considered adequate for the proposed application.

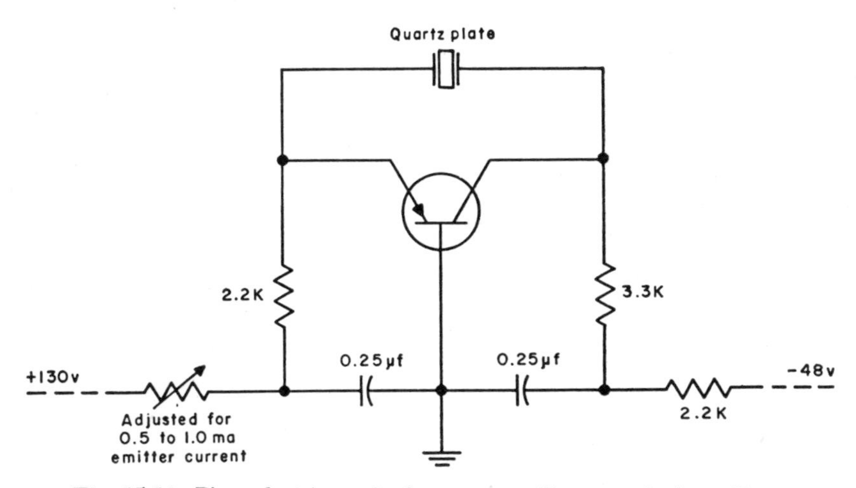

Fig. 15.10. Piezo-electric carrier frequency oscillator employing a Type 1729 point-contact transistor.

The transistor oscillator and amplifier required 0.8 w of total power less than that needed by the vacuum-tube circuit. The normal −48 and +130 v telephone office batteries supplied both circuits. More suitable power supply voltages, when available, can increase this power economy to more than 1.25 w. The saving of even such a small amount of power is important to reduce heating, because of the present-day practice of crowding the maximum number of miniature tube circuits into a small space.

The circuit of Fig. 15.10 is simple because the collector alternating current is in phase with the emitter alternating current in transistors. Therefore we can form an oscillator by feeding the collector current back to the emitter through a series-resonant circuit or its equivalent, a piezoelectric crystal. Also, the fed back collector current must be larger than the emitter current.

The supply voltages and the resistors in series with them initially determine the operating point Q in Fig. 15.11(A). When the circuit oscillates, the collector current and voltage follow the a-c load line. As indicated in Fig. 15.11(B), alpha decreases at both high and low

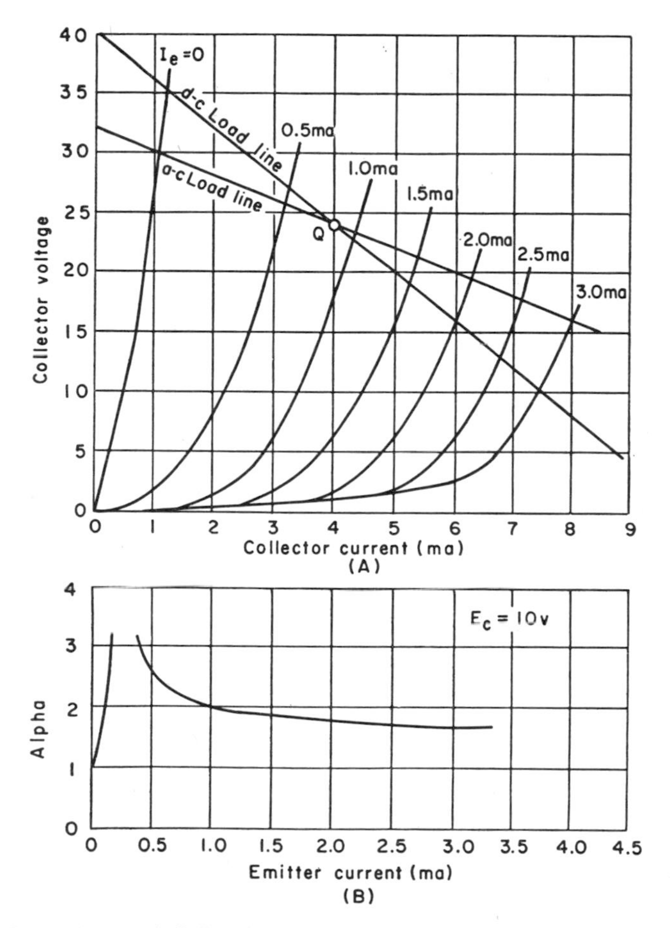

Fig. 15.11. (A) Collector characteristics of point-contact transistor, showing a-c and d-c load lines. (B) Variation of alpha with emitter current, for constant collector voltage.

emitter currents. This causes limiting action to occur on the peaks of the cycle.

It can be shown by mathematical analysis that the conditions for oscillation are approximately[3]

$$\alpha \geqq 1 + \frac{R_o}{R_L} + \frac{R_o}{r_c} \tag{9}$$

where R_o is the equivalent resistance of the piezoelectric plate, R_L is the collector load resistor, and r_c is the collector resistance of the transistor. Since r_c in point-contact transistors has values from 15,000 to 20,000 ohms, the third term of Eq. (9) is of second-order importance, and may be neglected. Because the alpha of most point-contact transistors is no larger than 2 over much of their operating range, and small size piezoelectric plates have an R_o from 2000 to 6000 ohms, R_L is limited to similar values.

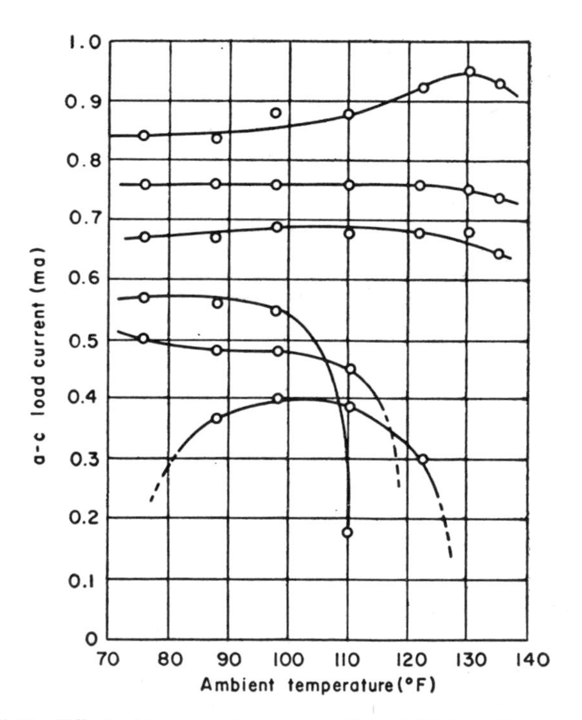

Fig. 15.12. Effect of temperature on six Type 1729 transistors in piezoelectric oscillator.

Equation (9) brings out an important difference between the customary vacuum tube oscillator and a direct-coupled emitter-collector circuit oscillator with a point-contact transistor. Although most vacuum tube oscillators have considerable excess gain, this transistor oscillator has practically no reserve current amplification. Therefore we might expect this transistor circuit to show considerable variations in operation.

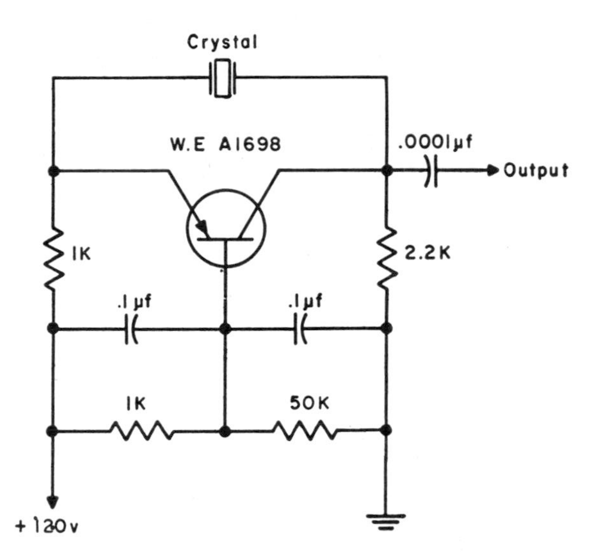

Fig. 15.13. Crystal-controlled oscillator utilizing a Type A1698 point-contact transistor.

Figure 15.12 demonstrates the effect of changing transistors in the curves of load alternating current versus temperature for six Type 1729 transistors.[3] The output and maximum operating temperatures vary widely. A large decrease in r_c causes oscillation failure at high temperatures; this phenomena is quite similar to the reverse current increase in germanium diodes at elevated temperatures.

A crystal-controlled oscillator[4] employing a Type 1698 point-contact transistor is described in Fig. 15.13. This oscillator operates from a single power supply. A 0.0001 μf capacitor isolates the output from the collector direct voltage.

Figure 15.14 shows the circuit of a 100 kc/sec precision transistor oscillator.[10] A Type 2517 junction transistor drives a high-quality

100 kc/sec GT-cut quartz crystal. A mercury cell supplies 1.35 v at 100 μa to the device, and should last more than five years.

This transistor oscillator employs the grounded-emitter configuration. The tank circuit is designed to oscillate at 100 kc/sec, and consists of a 6 mh inductance and a 350 $\mu\mu$f capacitor connected in the collector lead. This tuned circuit develops an output of 0.8 v, which is too large to apply directly to the crystal. Therefore an attenuator, composed of a 40 $\mu\mu$f and a 0.01 μf capacitors in series from the collector to ground, is utilized to reduce the voltage. The junction be-

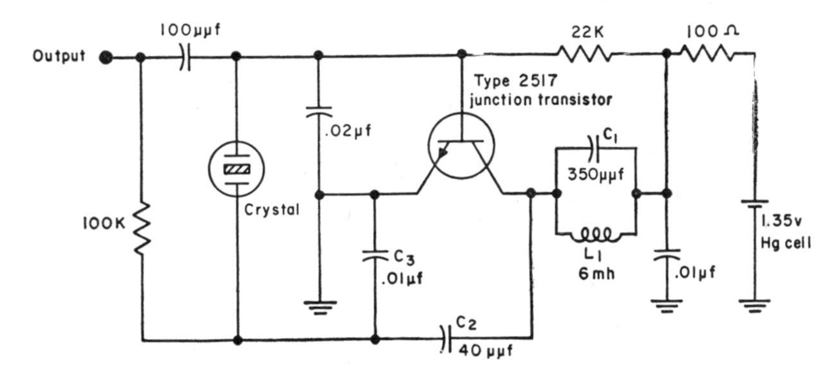

Fig. 15.14. Circuit of a precision oscillator employing a Type 2517 junction transistor.

tween these capacitors supplies about 60 μa driving current for the crystal. A 100 $\mu\mu$f capacitor couples the 3 mv crystal voltage to the output.

A high-stability crystal oscillator must have a constant phase shift in the feedback loop associated with the crystal and constant amplitude of oscillation. Large, stable, "swamping" capacitors at both crystal connections and highly stable components in the remainder of the circuit provide the constant phase shift. Transistor operation with collector-voltage limiting produces excellent amplitude stability.

A $1\frac{3}{4}$ in. diameter by 7 in. brass tube encloses all the components including the power supply. The crystal, mounted in an evacuated glass envelope, takes up more than half of the space in the tube. A Bakelite frame supports the transistor, coil, capacitors, and resistors. This frame may be "potted" in casting resin to increase the rigidity of the section. A Bakelite shield insulates the mercury cell from the metal housing. This cell, which is only about $\frac{1}{2}$ in. thick, is located at the base of the assembly.

The frequency stability with change in temperature is about 1 part in 10^8 per degree C, and with change in supply voltage is approximately 1 part in 10^8 per 0.10 v. When the transistor oscillator was compared with the standard oscillators controlling the transmissions of radio station WWV, the short time variations were about ± 3 parts in 10^{10}, and the long interval drift (in days) was about 3 parts in 10^9 per 24 hours. These values compare favorably with those of vacuum tube standard oscillators when first installed. As the quartz-crystal unit of a conventional type standard oscillator ages, the frequency drift normally decreases. Because of the recent development of this transistor oscillator there has not yet been time to accumulate data on the long-time stability in years.

Previously rather complex temperature control equipment (for operating temperatures as high as 60°C) and special highly reliable power supplies were needed for standard quartz oscillators or quartz clocks. The small size of the transistor oscillator makes possible more convenient and portable temperature control devices. The new unit was tested at 0°C. Merely placing the oscillator in a Dewar flask with crushed clear ice gave reasonable temperature stability. The lowered temperatures reduced drift and increased the Q of the quartz crystal. A readily portable, continuously oscillating frequency standard is now available for carrying to all parts of the world.

References

1. Hans E. Hollmann, "Transistor Oscillators," *Tele-Tech and Electronic Industries*, Vol. XII, No. 10, Oct. 1953, pp. 82–83.
2. *CBS-Hytron Transistor Manual, An Introduction to Transistor Theory, Data, and Applications, Bulletin E 212*, CBS-Hytron, A Division of Columbia Broadcasting System, Inc., Danvers, Mass.
3. R. S. Caruthers, *Some Experimental and Practical Applications of Transistor Oscillators*, Bell Telephone Laboratories, Inc., 1951.
4. John A. Doremus, "Point-Contact and Junction Transistors," *Radio-Electronic Engineering Section, Radio and Television News*, April 1952.

5. *RCA Transistors, Tentative Data Sheet, Form SCD-104,* Radio Corp. of America, Tube Department, Harrison, N. J., 1953.

6. B. N. Slade, "The Control of Frequency Response and Stability of Point-Contact Transistors," *Proc. IRE,* Vol. XL, No. 11, Nov. 1952, pp. 1382–1384.

7. Hans E. Hollmann, "Self-Oscillating UHF Transistors," *Tele-Tech and Electronic Industries,* Vol. XIII, No. 4, April 1954, pp. 75–77.

8. Reprinted with permission of Richard F. Shea, *Principles of Transistor Circuits,* 1953, John Wiley & Sons, Inc., New York, p. 61.

9. D. E. Thomas, "Transistor Amplifier-Cutoff Frequency," *Proc. IRE,* Vol. XL, No. 11, Nov. 1952, pp. 1481–1483.

10. Peter G. Sulzer, "A Precision Transistor Oscillator," *Electronic Design,* Vol. I, No. 2, Feb. 1953, pp. 6–7.

Chapter 16

AMPLITUDE MODULATION AND DETECTION WITH TRANSISTORS

1. *Continuous wave transmitters*

The simplest way to modulate a radio frequency oscillator to convey intelligence is to key it, or to start and stop the carrier in dots and dashes of the international Morse code.

Figure 16.1 is the circuit of a crystal-controlled transistor transmitter[1] which operates in the 2 m band; amateur radio station K2AH had a 12-element beam antenna for the 146 mc/sec band. This keyed oscillator employs an experimental high-frequency point-contact transistor in a Colpitts-type circuit.

The quartz crystal is a 16 mc/sec device which was intended to operate at its fifth harmonic, or 80 mc/sec. Actually it gave excellent control of oscillation at its ninth harmonic. The crystal functions in

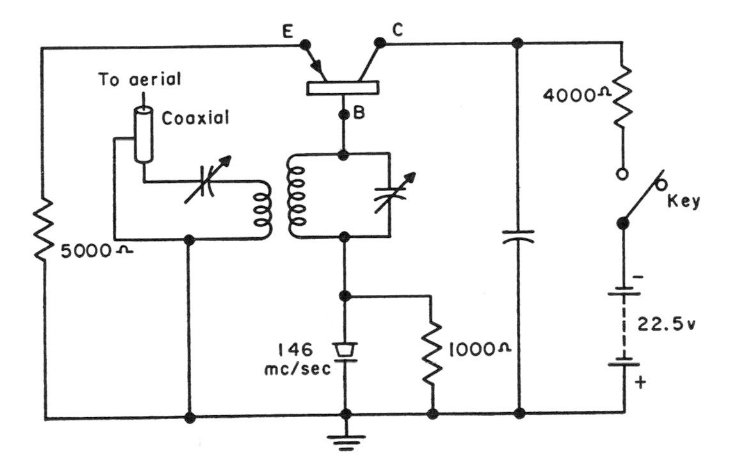

Fig. 16.1. Circuit of a 146-mc/sec crystal-controlled transistor transmitter.

the low-impedance or series mode, and by-passes the 1000 ohm resistor in series with the tuned circuit at the operating frequency, permitting the circuit to oscillate. At other frequencies the crystal has a high impedance which prevents oscillation.

A $22\frac{1}{2}$ v miniature hearing-aid battery supplies power for the transmitter. However, because of the voltage drop in the series resistors, the collector to base voltage is only about 10 v. Since the collector current is about 3 ma, the transistor input power is 30 mw. The antenna power is estimated as 30 to 50 μw.

Several amateur stations were worked by continuous wave at distances up to 25 miles, with the signals reported as RST559.

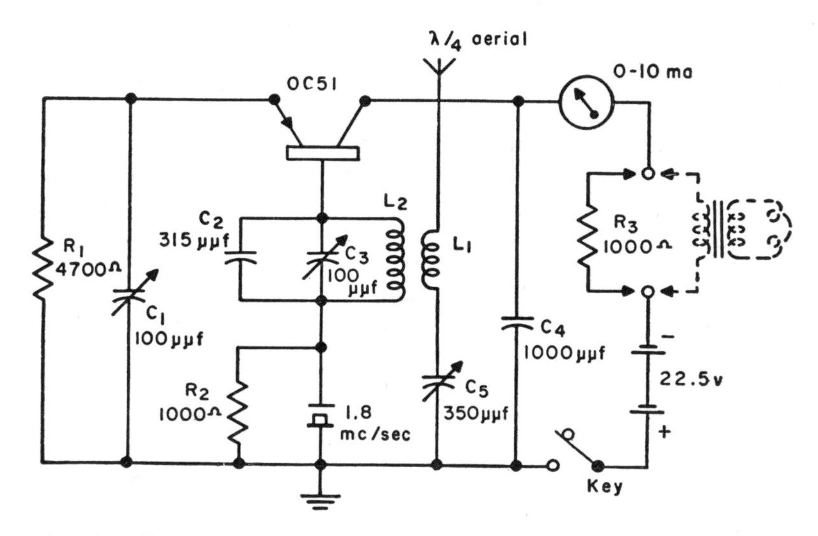

Fig. 16.2. Circuit of 160 meter crystal-controlled transistor transmitter. L_1 is 7 turns overwound on L_2; L_2 is 32 turns 16 SWG tinned copper, $1\frac{1}{2}$ in. diameter and $2\frac{1}{2}$ in. winding length.

Figure 16.2 shows the circuit of a somewhat similar crystal-controlled transistor transmitter[2] operating in the 160 m band. An OC51 point-contact transistor operates in a negative-resistance base oscillator which a 1.8 mc/sec crystal controls over about 1 kc. Without the crystal, the circuit still oscillates, but the excellent keying properties are sacrificed and more noise modulates the broader emitted wave at some frequencies.

The adjustment of C_1 is somewhat critical and is set to give maximum power output. Adjust C_3 until the crystal locks the oscillation and gives good keying qualities. The value of C_2 may be reduced to provide a useful output up to 3.8 mc/sec.

A quarter-wave horizontal wire antenna is operated against ground. Since the antenna current is only 30 μa, an absorption wave meter with a 50 μa indicator, or its equivalent, is required.

This transmitter with an input power of 20 to 100 mw has worked 20 stations on the 1.8 megacycle band with reports varying from RST599 at 3 miles to RST339 at 30 miles.

As indicated, the circuit also functions as an oscillating detector type of receiver for local continuous wave operation with head phones plugged into the collector circuit instead of resistor R_3. Good reception and break-in operation were obtained.

2. *Duality amplitude modulators*[3]

Some interesting amplitude modulator circuits for point-contact transistors have been devised by the principle of duality. The purpose of these circuits is to produce a carrier frequency wave with a desired envelope.

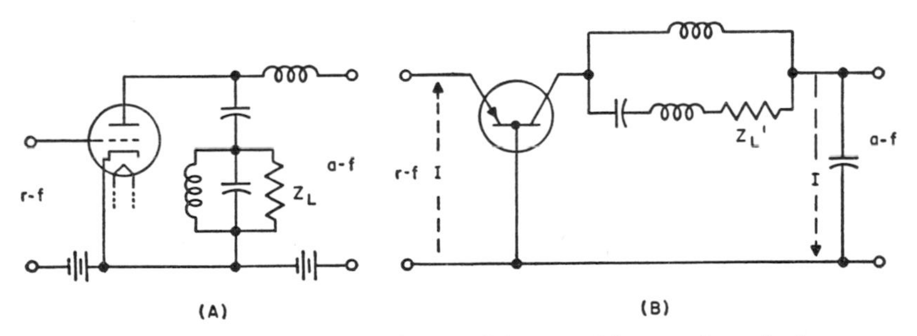

Fig. 16.3. Vacuum tube plate modulator and its transistor dual.

Figure 16.3 represents a vacuum tube plate modulator and its transistor dual. This circuit operates on the principle that the output of a class C amplifier varies directly with the plate supply voltage. The class C vacuum tube circuit of Fig. 16.3(A) amplifies the carrier frequency wave, and the audio modulating voltage varies the supply voltage. The modulating voltage, therefore, changes the peak output voltage. In the class C dual transistor circuit of Fig. 16.3(B) an audio modulating current varies the collector supply current. The modulating current thus changes the total supply current which determines the output.

Figure 16.4 shows a constant-current modulator and its dual. The two tubes in Fig. 16.4(A) draw a total supply current which is approximately constant. In a class C amplifier the output is also proportional to the supply current. A single constant-current power supply formed by a battery in series with an audio frequency choke is connected to the output of the audio amplifier in shunt with the output of the class C amplifier. The plate current of the class C amplifier at any instant is the difference between the total supply current

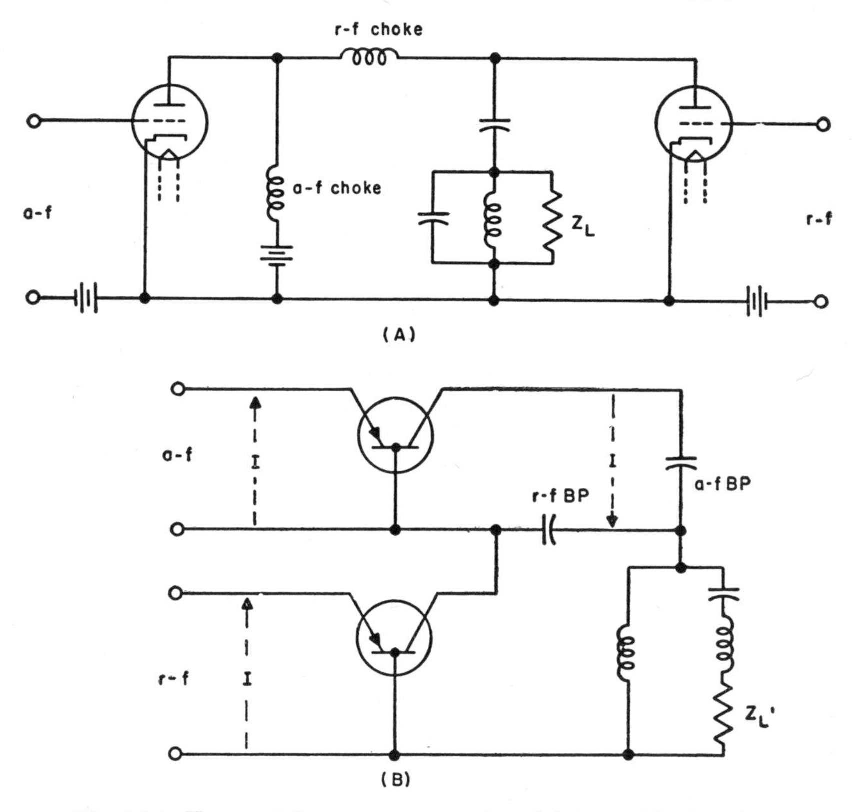

Fig. 16.4. Vacuum tube constant-current modulator and its transistor dual.

and the plate current of the modulator tube. Thus the class C amplifier output is inversely proportional to the plate current and grid voltage of the modulator tube. In the dual of Fig. 16.4(B) we have a class C transistor amplifier connected in series with a class A transistor modulator supplied by a constant-voltage source consisting of a large by-pass capacitor *AFBP* in shunt with a constant-current supply. The instantaneous collector voltage of the class C amplifier is the difference between the supply voltage and the collector voltage

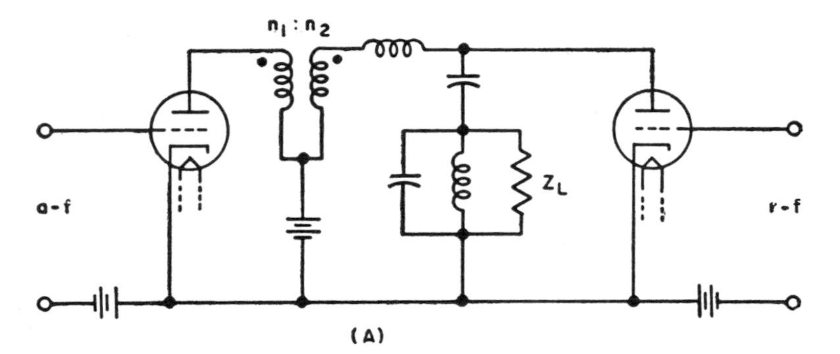

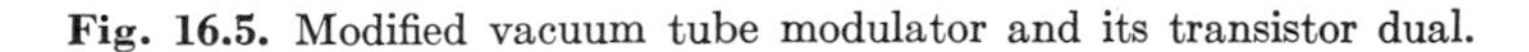

Fig. 16.5. Modified vacuum tube modulator and its transistor dual.

of the transistor modulator. Since the class C amplifier output varies directly with its supply voltage, the output will be proportional to the emitter current of the transistor modulator.

The circuits of Fig. 16.4 do not produce 100 per cent modulation because the modulator element cannot utilize all the available power supply current or voltage. Figure 16.5 shows the circuits of a modified vacuum tube constant-current modulator and its transistor dual which employs transformers to overcome this limitation. The transformer somewhat increases the current or voltage variations in the modulator unit. For the transformer in each circuit $n_2 > n_1$, and although the total supply current or voltage no longer remains constant, the change is small.

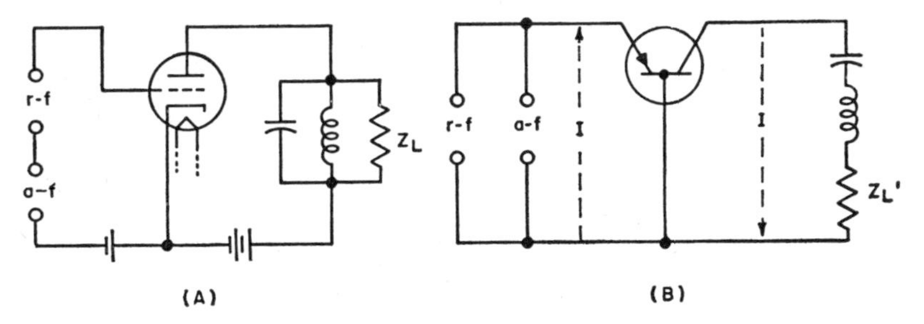

Fig. 16.6. A vacuum tube grid modulator and its transistor dual.

Figure 16.6 presents the circuit of a vacuum tube grid modulator and its transistor dual. Modulation products are directly produced by nonlinearity of the device transfer characteristics near cutoff. The grid voltage bias in the tube is sufficient to cause approximate plate current cutoff, whereas the emitter current bias in the transistor is adequate to give approximate collector voltage cutoff. A tuned output circuit selects the required modulation products. We can employ these circuits as large-signal devices, where modulation products are produced by the total nonlinearities, or as small-signal units, operating on the square law principle.

3. *Two amplitude modulated crystal oscillators*

Figure 16.7 is the circuit of a 7 mc/sec crystal-controlled transistor oscillator[4] which is amplitude modulated by a carbon microphone.

This oscillator utilizes a point-contact transistor in a grounded-base circuit with the 7 mc/sec crystal itself providing the feedback from collector to emitter. The parallel circuit in the collector lead resonates at 7 mc/sec. The inductance L consists of about 16 turns of No. 24 wire wound on a form $\frac{3}{8}$ in. in diameter. The carbon microphone in series with the supply voltage collector-modulates the oscillator. The antenna is inductively coupled to the tank circuit by a few turns of insulated wire wound over inductance L. Although this transmitter will cover only a short range, it does have possibilities for office intercommunication.

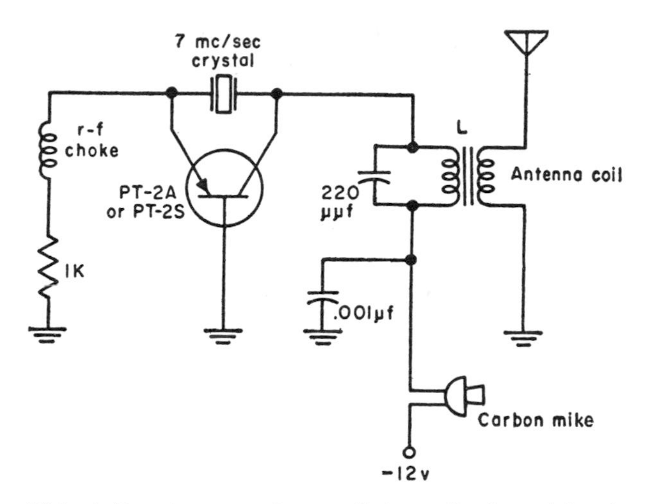

Fig. 16.7. A 7-mc/sec crystal-controlled amplitude-modulated transistor oscillator.

Figure 16.8(A) shows the circuit of a frequency-stabilized transistor oscillator[5] employing a 400 kc/sec crystal between collector and base and a parallel-resonant circuit between collector and emitter. The tank circuit's resonant frequency f_o should be about 10 to 20 per cent less than the crystal's frequency for maximum feedback. The transistor is a CK722 junction unit.

As indicated in Fig. 16.8(B), a diode D shunting the tank circuit produces a simple, effective amplitude modulation. The modulating voltage V_m varies the diode impedance, causing a Q modulation. The large capacitor C_D with its high by-pass resistor R_D supplies a self-adjusting bias, automatically establishes a sensitive operating point, and hence furnishes automatic volume control.

Figure 16.8(C) is a practical scheme for voice modulating this 400 kc/sec crystal-controlled transistor oscillator. The carbon microphone M receives rectified radio frequency energy from the diode D. The microphone modulates the self-adjusting bias which varies the diode impedance. The changing microphone resistance is transformed

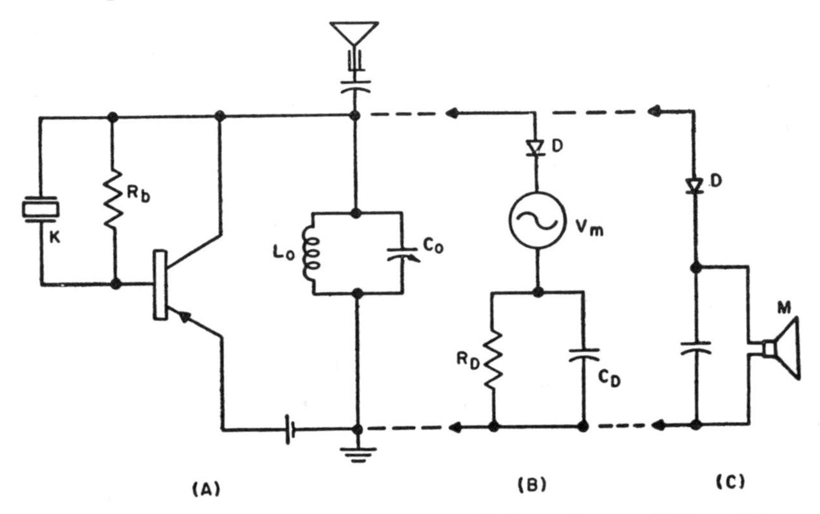

Fig. 16.8. (A) 400-kc/sec crystal-controlled transistor oscillator. (B) Q-modulation circuit for external modulating voltage, and (C) Q-modulation circuit for carbon microphone.

into the tank circuit by the nonlinear diode resistance, achieving the Q modulation without subjecting the microphone to radio frequency energy. Although it would be much more economical of power to supply the microphone directly from a d-c supply, this Q modulation circuit greatly aids subminiaturization by eliminating a sizable microphone transformer. The circuits of 16.8(A) and 16.8(C) in combination give 40 per cent amplitude modulation, when powered by two 1.5 v batteries.

4. *Two transistor amplitude modulators*

Figure 16.9 is a circuit diagram of an amplitude modulation system embodying an invention by Koros.[6] Disregarding for the present the connection through lead 34 between modulation signal source 26 and emitter electrode 13, this circuit operates in a conventional manner. The carrier wave developed by source 22 is effectively impressed between emitter 13 and base 12. Accordingly, an amplified version of the carrier wave appears at the output terminals 37. It is well known that emitter 13 and base 12 operate as a peak rectifier of the

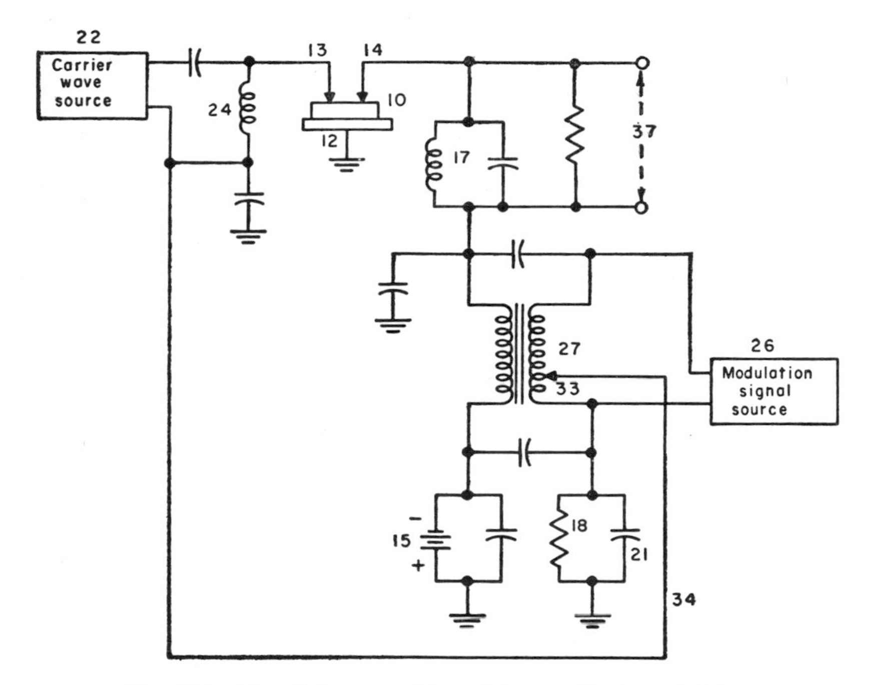

Fig. 16.9. Circuit diagram of transistor amplitude modulator.

impressed carrier wave. The rectified direct current flows through choke coil 24, lead 34, tap 33, the lower portion of primary winding 27, and bias network 18 to ground, that is, to base 12. The rectified current eventually builds up a charge across capacitor 21 which biases the emitter electrode 13. The thus developed bias voltage preferably is of such a magnitude as to provide class C operation of the semi conductor device 10.

The collector bias voltage supplied by battery 15 is modulated by the modulation signal source 26 in accordance with the modulation signal. Accordingly, the amplified output wave which may be obtained from output terminals 37 has its amplitude modulated in accordance with the modulation signal.

However, this amplitude modulated output wave also may have an undesired phase modulation. This phase modulation is due to a leakage current which is inherently present in the device 10 and which flows essentially between emitter 13 and collector 14. Since this leakage current may be out of phase with the amplitude modulated output wave, phase modulation is produced.

A predetermined portion of the modulation signal is impressed through adjustable tap 33, lead 34, and choke coil 24 on the emitter electrode 13 and base electrode 12. Consequently both the carrier wave impressed on device 10 and the amplified carrier wave developed in resonant circuit 17 are modulated simultaneously by the modulation signal. In this manner the undesired phase modulation of the amplitude modulated output carrier wave is substantially eliminated.

Figure 16.10 shows the circuit of another transistor modulator invented by Koros.[7] A high-frequency carrier is impressed between emitter and ground. Rectified current through this circuit flows

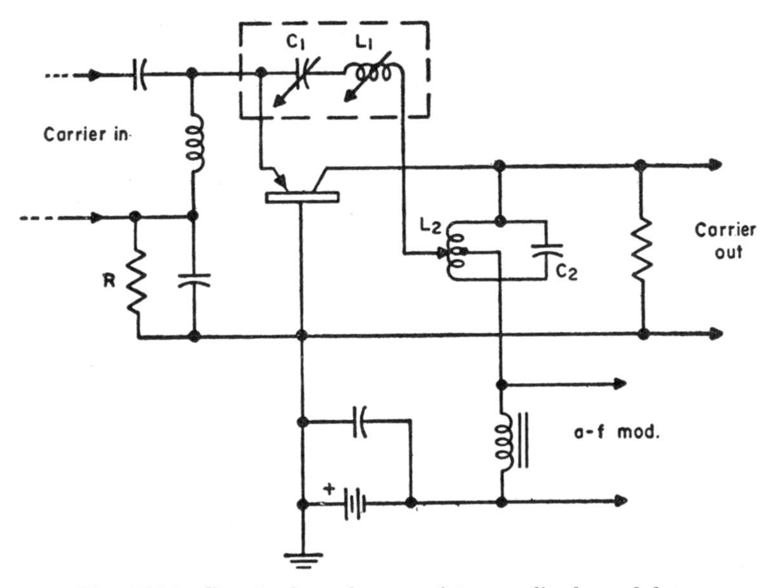

Fig. 16.10. Circuit of another transistor amplitude modulator.

through R to generate bias for the emitter. An audio frequency signal feeds the collector and modulates the carrier.

Ohmic leakage from emitter to collector causes a carrier component to arrive at the collector out of phase with the desired amplified signal. To cancel this phase distortion, part of the carrier input is fed directly through network $L1$-$C1$ to the tank $L2$-$C2$. Complete cancellation is effected by tuning $L1$-$C1$ and choosing the correct tap point on $L2$.

5. *Amplitude detection*

Either diodes or transistors can act as amplitude modulation detectors.[8] Figure 16.11(A) indicates a diode detector circuit. For linear detection with a diode, the output of the intermediate frequency amplifier must be at a comparatively high voltage level. Since the diode feeds the detected signal into the low impedance of the following audio stage, an audio frequency matching transformer is needed for good efficiency.

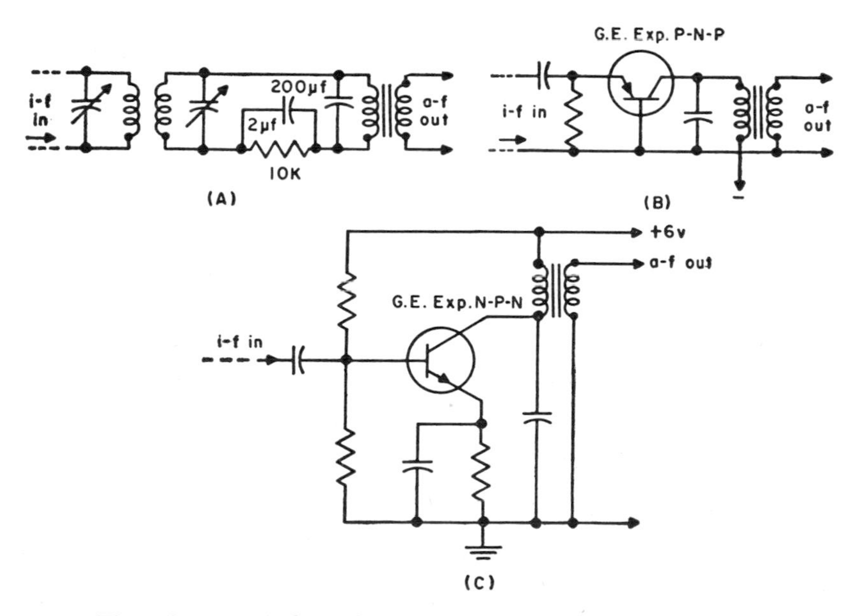

Fig. 16.11. Typical amplitude modulation detectors. (A) Germanium diode, (B) grounded-base P-N-P junction transistor, (C) grounded-emitter N-P-N junction transistor.

Transistor detectors have several advantages over diode detectors. Transistors function essentially as linear detectors at lower power levels than diodes although both transistors and diodes operate as square law detectors at low signal levels. Since the transistor detector also functions as the first audio amplifier, it develops fairly large power gain. This is especially true of the ground-emitter circuit where typical gain is 20 db referred to modulation power. Transistor detectors supply the d-c control power necessary for automatic gain control of transistor amplifiers. Diode detectors normally give insufficient d-c control power for automatic gain control, and would need an additional d-c amplifier in the feedback path or an extra intermediate frequency stage.

Figure 16.11(B) is the circuit of a grounded-base detector for which a typical input impedance is 3000 ohms. Figure 16.11(C) gives a grounded-emitter transistor detector; a typical input impedance is 20,000 ohms. The grounded-emitter connection generally produces greater gain.

Amplitude modulation detectors for point-contact transistors have been derived from well-known types of vacuum tube detectors by applying the principle of duality.[3] The function of these circuits is to obtain an output wave proportional to the envelope of the amplitude modulated input wave.

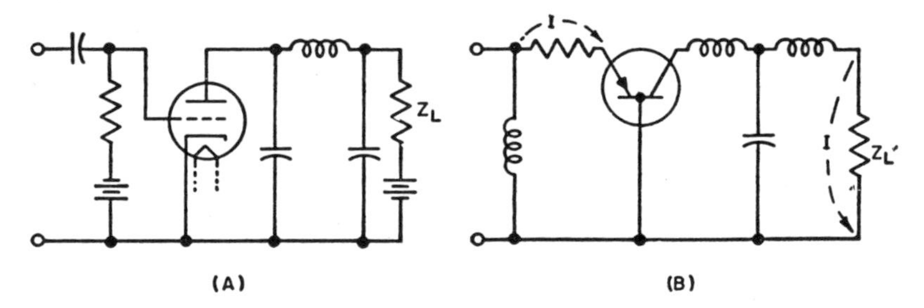

Fig. 16.12. Vacuum tube plate detector and its transistor dual.

Figure 16.12 gives the circuits of a vacuum tube plate detector and its transistor dual. The plate detector is basically a class B amplifier, is biased approximately to plate current cutoff, and has a low-pass filter in its output circuit. It rectifies the positive alternations of the input signal and cuts off the negative alternations. The filter prevents the radio frequency pulsations from reaching the load impedance Z_L

and produces an output proportional to the average of the positive alternations of the input signal. This is also proportional to the envelope for a true amplitude modulated wave.

The transistor dual functions in a similar manner. The circuit is a grounded-base amplifier with a low-pass filter in the collector circuit. The emitter current biases the transistor to collector voltage cutoff. The circuit amplifies the negative alternations of the input signal and cuts off the positive alternations. The collector voltage consists of negative radio frequency alternations of changing amplitudes. The filter smooths them, and the output is a replica of the envelope of the input signal.

If these circuits are to function properly, it is important that the plate detector filter have low input impedance outside of the pass band, and that the transistor dual filter have low input admittance outside of the pass band. Otherwise the form of the filter is not restricted.

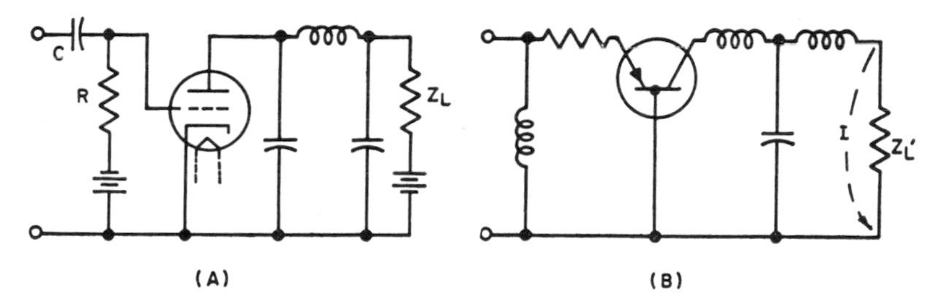

Fig. 16.13. Vacuum tube grid-leak detector and its transistor dual.

Figure 16.13 shows the circuits of a vacuum tube grid leak detector and its transistor dual. In the vacuum tube circuit the incoming signal drives the grid positive, the grid draws current and charges capacitor C, and later this capacitor discharges through the resistor R. The time constant of this grid leak bias circuit is made sufficiently short that the bias can follow the envelope of the input wave. The total grid voltage consists of the input signal and an additional voltage proportional to the envelope of the modulated wave. The entire grid signal is amplified by the tube, and the output filter removes the high-frequency pulsations. The transistor dual operates in a corresponding fashion except that emitter current replaces grid voltage.

6. *Automatic gain control*

A decrease in either emitter current or collector voltage causes transistor amplifier gain to decrease.[8] Therefore we can design at least two kinds of automatic gain control circuits.

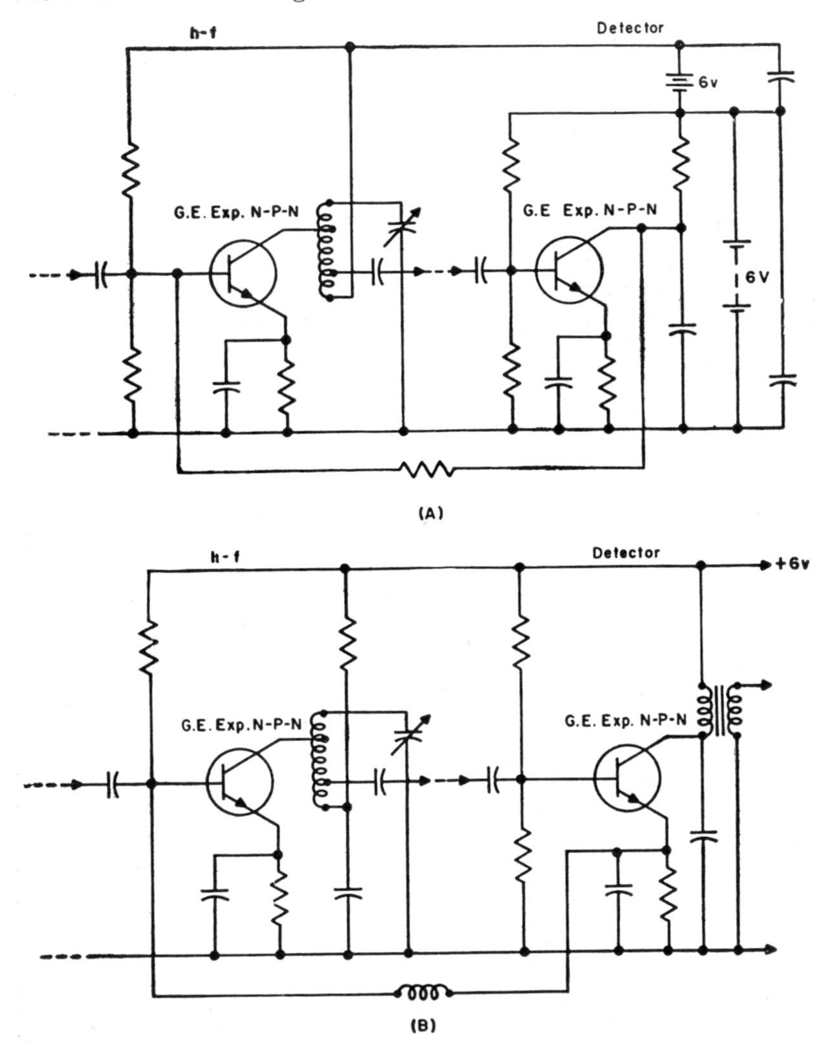

Fig. 16.14. Automatic gain control circuits with (A) emitter-current control and (B) collector-voltage control.

Control power is needed for both types. A transistor detector can easily supply this d-c power which the controlled a-c stage can increase if it also functions as a d-c amplifier.

When we employ emitter current control, we apply the control voltage to the base of the controlled stage. The transistor amplifies the resulting variations of base direct current, producing large changes in emitter current and gain.

When we utilize collector voltage control, we likewise apply the control voltage to the base. The transistor amplifies variations of base current to produce larger changes in collector current. A resistor placed in the collector circuit causes a voltage drop which varies the collector voltage and gain.

Figure 16.14 describes both of the above types of automatic gain control circuits: (A) utilizes emitter current control, and (B) employs collector voltage control.

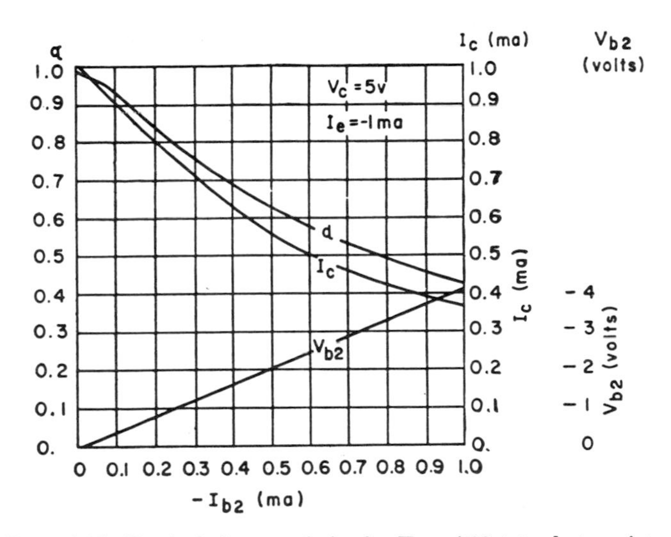

Fig. 16.15. Typical characteristics for Type 700 tetrode transistor.

Type 700 tetrode transistor[9] is an N-P-N grown junction unit constructed with two base layer connections so that the current gain may be varied. It is especially designed for low-level, low-frequency, automatic gain control circuits which require small size, long life, reliability, and operational economy. In a typical grounded-emitter amplifier, less than 100 μa introduced into the second base lead can attenuate the output signal 20 db.

Figure 16.15 shows typical characteristics for the Type 700 tetrode transistor. These indicate that a change of 4 v in the bias of the second base lead with respect to the first base lead causes alpha to vary from about 0.95 to 0.42. The corresponding changes in output current are from about 1 ma to 0.37 ma.

References

1. G. M. Rose, "Transistor, or 25 Miles on a Hunk of Germanium," *QST*, Vol. XXXVII, No. 3, March 1953, p. 14.
2. A. Cockle, "160-Metre Transistor Transmitter," *Wireless World*, Vol. LX, No. 5, May 1954, p. 217.
3. R. L. Wallace, Jr. and G. Raisbeck, "Duality as a Guide in Transistor Circuit Design," *Bell System Tech. J.*, Vol. XXX, April 1951, pp. 381–418.
4. *CBS-Hytron Transistor Manual, An Introduction to Transistor Theory, Data, and Applications, Bulletin E 212*, CBS-Hytron, A Division of Columbia Broadcasting System, Inc., Danvers, Mass.
5. Hans E. Hollmann, "Transistor Oscillators," *Tele-Tech and Electronic Industries*, Vol. XII, No. 10, Oct. 1953, pp. 82–83.
6. Leslie L. Koros, "Transistor Amplitude Modulator," *U. S. Patent 2,629,858*, assigned to Radio Corporation of America.
7. Leslie L. Koros, "Transistor Modulator," *U. S. Patent 2,644,925*, assigned to Radio Corporation of America.
8. Arthur P. Stern and John A. A. Raper, "Transistor AM Broadcast Receivers," *Convention Record of IRE, 1954 National Convention, Part 7, Broadcasting and Television*, pp. 8–14.
9. *Data Sheet, Type 700 Tetrode Transistor*, Texas Instruments, Incorporated, Dallas, Texas, March 1954.

Chapter 17

FREQUENCY MODULATION AND DEMODULATION WITH TRANSISTORS

1. *Introduction*

This chapter describes several FM oscillators to demonstrate the production of frequency modulation with transistors. Since none of these devices is intended to transmit on the air, no piezo-electrical crystal is employed to control the center frequency. The distance covered is only a few hundred feet. Practical applications of these circuits include wireless microphones and phonograph pickups.

2. *A 10.75 mc/sec transistor FM oscillator*[1]

Figure 17.1 is the circuit for a 10.75 mc/sec transistor FM oscillator. In this circuit the transistor operates in three different ways: it oscil-

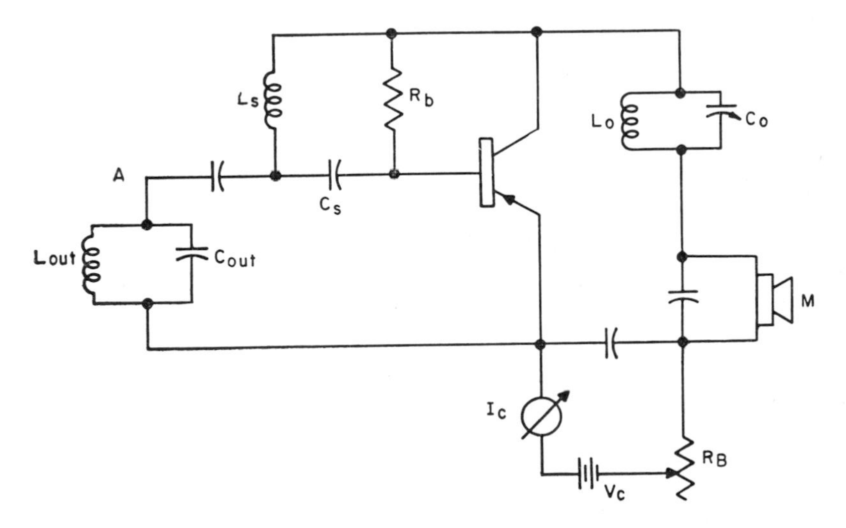

Fig. 17.1. 10.75-mc/sec FM oscillator employing a junction transistor.

lates at a fundamental frequency f_o near its alpha cutoff, it multiplies the frequency f_o and energizes the output tank $L_{out}C_{out}$ at a high harmonic, and it acts as a reactance modulator. A circular multiplication around the feedback loop produces the harmonics. This occurs because of the highly nonharmonic nature of the whole oscillating system; in other words, frequency variations cause its frequency-determining characteristics to change. Multiple resonances occur like those in a superregenerative circuit. Although the collector tank circuit L_oC_o and the feedback circuit L_sC_s resonate at f_o, the feedback loop is closed for the harmonics which coincide with sidepeaks, whereas the intervening harmonics are suppressed.

The circuit of Fig. 17.1 employs the circular frequency multiplication principle with a junction transistor. The master oscillator is tuned to 1.2 mc/sec, whereas the output circuit operates at 10.75 mc/sec, the ninth harmonic.

The collector voltage frequency-modulates this transmitter. The intermediate-frequency amplifier of a standard FM receiver can pick up the 10.75 mc/sec output signal. The voltage drop across the carbon microphone M in the collector circuit easily develops the modulating voltage of ± 1 v needed to give a 100 per cent FM equivalent to a frequency swing of ± 1 per cent. A fine adjustment of the carrier frequency is provided by the variable resistor R_B in the battery circuit. Automatic frequency control can be accomplished by a reference discriminator or receiver to control the collector current automatically.

3. *Transistor operated FM radiophone transmitter*[2]

The circuit of a transistor operated FM radiophone transmitter is shown in Fig. 17.2. The transmitter employs an M1832 point-contact transistor as a combined 106 mc/sec radio frequency oscillator and frequency modulator, and a Type A1858 junction transistor as an audio amplifier. The complete transmitter occupies a plastic container only about $\frac{2}{3}$ the size of a pack of cigarettes.

The audio amplifier is required only when the crystal microphone is utilized with the transmitter. A crystal phonograph pickup with the proper step-down transformer will modulate the transistor directly. The A1858 junction transistor in the audio amplifier is connected in a common-emitter circuit to give a large audio current gain. Resistor R_1 in the emitter circuit and the voltage divider, consisting of resistances R_2 and R_3 across the battery terminals, stabilize the d-c operating point of the junction transistor. This voltage divider is adjusted so that the IR drop across R_2 equals the product of the emitter resistance R_1 and the approximate collector current desired, which is 250 μa. Component C_1 is an audio bypass capacitor. A high ratio step-down transformer T_1 matches the high-impedance crystal microphone to the low-impedance transistor input. Resistances R_4 and R_6 and capacitance C_2 couple the output of the audio amplifier to the input of the oscillator modulator.

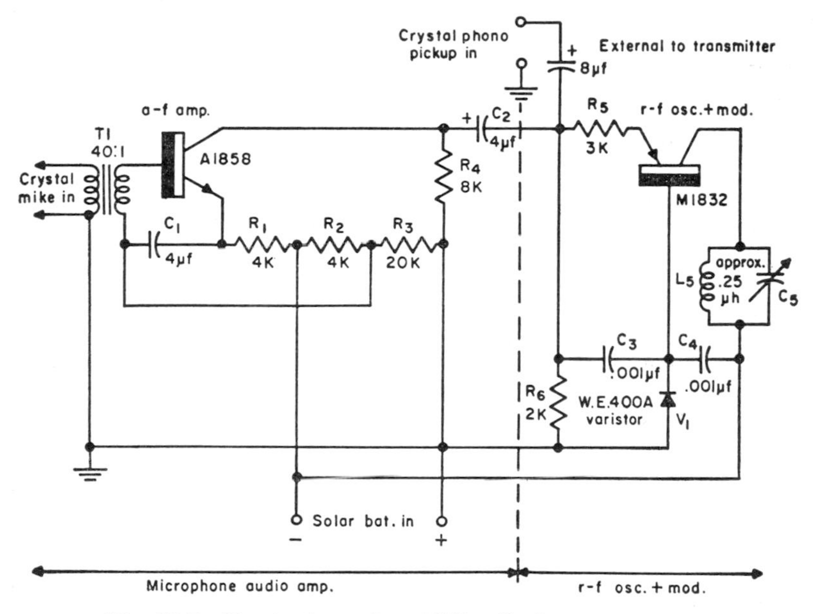

Fig. 17.2. Circuit of transistor FM radiophone transmitter.

In the oscillator modulator circuit the coupling required for oscillation is provided by the emitter-to-collector capacitance of the transistor, its socket, and external connections.

The magnitude of the current gain of a transistor is not constant with frequency. It begins to decrease as frequency is increased toward and beyond the cutoff frequency. Accompanying this decrease in current gain, there is a corresponding phase shift in the current gain of the transistor. The transistor oscillates at a frequency well above its critical cutoff frequency where this phase shift has the proper magnitude to compensate for the phase shift in the emitter-to-collector coupling capacitance. Although the value of the emitter-to-collector capacitance is not critical it is possible to make it too large for oscillation in the v.h.f. region. It is therefore important to keep the oscillator circuit assembly and wiring compact and not increase this capacitance by long emitter and collector leads.

The tank coil L_5 is not critical. It may consist of six turns of No. 22 copper wire wound on a $\frac{3}{8}$ in. diameter mandrel at about 10 turns to the inch. Tank capacitor C_5 tunes this coil to the desired oscillating frequency. The parasitic capacitances of the transistor also contribute to the tank circuit capacitance. Also the oscillator operates slightly off the exact tank circuit resonant frequency. The tank circuit frequency is therefore adjusted only approximately in the initial assembly and is tuned to the proper frequency when the circuit is actually oscillating. An adjustable trimming capacitor is included as part of C_5 to obtain a total range of oscillation frequency of about 10 mc/sec.

Frequency modulation is obtained because the cutoff frequency of the transistor is not constant but shifts when the operating point of the transistor is changed. The phase shift of the transistor current gain also changes as a result of this shift in cutoff frequency. This change in phase shift requires the frequency of the oscillator to change to keep the oscillator coupling in proper phase at the oscillation frequency. When an audio signal is fed into the emitter of the transistor oscillator, the operating currents of the transistor are changed in accordance with the instantaneous magnitude of the audio signal. This changes the cutoff frequency of the transistor which in turn changes the frequency of oscillation of the oscillator. This is frequency modulation by transistor current gain frequency-cutoff shift.

Resistor R_5 in the emitter circuit of the oscillator prevents relaxation oscillations which may occur in v.h.f. point-contact transistors. Such relaxation oscillations are caused by emitter-to-ground capacitance combined with positive feedback through the internal base resistance of the transistor. Resistance R_5 is placed directly on the transistor emitter terminal to isolate all other connections to the emitter and limit the emitter-to-ground capacitance to that of the transistor and its socket. By holding down the total emitter-to-ground capacitance, relaxation oscillations are avoided.

Diode V_1 in the base of the oscillator provides emitter bias without recourse to a second potential source. Resistor R_6 provides a d-c emitter current path for the oscillator transistor which is of sufficiently high resistance to avoid shorting the audio input.

Components C_3 and C_4 are radio frequency bypass capacitors to return the v.h.f. frequencies in the emitter and collector directly to the base without passing through the biasing circuits.

The voltage and current required to operate this transmitter are only 4 v and 3 ma respectively, or a total power requirement of just 12 mw. A 10-cell Bell solar battery has a normal open-circuit voltage of 5 v and a total power output of about 250 mw. Therefore the transistor transmitter can be operated from such a battery even when the weather is cloudy.

No antenna is shown coupled to the oscillator tank circuit. An antenna is omitted to limit the range of transmission to the few hundred feet required for experimental and demonstration purposes. A standard commercial FM receiver is employed to receive the signals transmitted by this solar-powered transmitter.

4. *A 100 mc/sec transistorized FM transmitter*[3]

A 100 mc/sec FM transmitter utilizing a Type 2N33 point-contact transistor is diagrammed in Fig. 17.3. A circular frequency multiplication of the internal transistor frequency occurs in this transmitter. A tank circuit in the collector lead operates at the second or third harmonic, and produces frequencies in the 100 mc/sec range. Frequency modulation is accomplished by varying the collector current a small amount about its quiescent value. Hence about 100 mv output from a piezoelectric pickup of a record player produces a 100 per cent frequency swing and an extremely simple, high-fidelity frequency modulation.

5. *Frequency demodulation with transistors*

The conventional semiconductor discriminator employing two germanium diodes is well known and will not be discussed here.

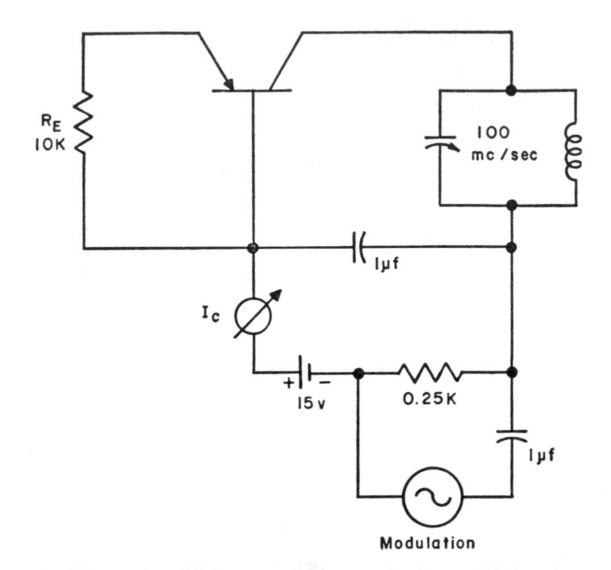

Fig. 17.3. 100-mc/sec FM transmitter employing a 2N33 point-contact transistor.

Figure 17.4 shows the circuit of a transistor FM detector utilizing a special symmetrical transistor.[4] When negative bias is applied to the base of such an alloy P-N-P junction transistor, some emitter-collector current will flow in either direction, depending on the polarity of the collector voltage. A signal generator or the intermediate

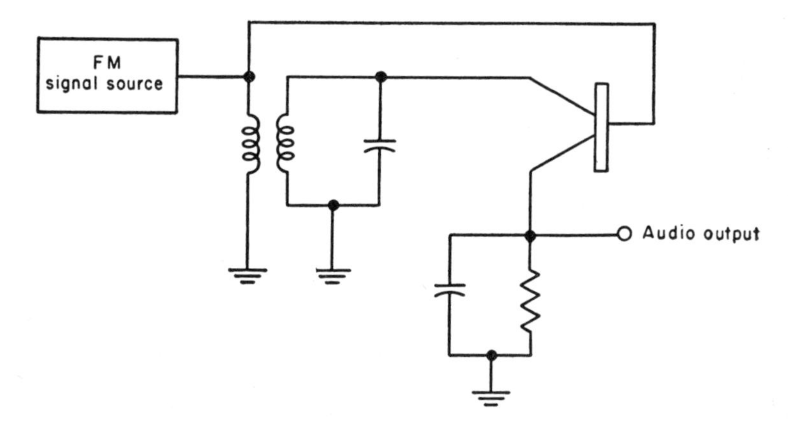

Fig. 17.4. FM detector employing a symmetrical transistor.

frequency amplifier of a conventional FM receiver feeds the transformer. The base-emitter circuit of the P-N-P transistor receives the FM signal output from the source. During the positive alternation of the wave applied to the base, the emitter-collector circuit of the P-N-P transistor is effectively opened and no current flows through the output resistor. During each negative alternation, the emitter-collector circuit conducts. For N-P-N transistors the conditions are reversed.

The signal developed across the secondary of the transformer determines the magnitude and direction of the current flow during the conductive periods. When the applied frequency is equal to the resonant frequency, the voltage across the secondary is 90° out of phase with the voltage across the primary. For this condition the load resistor will have a zero direct voltage drop across it. When the frequency increases, the secondary voltage lags the primary voltage by an angle less than 90°; when the frequency decreases, it will lag by an angle more than 90°. (Of course, the lagging phase relationship can be changed to a leading one by reversing the leads of the transformer secondary.) As the phase relationship changes, the voltage developed across the load resistor varies with the frequency modulation. The current tends to remain constant with varying signal amplitude.

References

1. Hans E. Hollmann, "Transistor Oscillators," *Tele-Tech and Electronic Industries*, Vol. XII, No. 10, Oct. 1953, pp. 82–83.

2. D. M. Chapin and D. E. Thomas, "Solar Battery Powers Transmitter," *Radio Electronics*, Vol. XXV, No. 8, Aug. 1954, pp. 76–78. Copyright 1954 by Gernsback Publications, Inc.

3. Hans E. Hollmann, "Self-Oscillating UHF Transistors," *Tele-Tech and Electronic Industries*, Vol. XIII, No. 4, April 1954, pp. 75–77.

4. George Clifford Sziklai, "Symmetrical Properties of Transistors and Their Applications," *Proc. IRE*, Vol. XLI, No. 6, June 1953, pp. 717–724.

Chapter 18

TRANSISTOR RADIO AND TELEVISION RECEIVERS

1. *A two-transistor radio receiver*[1]

A two-transistor standard broadcast radio receiver is shown in Fig. 18.1. The first transistor is used as a detector-amplifier, whereas the second transistor is employed as an audio amplifier. By using grounded-emitter circuits, only one battery is required. Mutual cou-

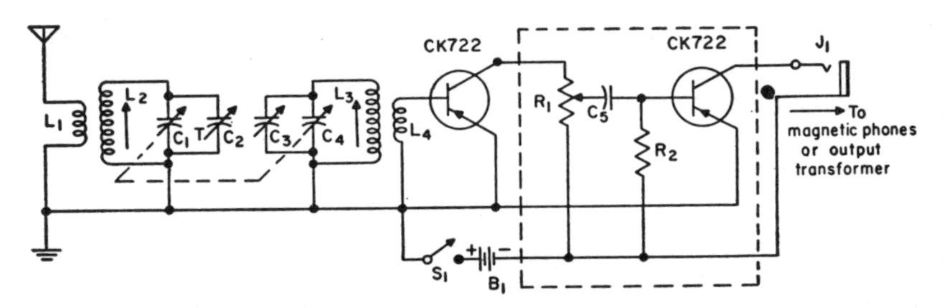

Fig. 18.1. Two-transistor standard-broadcast radio receiver. R_1 is 20,000 ohm potentiometer; R_2 is approx. 250,000 ohms, $\frac{1}{4}$ w resistor; C_1, C_4 is two-gang, 365 $\mu\mu$f, capacitor (I.C.A.534); C_2, C_3 are trimmers on C_1, C_4; C_5 is 10 $\mu\mu$f, 25 v electrolytic capacitor; L_1, L_2 is antenna coil (Merit 380); L_3, L_4 is detector coil (Merit 382, modified); S_1 is S.P.S.T. switch; J_1 is output jack; B_1 is 3 v battery (Burgess 422); two CK722 junction transistors (Raytheon) are utilized.

pling between the antenna and detector coils is obtained by placing these coils close together with 1 in. separation center to center. The detector coil requires modification to match the input impedance of the first transistor. This is accomplished as illustrated in Fig. 18.2. The antenna winding of the Merit type 382 coil should be removed carefully. After the leads are unsoldered, this winding can be slid from the end of the coil form. Then 50 turns of this wire should be scramble wound on the core close to the first pi of the tuning coil.

A good coil dope should be used to cement the new detector coil in place.

Resistor R_2 should have a value to make the collector current of the second transistor about 1 ma. The strength of the received signal determines the collector current of the first transistor; a strong signal will give an average current of about 200 μa. Two penlight cells should give a battery life of at least 100 hours.

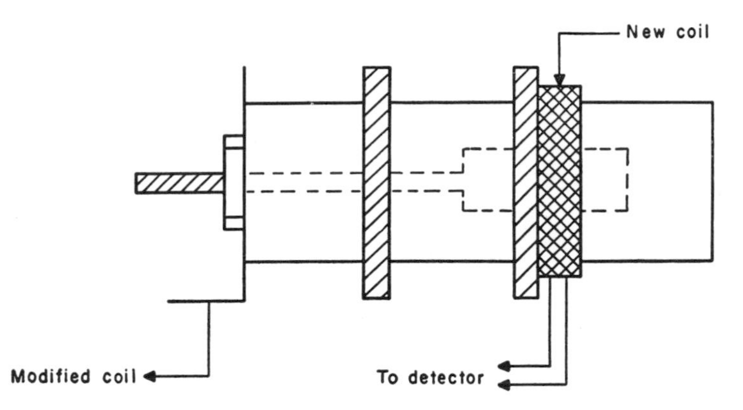

Fig. 18.2. Detector coil modification.

The correct load impedance for the output stage is about 2000 ohms. Therefore magnetic phones may be connected directly in the output collector circuit. A matching transformer should be used for low-impedance phones or loudspeaker. The receiver output power is approximately 1.5 mw.

2. *A transistorized superheterodyne broadcast receiver*[2]

An eight-transistor superheterodyne broadcast receiver is shown in Fig. 18.3. This receiver employs one radio frequency amplifier stage (550 to 1550 kc/sec), a mixer, a local oscillator tuning 455 kc/sec above the signal frequency, a three-stage 455 kc/sec intermediate frequency amplifier, a 1N34 diode detector, and a two-stage audio amplifier. The over-all gain of the receiver is about 90 db. The gain control consists of two ganged potentiometers, one in the input of the first radio frequency stage and the other in the input of the first intermediate frequency amplifier. Each of these gives a maximum of about 50 db attenuation, or a total range of 100 db. Since ordinary transistors have a sharp cutoff characteristic, automatic volume control normally cannot be used. It is not advisable to vary the operating conditions of sharp-cutoff transistors, since cross modulation usually occurs on strong signals.

The sensitivity of this receiver is approximately 200 μv for an output of 6 mw at 1000 cps. The output signal-to-noise ratio is 10 db, and is limited by the input transistor noise. The maximum audio output is about 15 to 20 mw with 5 per cent harmonic distortion at 1000 cps. The selectivity curve is about 9 kc/sec wide between points which are 6 db down. Between points which are 60 db down, the band width is approximately 80 kc/sec. Hence the selectivity ratio is about 10.

The power requirements of this receiver are 3 v at 8 ma for the emitter circuits, and 30 v at 30 ma for the collector circuits, or slightly less than 1 w of battery power.

Since the transistor is a current-operated device, a well-regulated current bias must be provided. Otherwise a serious distortion may result and the danger of burning out the transistor may be increased. The simplest way of securing current regulation is to use a limiting resistor in the input bias circuit.

In the grounded-base circuit, which is used in all the amplifier stages in this receiver, the input impedance of the transistor is much lower than the output impedance of the preceding transistor. Therefore impedance (and voltage) stepdown transformers are needed between stages.

In spite of the above conditions which are peculiar to transistors, the circuit of this receiver resembles that of a receiver employing vacuum tubes.

3. *A transistor pocket radio receiver*

The Regency Model TR-1 is the first commercially available transistor radio receiver. It is pocket size, measuring only 3 by 5 by $1\frac{1}{4}$ inches, and weighing less than 12 ounces. Figure 18.4 shows the circuit. A ferrite bar antenna picks up the signal. A TI233 transistor is utilized in the mixer-oscillator stage, followed by two TI222 units in 262 kc/sec neutralized intermediate frequency amplifiers, a diode

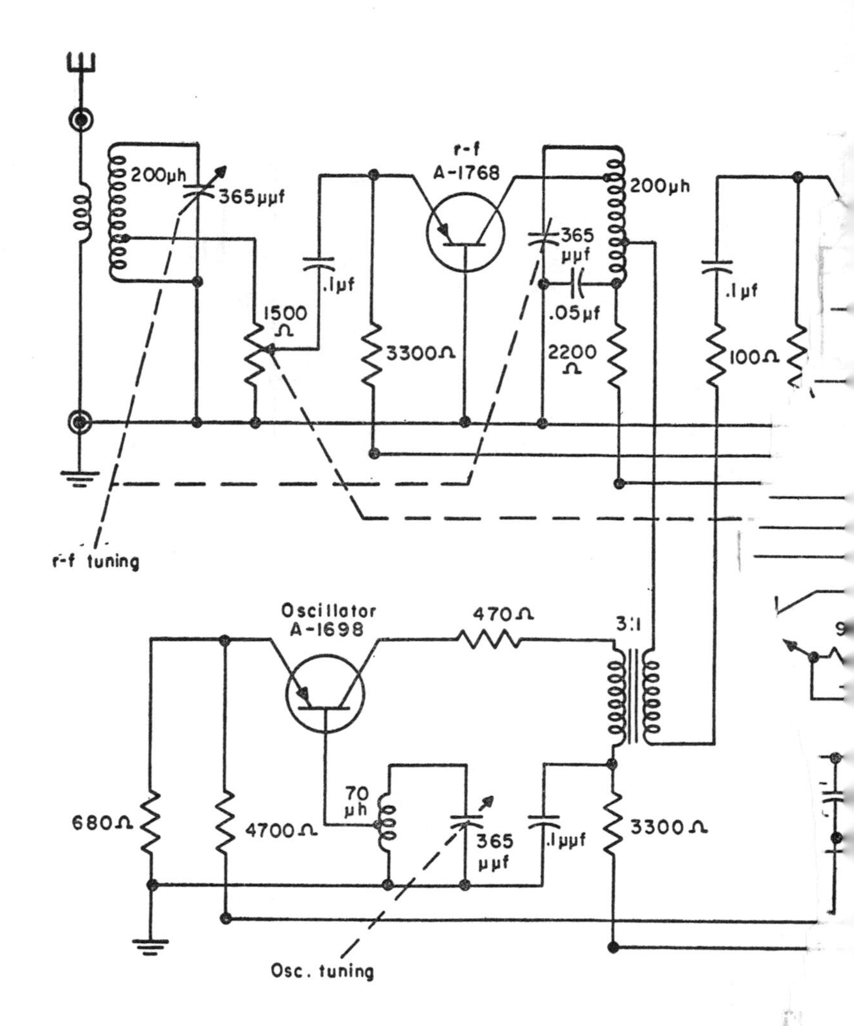

200μh
365μμf
r-f
A-1768
200μh
365
μμf
.1μf
.05μf
1500
Ω
3300Ω
2200
Ω
.1μf
100Ω
r-f tuning
Oscillator
A-1698
470Ω
3:1
70
μh
680Ω
4700Ω
365
μμf
.1μμf
3300Ω
Osc. tuning

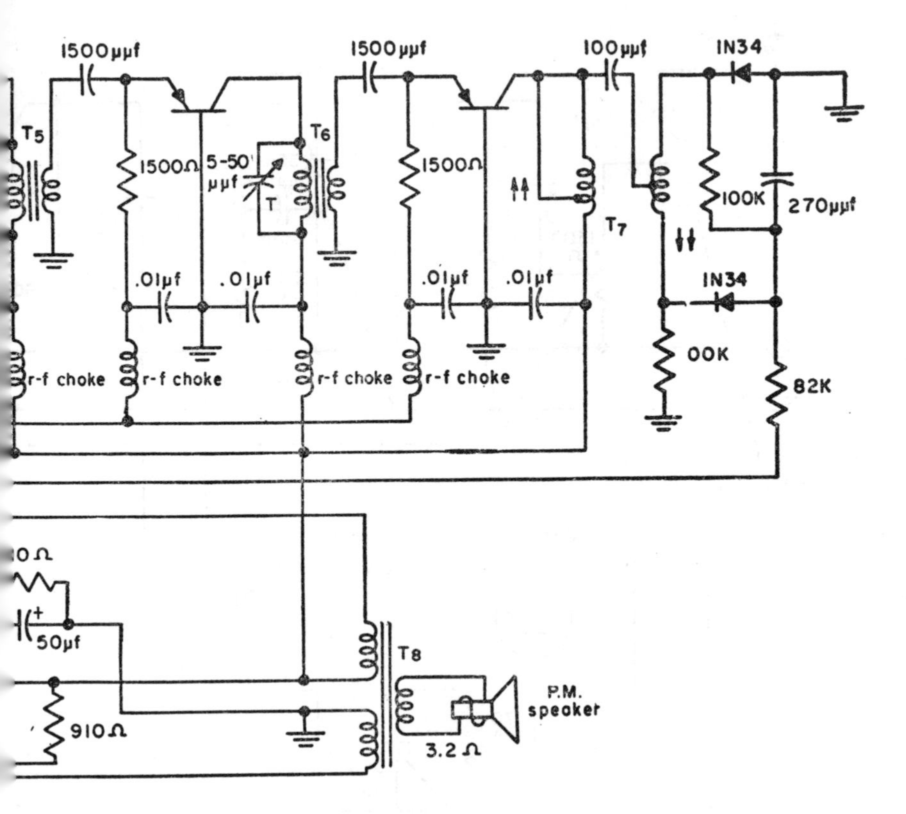

1500μμf
1500μμf
100μμf
IN34
T5
T6
1500Ω
5-50 μμf
T
1500Ω
T7
100K
270μμf
.01μf
.01μf
.01μf
.01μf
IN34
r-f choke
r-f choke
r-f choke
r-f choke
00K
82K
0Ω
50μf
T8
P.M. speaker
910Ω
3.2Ω

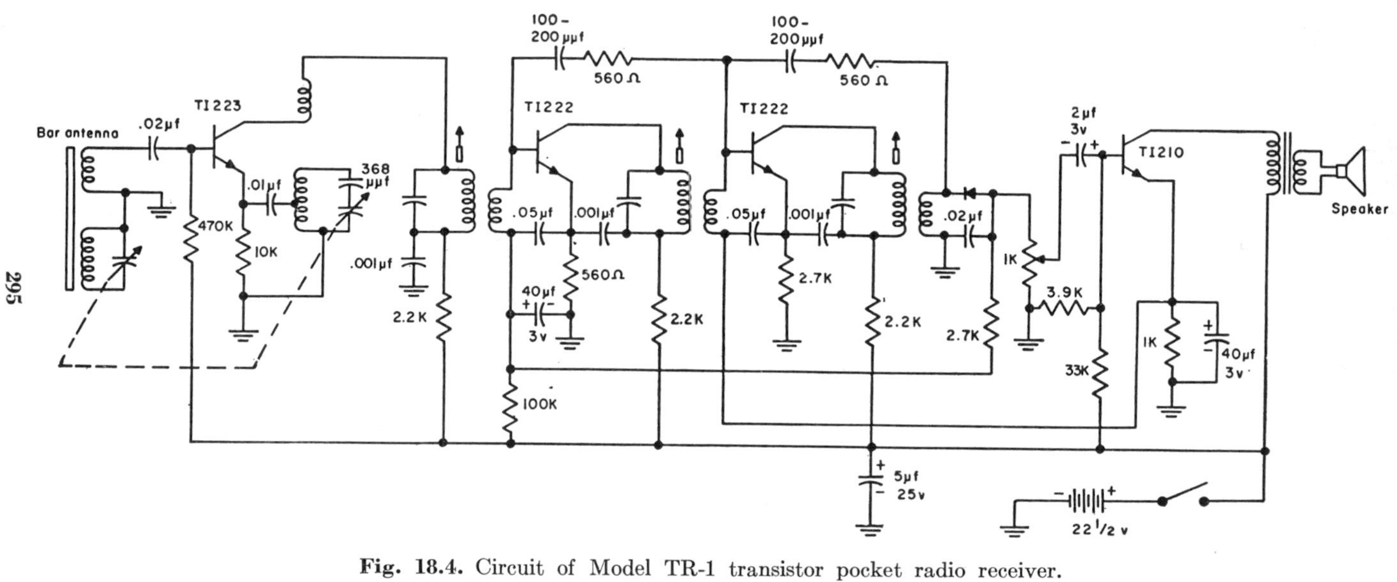

Fig. 18.4. Circuit of Model TR-1 transistor pocket radio receiver.
Courtesy of Regency Division, I.D.E.A., Inc.

detector, and a TI210 transistor in the audio amplifier which drives a $2\frac{3}{4}$ inch loudspeaker. The power output is 12 mw with approximately 6 per cent distortion. The set operates from a $22\frac{1}{2}$ v photoflash battery.

4. *A portable transistor FM receiver*[3]

Figure 18.5 illustrates the circuit of a transistorized, tubeless FM receiver. This receiver includes a built-in retractible dipole antenna, and employs 11 transistors and 4 germanium diodes. Because of the characteristics of available transistors, several compromises were necessary in the design. Since amplification at 100 mc/sec was not possible with current transistors, no radio frequency stage was used. Also, since a low gain per stage was obtained at the usual 10.7 mc/sec intermediate frequency for FM receivers, a 5 mc/sec intermediate frequency was selected.

A self-contained antenna in the form of a collapsible dipole antenna is incorporated into the receiver. This consists of a pair of steel measuring tapes mounted at the top ends of the cabinet. These tapes are silver plated and connected by a metal strip to form a simple bent dipole. When better reception is required, a jack at the center enables a twin lead from a roof-top antenna to be substituted.

The mixer consists of a pair of 1N54A germanium diodes in a balanced circuit. The local oscillator employs a circuit like a shunt-fed Hartley, with a selected point-contact transistor similar to the RCA 2N33. The oscillator capacitor tunes this circuit over the range of 83 to 103 mc/sec, and is ganged with the mixer capacitor. The trimmer consists of a ferrite slug. The oscillator operates below the carrier frequency to give sufficient excitation, since the oscillator output diminishes with frequency. Small changes in battery voltage had little effect on the transistor oscillator, approximately 5 v being required to shift the frequency one FM channel, or 200 kc/sec. No noticeable frequency shift due to temperature change developed from ordinary operation of the receiver over an approximate temperature range of 20°F. The mixer inductance L_1 has two taps on each side of the center tap to which the oscillator input is attached. These taps give an approximate impedance match for the antenna, the diodes, and the radio frequency tuning capacitor. The mixer feeds the 5-

mc/sec intermediate frequency signal to the first intermediate frequency transformer with a conversion loss of approximately 2.3.

The intermediate frequency amplifier consists of six point-contact transistors connected in grounded-base circuits. Intermediate frequency transformers T_1 to T_6 have toroidal windings. Their small external fields permit them to be placed close together without causing instability. Only the primaries of these transformers are tuned by ceramic trimmers, with tight coupling between each primary and secondary. Ferrite "doughnuts" $\frac{1}{2}$ in. outside diameter, $\frac{3}{16}$ in. inside diameter, and $\frac{1}{16}$ in. thick are used for the cores. The primaries and secondaries are wound opposite each other on these cores in single layers of No. 36 enameled wire with 65 turns for the primaries and 12 turns for the secondaries. This turns ratio approximately matches the impedance of one collector to that of the following emitter. Isolation of stages is accomplished by supplying the collectors through separate LC filters from the common $-22\frac{1}{2}$ v battery. Likewise, there are individual LC filters, decoupling the emitters from their common $+1\frac{1}{2}$ v supply. The emitter current per stage is limited to less than 1 ma by series 1500 ohm resistors. Each stage has an average gain of about 11 db or 3.6 times. This results in an over-all gain of 67 db, or 2200 times. Strong signals cause the final stages to limit due to overloading.

A conventional discriminator circuit employing a pair of 1N34 germanium diodes comprises the FM detector. Transformer T_7 is an ordinary slug-tuned transformer with the primary tapped to match the last intermediate frequency transistor.

The audio system is quite unusual. The driver consists of a two-stage grounded-collector (emitter-follower) amplifier using RCA 2N34 junction transistors. This amplifier has a low output impedance suitable for driving a complementary-symmetry, push-pull output stage employing a pair of experimental junction power transistors. The output transformer T_8 has a split primary so that only one battery is necessary to power the P-N-P and N-P-N output transistors. Each primary has a step down ratio of 11.5 to 1 to the secondary, which is connected to a 3.2 ohm voice coil. The over-all power gain of the audio system is 46 db, and the maximum undistorted power delivered to the speaker is 75 mw.

A light hearing-aid battery supplied collector power for this experimental receiver. With the total collector current of 60 ma, the battery life was about 10 hours. A penlight cell was sufficient for the 6 ma total emitter current.

With only the internal collapsible antenna, the receiver operated satisfactorily under normal strong-signal conditions over the FM band.

5. *A transistorized television receiver*[4]

A block diagram of an experimental transistorized television receiver is given in Fig. 18.6. A loop antenna picks up the signal to op-

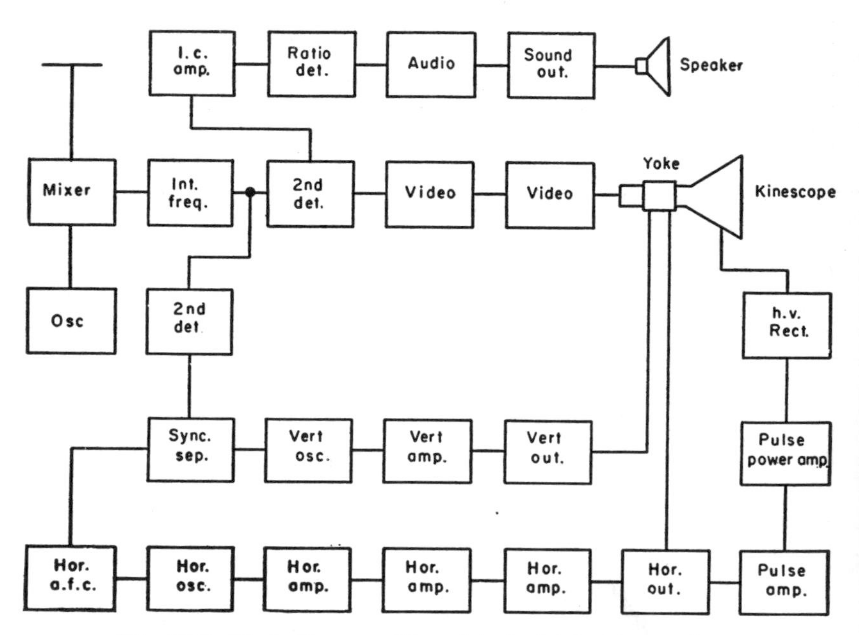

Fig. 18.6. Block diagram of transistorized television receiver.

perate the receiver, a pair of crystal diodes is used in the mixer for combining the signal with the local oscillator, and six stages of grounded-base, point-contact transistors amplify the resulting difference signal. Independent signals for the sync and video amplifier are supplied by two second detectors. Four intercarrier frequency stages amplify the intercarrier sound from the video detector, and then a ratio detector demodulates it. The resulting audio signal is amplified by a grounded-collector stage (emitter-follower stage) which drives a complementary symmetry push-pull stage. For amplifying the video signal a combination amplifier employs both a grounded-emitter junction transistor and a point-contact transistor. This has the advantages of both higher input impedance and high-frequency response.

A loop antenna was used to make the receiver completely self-contained. The loop is made of sheet brass strips bent at a right angle, and fits the top outside edges of the case, which is 12 by 13 by 7 inches. The inductance of the loop measured 1 μh at 25 mc/sec, requiring only 6 $\mu\mu$f to resonate it at 68 mc/sec. The loop is broken at the middle of the front side for the tuning capacitor. A coil is placed in parallel with the tuning capacitor and the loop to reduce the inductance of the loop and to give an impedance match for the mixer diodes. The inductance of the coil and loop combination is about 0.5 μh, permitting a greater minimum tuning capacitance. The mixer diodes are connected to balanced taps at intermediate impedance points on the coil to insure maximum power transfer.

Figure 18.7 shows the schematic diagram of the local oscillator, mixer, and first two intermediate frequency amplifiers. A Type

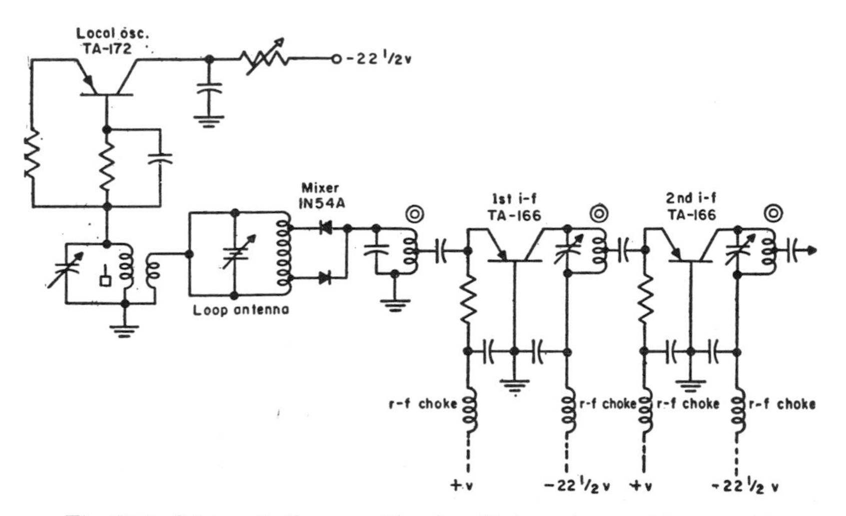

Fig. 18.7. Schematic diagram of local oscillator, mixer, and first two i-f amplifiers.

TA-172 point-contact transistor developed for high-frequency oscillators is used for the local oscillator. A signal of 60 mc/sec is generated by a suitable oscillator circuit for mixing with the 67.25 mc/sec carrier of channel four. A two-turn pickup coil is wound over the oscillator tank to couple the local oscillator signal to the midpoint of the loop. The signal across this pickup coil is 1 v.

The mixer employs two 1N54A crystal diodes in a balanced circuit. The input to the first intermediate frequency amplifier has a tapped coil for impedance matching. The inductance of this coil is 50 μh. Ferrite toroids are used for the coils in all the tuned intermediate frequency stages to reduce stray magnetic fields and to minimize shielding problems. The high coupling coefficients obtainable make possible large impedance transformation ratios. The mixer circuit has a gain of -6 db or a two-to-one loss of signal voltage with 1 ma total diode mixer current.

Stagger tuning is employed for the intermediate frequency amplifiers. Type TA-166 point-contact transistors are connected in grounded-base circuits in the intermediate frequency amplifier stages. Tapped coils match the collector of one stage to the emitter of the following stage. A $22\frac{1}{2}$ v battery supplies the collector voltage for the

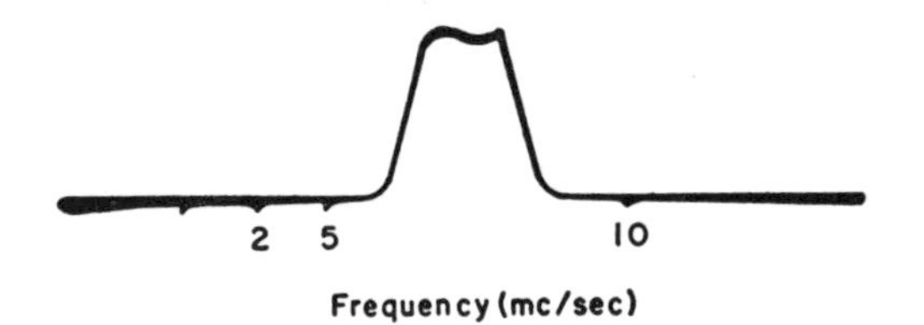

Fig. 18.8. Frequency response of the i-f amplifiers.

whole receiver, but individual *LC* filters provide decoupling for each collector circuit. Since Type TA-166 transistors are short-circuit stable, it was unnecessary to keep the collector circuit impedance high outside of the pass band. A penlight cell supplies the emitter bias, which is fixed at about 1 ma. The six stages and the second detector give an over-all power gain of 47 db for the pass band displayed in Fig. 18.8. The characteristic rises between 6.5 and 7.5 mc/sec, and is flat between 7.5 and 9.5 mc/sec.

A transistor was used for the second detector rather than a crystal detector. When a crystal detector was employed, an extremely low rectification efficiency resulted because of the relatively low input impedance of the video amplifier. Also, since the crystal rectifier worked into an a-c load resistance which was equal to or less than the d-c load, there was severe negative peak clipping.

The last intermediate frequency transformer has two windings and is double tuned. The secondary is tapped to match the emitter of the point-contact Type TA-166 transistor detector. This transistor has no emitter bias; the low side of the secondary is grounded. The emitter and base of the transistor serve as a crystal rectifier, and the rectified signal is amplified by the current gain, alpha, of the transistor. The collector load impedance was made small so as not to affect adversely the frequency response of the video amplifier.

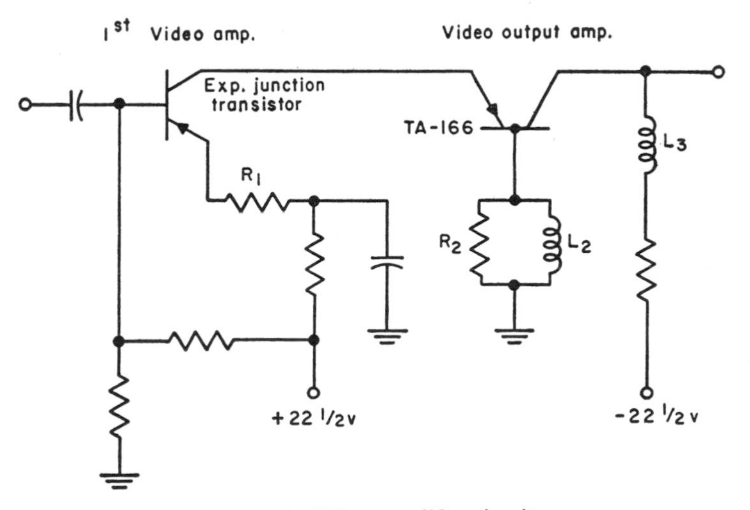

Fig. 18.9. Video amplifier circuit.

Figure 18.9 shows the circuit of the video amplifier. The first video amplifier stage employs a junction transistor in a grounded-emitter circuit to give a fairly large input impedance. A Type TA-166 point-contact transistor is used in the video output amplifier to give the required high-frequency response.

The amplifier has a low-frequency voltage gain of 20. The frequency response of the video amplifier is displayed in Fig. 18.10. The response of the amplifier without equalization is shown in (a). The response indicated in (b) results when video peaking coil L_3 is placed in the collector circuit of the point-contact transistor. In (c) is illustrated additional equalization given by the degenerative feedback resistor R_1 in the emitter circuit of the junction transistor. As shown in (d), R_2 and L_2 can provide positive feedback in the base of the point-contact transistor, since the junction transistor has a high output impedance. When a low-Q series circuit resonant at 1 mc/sec by-passes R_1, the result is as indicated in (e). The input signal generator in the above figures has a source impedance of 1000 ohms.

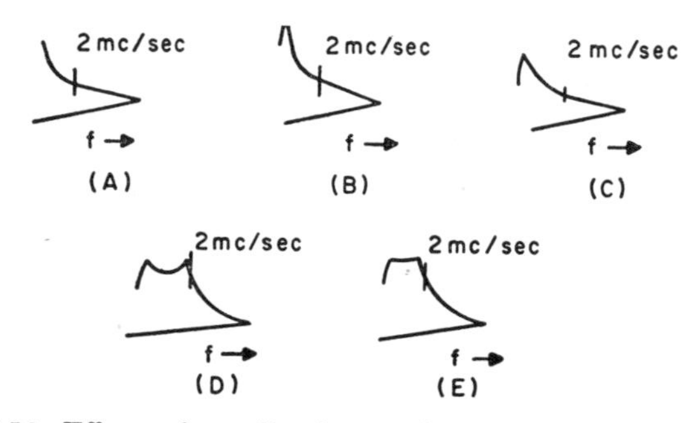

Fig. 18.10. Effects of equalization on the frequency response of the video amplifier.

For good frequency response and limited power dissipation it was necessary to restrict the voltage swing of the point-contact transistor in the output stage. Since prior measurements had shown that an 8 v peak-to-peak swing in the output was sufficient for good picture contrast, the bias was adjusted for this amount with the 2700 ohm load resistance. Later all this allowable swing was utilized for the actual picture signal, and thus the sync pulses were lost in driving the amplifier into the saturation region.

It was essential to have a separate sync amplifier because of the above sync elimination. Another second detector was provided to prevent excessive loading of the first second detector by this additional amplifier. To take less of the available signal power, a lower impedance tap is placed on the driving transformer to feed the extra detector, which is similar to the video detector.

The video detector circuit has a sound take-off trap which provides the intercarrier sound signal. Four stages tuned to the intercarrier frequency, 4.5 mc/sec, amplify the signal. The first three stages are peaked at 4.5 mc/sec, but are otherwise like the picture amplifier stages. The fourth stage feeds a standard ratio detector transformer which is modified for a lower source impedance. The demodulator has 120 kc peak separation and provides about 1 v of audio output.

The audio system is of unusual design. An emitter follower stage drives a complementary symmetry push-pull output circuit employing a P-N-P transistor and an N-P-N transistor.

The following is a description of the vertical deflection system. The vertical yoke has an equivalent circuit consisting of a 65 ohm resistance in series with a 45 μh inductance. The proposed picture height is three inches, requiring a three-inch beam deflection and a peak-to-

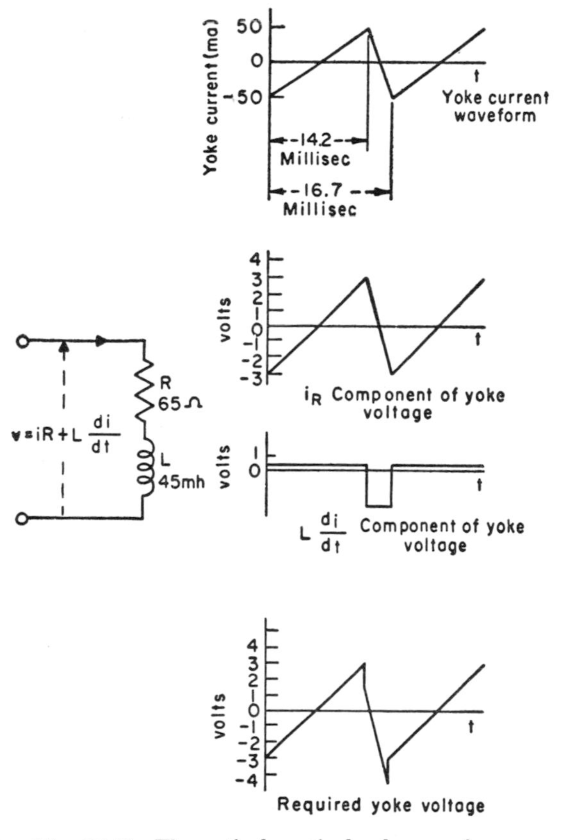

Fig. 18.11. Theoretical vertical yoke waveforms.

peak current of 100 ma. The ideal waveforms necessary to obtain linear deflection are shown in Fig. 18.11.

Figure 18.12 gives the simplified circuit of a synchronized relaxation oscillator employing a TA-165 point-contact transistor and generating the waveform to energize the yoke. The applied voltage gives the base of the transistor a negative potential equal to the product of the leakage current across the collector rectifying contact, and the base resistor R_3.

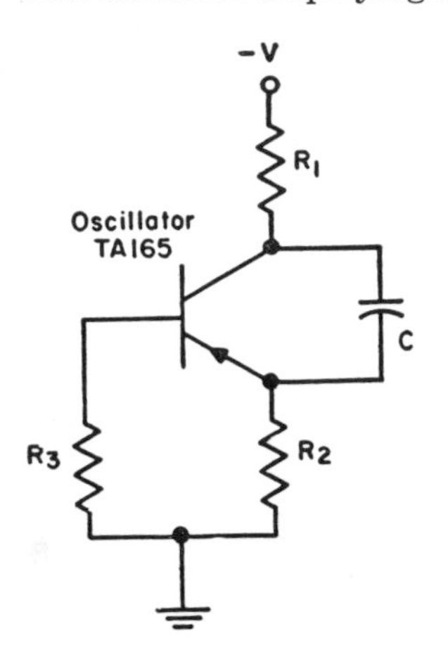

Fig. 18.12. Vertical oscillator schematic diagram.

Because of the current which flows through R_2 to charge capacitor C, the emitter voltage is also negative. There is negligible conduction through the emitter-collector path of the transistor as long as the emitter is more negative than the base. As the capacitor charges, the leakage current rises, and the charging current through R_2 decreases exponentially. Finally the emitter becomes positive with respect to the base. Then the capacitor starts to discharge through the emitter-collector path. Since the transistor has a current gain, alpha, greater than one, the base current increases more rapidly than the emitter current, and the action builds up until the capacitor is discharged. Then the cycle repeats.

Fig. 18.13. Waveforms of (A) vertical oscillator output, and (B) vertical yoke voltage.

Positive pulses are applied to the emitter at a rate somewhat faster than the free running rate for synchronization. Figure 18.13(A) illustrates the voltage waveform across R_1. By changing the ratio of the collector resistance to the emitter resistance, the ratio of the sawtooth to the pulse may be varied.

To couple the oscillator to a transistor amplifier without distortion of the generated waveform, two conditions must be met. First, the amplifier must have negligible loading effect on the oscillator. Second, a current instead of a voltage source must feed the amplifier. The first is due to the reactive output impedance of the oscillator. In addition to attenuating the output, any oscillator loading also distorts the waveform. The nonlinear input impedance of the transistor amplifier imposes the second condition. Although equal increments of base current generate equal increments of collector current, the former do not correspond to equal increments of base voltage. Figure 18.14

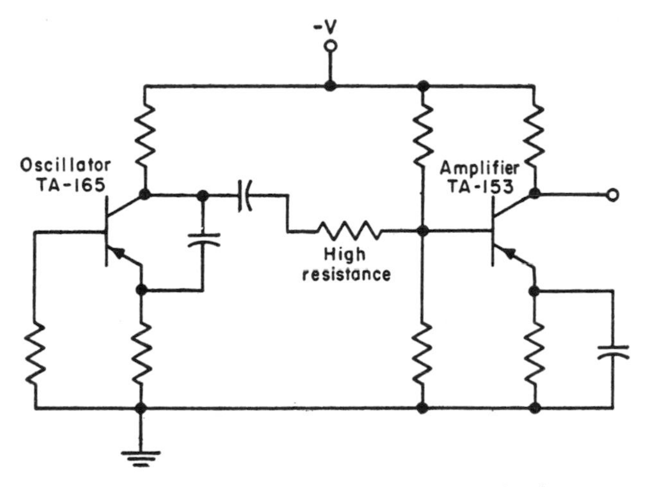

Fig. 18.14. Vertical oscillator coupling circuit.

shows how high-resistance coupling is used to meet the two conditions. Loading of the oscillator is prevented, and a constant current source is provided by this resistance.

The circuit of the three-stage vertical amplifier is given in Fig. 18.15. The first stage has a TA-153 junction transistor in a grounded-emitter, stabilized class A amplifier. The second or driver stage consists of a grounded-collector power-junction transistor having the low impedance to drive the output stage. Resistor R_1 and capacitor C_1 provide frequency-selective feedback, which compensates for distortion caused by the first two stages. For the output stage a P-N-P and N-P-N transistor are used in a grounded-collector, complemen-

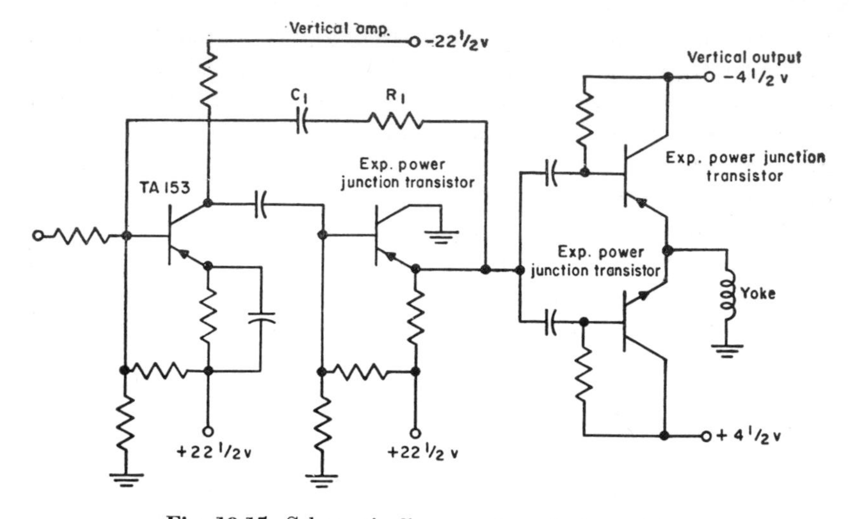

Fig. 18.15. Schematic diagram of vertical amplifier.

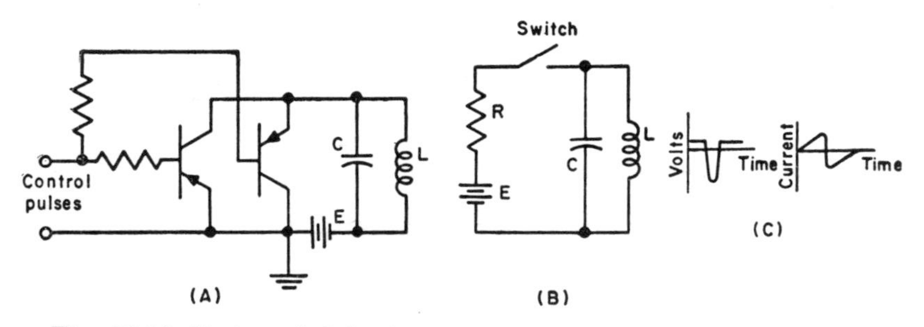

Fig. 18.16. Horizontal deflection design equations: (A) actual circuit; (B) equivalent circuit; (C) yoke wave forms.

(D) Design Equations

$$E = \frac{E_{T\max}}{1 + \frac{\pi(1-\delta)}{2\delta}} \qquad L = \left(\frac{K(1-\delta)E}{Df_R}\right)^2$$

$$I_{pp} = \frac{f_R D^2}{K^2 E(1-\delta)} \qquad \sqrt{LC} = \frac{\delta}{\pi f_R}$$

Where $E_{T\max}$ is maximum voltage across the transistors; δ is ratio of retrace time to the time for one complete cycle; K is a measurable constant depending on yoke construction and anode voltage; E is battery voltage in volts; D is deflection width in inches; f_R is line repetition rate in cps; I_{pp} is peak-to-peak deflection current in amperes; C is capacitance of yoke in farads; and L is inductance of yoke in henries.

tary symmetry push-pull amplifier. With this amplifier the vertical yoke may be directly coupled to the output without causing any decentering current. A class A efficiency of 24 per cent was achieved with this circuit; this compares favorably with the 33 per cent maximum theoretical value for a sawtooth wave. Figure 18.13(B) shows the voltage waveform across the yoke.

The horizontal deflection system will now be described. The principle of operation of the system is that linear bidirectional currents may be caused to flow in an inductive yoke, if a source of energy is periodically connected and disconnected by a fast switch. The circuits, design equations, and yoke waveforms for such a system are shown in Fig. 18.16.

When the transistor is applied as a switching element, there results a simple and efficient circuit which closely resembles an ideal switch. Instead of a single symmetrical transistor, two power-junction transistors are employed with their emitters and collectors cross-connected

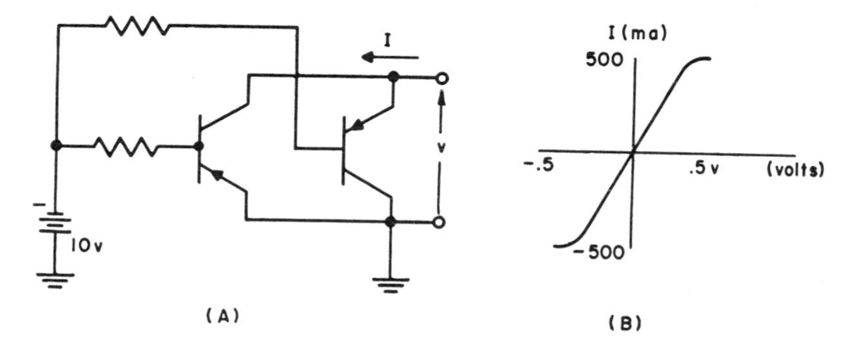

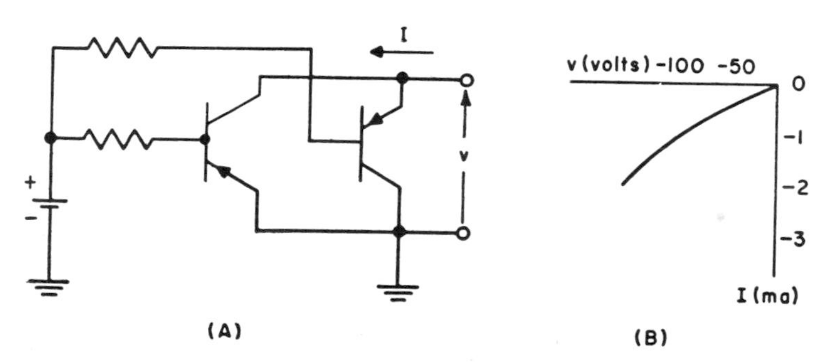

Fig. 18.17. Output characteristics of switching transistors.

as shown in Fig. 18.17(A). Figure 18.17(B) displays the output characteristics of these transistors for the "closed" and "open" conditions. The low effective resistance and the symmetry of the "closed" condition, and the high effective resistance of the "open" condition are to be noted.

To control the output transistors, their bases must be returned to a negative potential when they are conducting, and to a positive potential when they are cut off. A switching circuit to accomplish this is given in Fig. 18.18. This configuration, which uses two transistors,

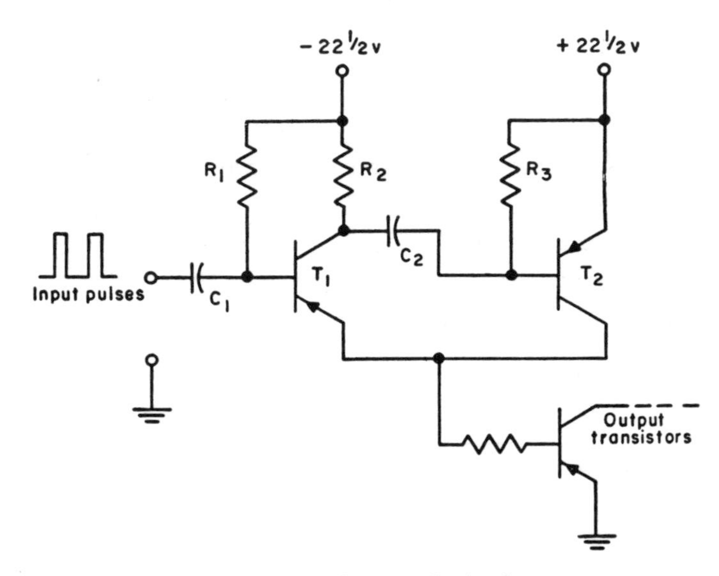

Fig. 18.18. Totem pole circuit.

is in essence a single-pole double-throw switch, and is known as the "totem pole" circuit. During the forward trace of the beam, transistor T_1 conducts heavily because of the large negative bias applied through R_1, while transistor T_2 is cut off. Hence T_1 connects the bases of the output transistors to the negative $22\frac{1}{2}$ v supply. When T_1 receives a positive pulse through C_1, then T_1 is cut off and a negative pulse appears across R_2. Capacitor C_2 couples this negative pulse to T_2, placing T_2 in a highly conducting state. During the positive pulse, T_2 connects the bases of the output transistors to the positive $22\frac{1}{2}$ v supply.

For operation of the horizontal deflection system, pulses, occurring at the line repetition rate and equal in width to the retrace time, are required. These pulses are generated by an oscillator similar to that for vertical deflection, except for the circuit elements which determine the frequency. Figure 18.19 shows the direct-coupled, complementary symmetry class B amplifier which is used to enlarge these pulses. With no input pulse, the output terminal is connected through R_1 to the negative $22\frac{1}{2}$ v supply, since both transistors are practically cut off. When a positive pulse is applied to the input, both transistors conduct heavily, and the P-N-P transistor connects the out-

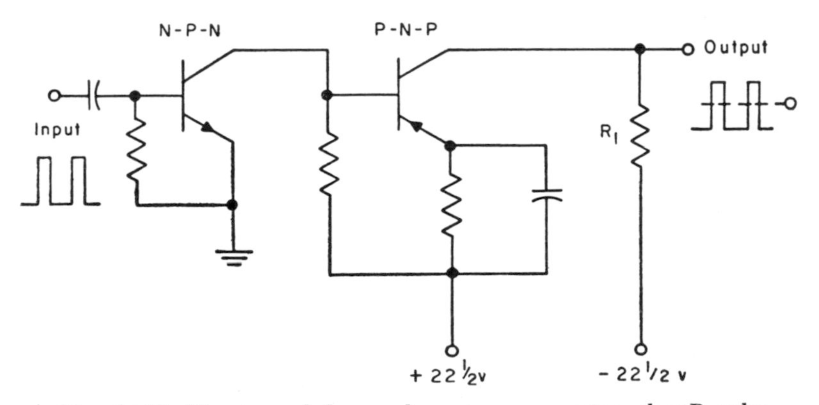

Fig. 18.19. Direct-coupled, complementary symmetry, class-B pulse amplifier.

put terminal to the positive $22\frac{1}{2}$ v battery. With this circuit, output pulses of about 40 v peak-to-peak are obtained from an input of 0.5 v peak-to-peak.

For the switching transistors available, driven sync was impractical because of the appreciable time delay between the application of a positive pulse and the "opening" of the yoke circuit. This delay is caused by the reactive effects of the input circuit of the switching transistors, and is approximately 15 μsec, or about 5 μsec longer than the time of the horizontal retrace of the video signal. It is possible to compensate for this delay by rephasing the horizontal oscillator with an automatic frequency control system such as that described in a later section.

Figures 18.20, 18.21, and 18.22 illustrate the waveforms observed at various points in the horizontal deflection system. Those of the yoke voltage and current are especially interesting because of their

Fig. 18.20. Waveforms of (A) horizontal oscillator output, and (B) input to totem pole circuit.

similarity to the theoretical waveforms previously shown in Fig. 18.16.

Figure 18.23 gives the schematic diagram of the synchronizing circuits. Two TA-153 junction transistors function as the sync separa-

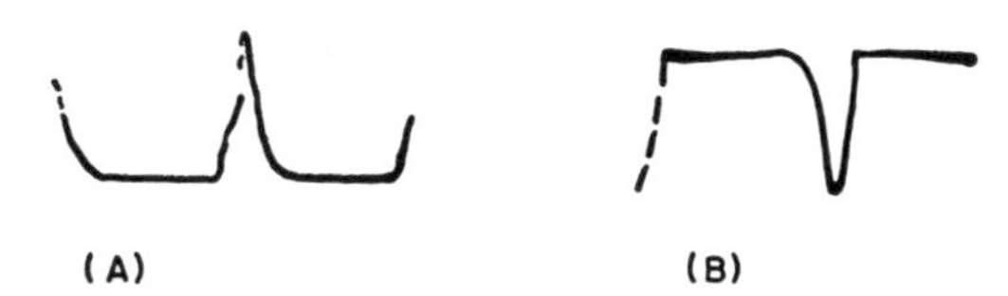

Fig. 18.21. Waveforms of (A) output to totem pole circuit, and (B) yoke voltage.

tor and amplifier. The sync separator operates in a grounded-base circuit. The emitter-base rectifier separates the sync pulses, which the collector circuit couples to the following amplifier. After the vertical pulses are integrated, another grounded-emitter stage amplifies them, and then they synchronize the vertical oscillator.

Fig. 18.22. Waveform of horizontal yoke current.

The symmetrical properties of the phase comparator transistor are utilized for the horizontal automatic frequency control system previously mentioned. The network R_1 and C_1 integrate the retrace voltage pulse from the deflection yoke. Without a negative sync pulse applied to its base, the phase comparator merely acts as a high resistance, and the integrated retrace pulse is a symmetrical sawtooth wave, since C_2 removes its d-c component. Therefore the base of the frequency-controlled transistor has no direct voltage. If the horizontal sync pulse arrives at the same time as the zero voltage of the sawtooth retrace, the operation is unchanged. Should the sync pulse occur while the retrace voltage is positive, the resulting low resistance of the phase comparator charges C_2. Capacitor C_2 discharges through resistor R_4 and the frequency-controlled transistor. This applies a small negative bias to the base of the frequency-controlled transistor,

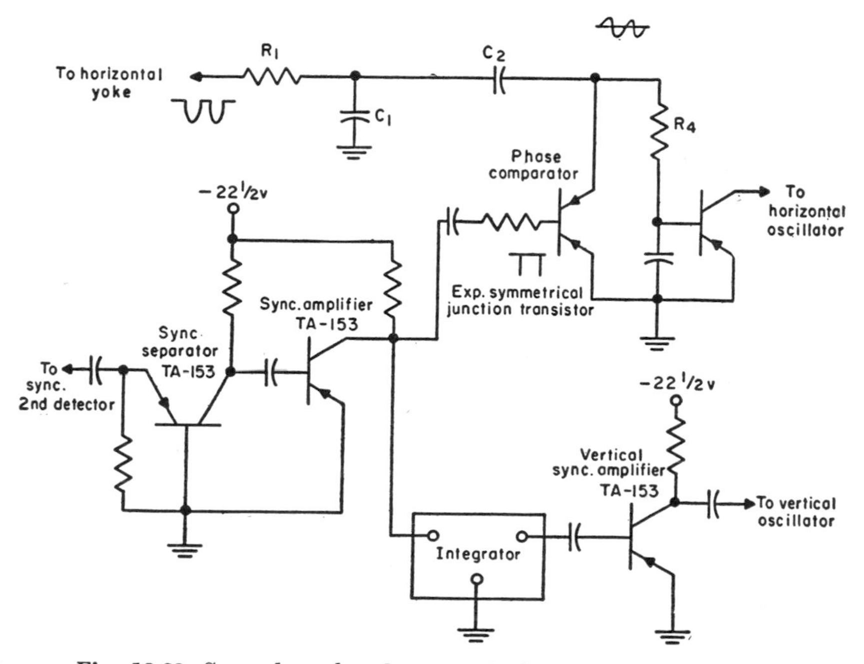

Fig. 18.23. Sync channel and automatic frequency-control circuits.

lowering its effective resistance and causing the horizontal oscillator to fire earlier than on the preceding cycle. The process goes on until the sync pulse coincides with the zero voltage point of the sawtooth retrace. If the sync pulse arrives when the sawtooth retrace is negative, the operation is reversed.

The 2000 v direct current for the kinescope is not readily obtainable from the deflection system, because the transistors limit the flyback voltage of the horizontal deflection system, and because no transformer is used. Hence a separate system, as shown in Fig. 18.24, was developed. A two-stage class B amplifier drives a tuned output transformer. The negative flyback pulse lightly drives the amplifier, causes the first transistor to conduct, and thus applies a conduction bias to the output stage. The output power transistor supplies energy at the horizontal frequency to the tuned transformer. The base circuit choke of the output transistor gives a low-resistance d-c path, and prevents any leakage current in either transistor from biasing the output to conduction except when a pulse arrives. The alternating current from the secondary of the tuned transformer is converted to pulsating direct current by a half-wave selenium rectifier, and filtered by a capacitor to supply the 2000 v direct current for the kinescope.

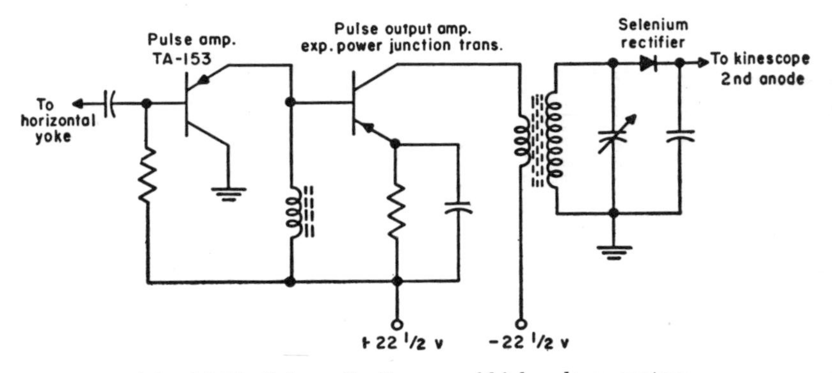

Fig. 18.24. Schematic diagram of high-voltage system.

The television receiver is portable with self-contained batteries. It consumes 13 w total power. The filament of the kinescope requires 3.6 w, or over 25 per cent. The 5FP4 kinescope gives a 3 by 4 in. picture with about 10 foot lamberts of highlight brightness. The signal channel is located on a vertical plastic shelf in the center of the receiver. The deflection chassis is mounted under the neck and socket of the kinescope. To provide the least disturbance to the rest of the receiver, the high-voltage supply is placed on the far side of the batteries. The receiver complete with batteries weighs 27 pounds.

The reception range of the receiver with the built-in loop was about five miles from WNBT. A simple dipole antenna held about 7 ft from the ground gave satisfactory reception for about 15 miles from the Empire State Building. The receiver has a sensitivity of approximately 5 mv/m. Since this sensitivity is not limited by noise, additional stages or available improved transistors could increase it considerably.

References

1. Robert K. Dixon, "Build This Transistor Receiver," *Radio and Television News*, Vol. XLIX, No. 2, Feb. 1953, pp. 35–37.

2. Emerick Toth, "Application of Transistors to Radio Receiver Circuitry," *NRL Report 4049*, Naval Research Laboratory, Washington, D. C., May 21, 1952, pp. 18–25.

3. R. C. Ballard, "A Portable Transistor FM-Receiver," *Tele-Tech and Electronic Industries*, Vol. XII, No. 8, Aug. 1953, p. 79.

4. G. C. Sziklai, R. D. Lohman, and G. B. Herzog, "A Study of Transistor Circuits for Television," *Proc. IRE*, Vol. XLI, No. 6, June 1953, pp. 717–724.

Chapter 19

TRANSISTOR RELAXATION OSCILLATORS

1. *Multivibrators*

Relaxation oscillation will occur if we connect the parallel combination of a resistor and a capacitor between the emitter and ground of a point-contact transistor utilizing base feedback. Figure 19.1 in-

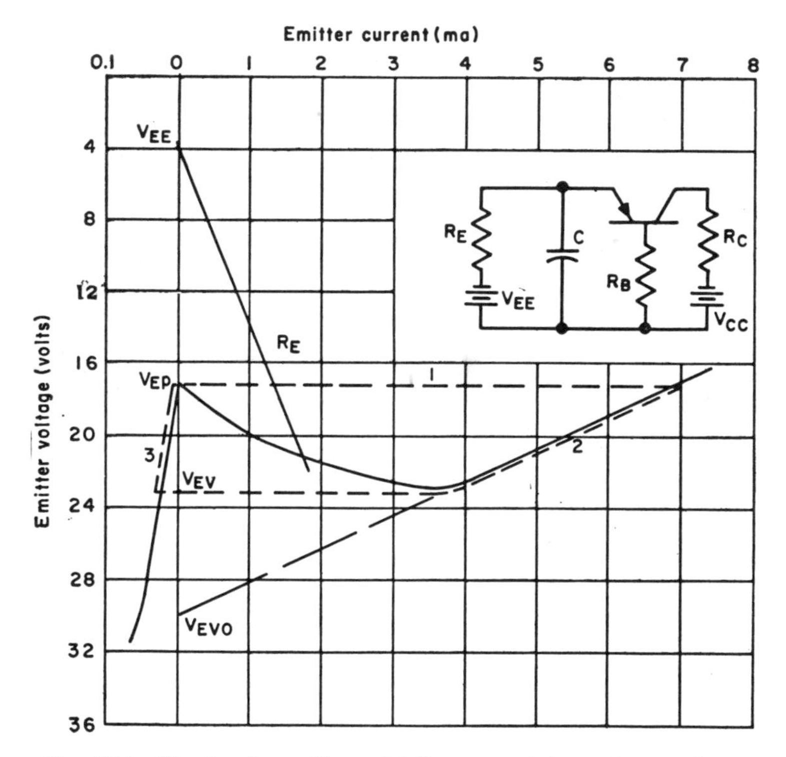

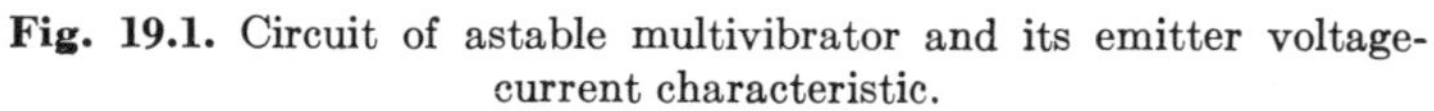

Fig. 19.1. Circuit of astable multivibrator and its emitter voltage-current characteristic.

dicates this kind of a circuit and its emitter voltage-current characteristic.[1] For the astable mode, the emitter load resistor R_E has a value such that the load line intersects the negative-resistance section of the characteristic. The transistor would ordinarily have a stable operating point. However, the capacitor C practically short-circuits R_E, and the operating point follows path 1, 2, and 3. Hence C alternately charges and discharges between potentials V_{EP} and V_{EV}. The capacitor discharges through a comparatively high emitter-input resistance in parallel with R_E when the operating point lies in a negative

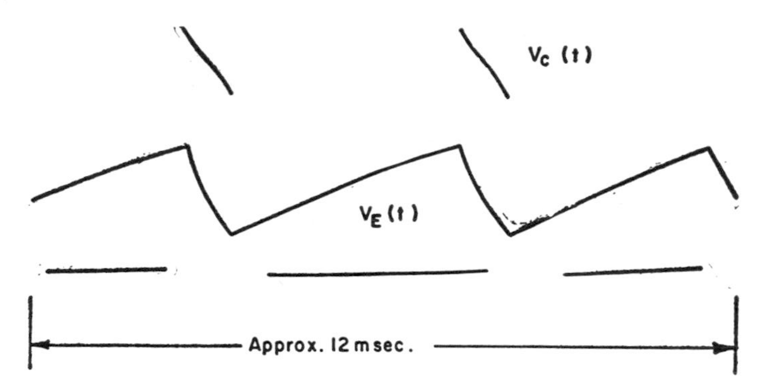

Fig. 19.2. Emitter voltage $V_E(t)$ superimposed on collector voltage $V_C(t)$.

low-current section. Capacitor C charges through R_E in shunt with a relatively low emitter-input resistance when the operating point occurs in the positive high-current area. The collector output consists of rectangular pulses. Collector-pulse duration occurs during high emitter-current operation, whereas the "dead time" between collector pulses is at low emitter current.

For a typical multivibrator utilizing a Type A-1698 point-contact transistor the waveforms of emitter and collector voltages are given in Fig. 19.2.

The quiescent time between collector pulses, or the time of operation in the low-current area, is

$$t_L = \frac{1}{\beta_L} \ln \frac{V_{EV}(R_E + R_{IN_L}) - (V_{EP}R_E + V_{EE}R_{IN_L})}{V_{EP}(R_E + R_{IN_L}) - (V_{EP}R_E + V_{EE}R_{IN_L})} \tag{1}$$

where $\beta_L = (R_E + R_{IN_L})/R_E R_{IN_L} C$.

The collector pulse duration, or the time in the high-current section is

$$t_H = \frac{1}{\beta_H} \ln \frac{V_{EP}(R_E + R_{IN_H}) - (V_{EVO}R_E + V_{EE}R_{IN_H})}{V_{EV}(R_E + R_{IN_H}) - (V_{EVO}R_E + V_{EE}R_{IN_H})} \qquad (2)$$

where $\beta_H = (R_E + R_{IN_H})/R_E R_{IN_H} C$.

The sum of t_L and t_H is the reciprocal of the repetition rate.

The above equations were verified experimentally by plotting the static $V_E - I_E$ characteristic as shown in Fig. 19.1. A negative resistance was produced by the circuit in this figure with $R_C = 2200$ ohms, $R_B = 6800$ ohms, $V_{CC} = -45$ v, and $V_{EE} = 0$ v. The emitter negative-resistance parameters found from this characteristic were $R_{IN_H} = 1820$ ohms, $R_{IN_L} = 240{,}000$ ohms, $V_{EV} = -23.0$ v, $V_{EVO} = -30.1$ v, and $V_{EP} = -16.8$ v.

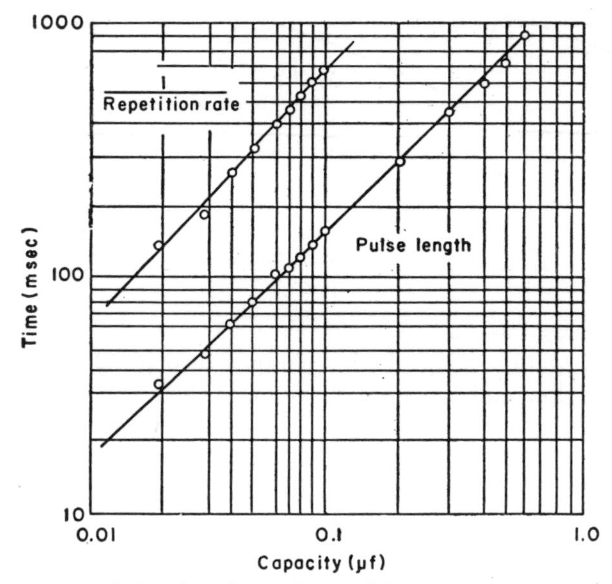

Fig. 19.3. Pulse duration and repetition rate versus capacity.

Figure 19.3 shows the variation of the calculated and measured collector pulse lengths and reciprocals of the repetition rates with capacitance. The circles indicate the measured values to about 5 per cent deviation. These curves show that the above formulas give accurate values for the pulse duration and repetition rate over an extensive range.

A free-running pulse generator utilizing a Type PT-2S point-contact transistor[2] is illustrated in Fig. 19.4. The pulse width and pulse frequency are adjustable. The value of the capacitor C determines the pulse width, whereas the 5000 ohm variable emitter resistor establishes the pulse frequency. The values shown in this circuit give a pulse width of 0.5 μsec, and a pulse frequency of about 500 kc/sec with the variable resistor set at approximately 2500 ohms.

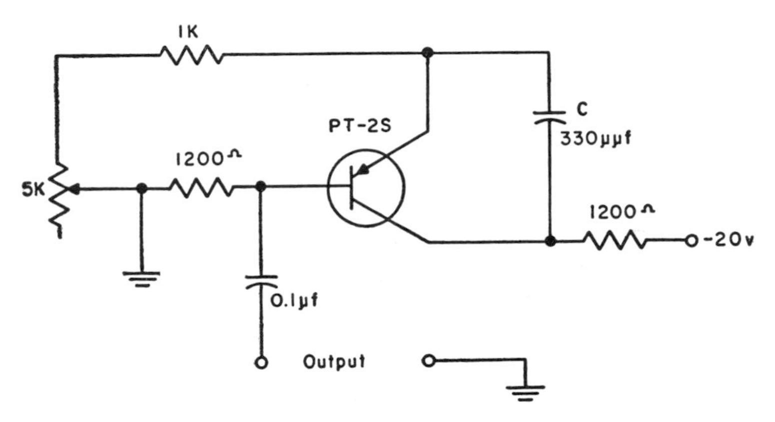

Fig. 19.4. Free-running pulse generator employing a PT-2S point-contact transistor. *Courtesy of Bendix Radio, Division of Bendix Aviation Corp.*

Pulse widths longer than 0.5 μsec may be obtained by employing a capacitor C larger than 330 $\mu\mu$f. An output pulse of about 5 v is obtained across the 1200 ohm base resistance through the 0.01 μf capacitor. This circuit requires only one 20-v battery supply.

A free-running emitter-coupled multivibrator[3] employing N-P-N junction transistors is diagrammed in Fig. 19.5. It operates as an approximate square wave generator, whose repetition rate we can adjust by changing the value of capacitor C_1.

We can explain the operation with the aid of Fig. 19.6, which represents the base-to-ground voltage of transistor T_2 versus time. This discussion neglects base-to-emitter potential differences when a transistor is turned on in its active region in which this circuit is intended to operate. The multivibrator changes its state when the base-to-ground potential of T_2 arrives at a value of E_1 for T_2 off and T_1 on, or a value of $E_1(R_3 + R_4)/R_4$ for T_1 off and T_2 on. This reasoning is not affected by capacitor C_2, a small peaking capacitance. We can make the "off" periods of T_1 and T_2 equal to one time constant of the exponential waveform on the base of T_2 by selecting the proper circuit parameters. The output "square wave" should then have minimum fractional time jitter. If we neglect the effects of the collector output impedance of T_1 and the base input impedance of T_2, these time con-

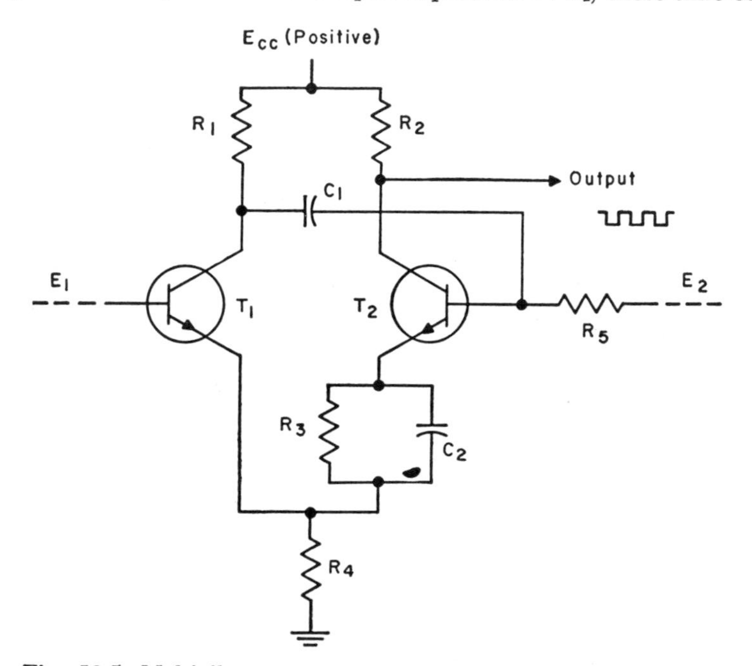

Fig. 19.5. Multivibrator square-wave generator employing N-P-N junction transistors.

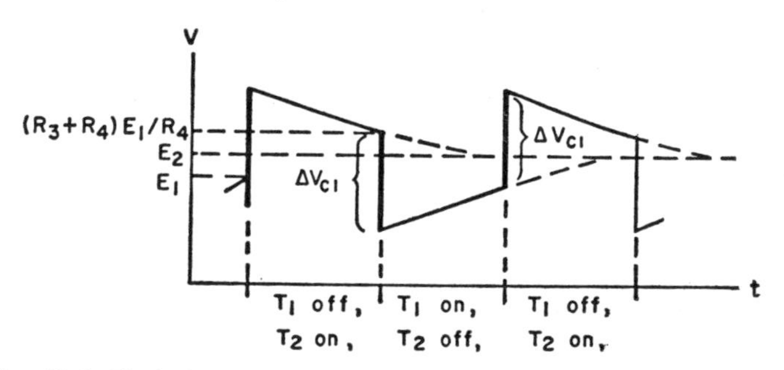

Fig. 19.6. Variation of base-to-ground voltage of transistor T_2 with time.

stants approximately equal $C_1(R_1 + R_5)$, and the repetition period of the output is theoretically about $2C_1(R_1 + R_5)$.

Assuming that the current gain α_1 of T_1 is constant and that the base input impedance of T_2 may be neglected, the relationships between the circuit constants can be given by

$$E_2 = E_1 + \frac{\Delta V_{c1}}{1 + \epsilon} \tag{3}$$

$$R_3 = \frac{2R_4\,\Delta V_{c1}}{E_1(1 + \epsilon)} \tag{4}$$

$$\frac{R_1R_5}{R_1 + R_5} = \frac{R_4\,\Delta V_{c1}}{\alpha_1 E_1} \tag{5}$$

where the jump in collector voltage of T_1,

$$\Delta V_{c1} \approx \alpha_1 \left(\frac{E_1}{R_4}\right)\left(\frac{R_1R_5}{R_1 + R_5}\right) \tag{6}$$

and $\epsilon = 2.718$.

For an experimental circuit the assumed values were $E_1 = 7.5$ v, $R_4 = 5600$ ohms, $\Delta V_{c1} = 7.5$ v, and $\alpha_1 = 0.95$ for Type 201 transistors. Utilizing Eqs. (3), (4), (5), and (6), the remaining circuit parameters were determined as $R_3 = 3000$ ohms, $R_1 = R_5 = 12{,}000$ ohms, $R_2 = 2200$ ohms, $E_2 = 9.5$ v, and $E_{cc} = 20$ v. The values of R_2 and E_{cc} were selected such that T_1 and T_2 operate in their active areas when they are turned on. Voltages E_1 and E_2 were conveniently obtained from a low-impedance voltage divider connected between E_{cc} and ground. The bleeder resistances from E_{cc} to ground were 2400 ohms, 470 ohms, and 1800 ohms, respectively. These resistors supplied open-circuit values of $E_1 = 7.7$ v and $E_2 = 9.7$ v. All resistors had 1 per cent tolerances.

For low-frequency operation, values of $C_1 = 1.0$ μf (actually 1.1 μf) and $C_2 = 0$ were selected. The corresponding theoretical repetition period of the output is 0.053 sec. The measured output period for 14 transistors was 0.033 sec ± 11 per cent with a duty cycle of 0.54 ± 8 per cent. Reducing the impedance of the voltage divider supplying E_1 and E_2 to one-fifth of its original value increased the ratio of measured to theoretical repetition periods from 62 per cent to 72 per cent with no change in duty cycle. Theoretically, the supply voltage E_{cc} should not affect the repetition period or duty cycle of the output. The measured variation of these quantities with E_{cc} for an average pair of transistors is given in Table 7.

For higher-frequency oscillation a value of $C_1 = 0.001$ μf (actually 0.00104 μf) was selected. Experiment showed that C_2 should be about 500 μμf to give the output the best shape without affecting its period.

TABLE 7. VARIATION OF REPETITION PERIOD AND DUTY CYCLE WITH SUPPLY VOLTAGE E_{cc}

E_{cc}, volts	Repetition period, sec	Duty cycle
5	0.017	0.53
10	0.027	0.54
15	0.031	0.55
20	0.033	0.56
25	0.034	0.55

The output now has a theoretical repetition period of 50 μsec. The measured output period for the same 14 transistors was 40 μsec ± 20 per cent with a duty cycle of 0.58 ± 7 per cent. The increase of the average ratio of measured to theoretical periods of the output and the greater variation of the measured period compared with the low-frequency values was caused by the low alpha cutoff frequencies of some of the transistors. The range of alpha cutoff frequencies was from 0.2 to 1.4 megacycles.

2. *Blocking oscillators*

Since the transistor has a much lower input impedance than output impedance, it would seem that we could design a transistor pulse generator employing an impedance-changing transformer to couple the output back to the input. Experiment has shown that almost any transistor will operate in a blocking oscillator.[4] It is easy to generate rectangular pulses with duration periods of less than 1 μsec and rise times as short as 0.01 μsec in 20 v pulses. Pulse repetition frequencies from low audio frequencies up to 2 megacycles may be achieved. Circuit analysis indicates that a transistor with a current gain of less than unity can give the desired negative resistance for oscillation. Therefore a junction transistor could be utilized.

Figure 19.7 shows the circuit and typical waveforms of a blocking oscillator employing an AN2891 point-contact transistor. For a free-running oscillator, emitter resistor R should be returned to a positive voltage as shown, so that it supplies the emitter with a constant current of approximately 1 ma. For circuit operation by trigger pulses, we normally return R to a negative voltage.

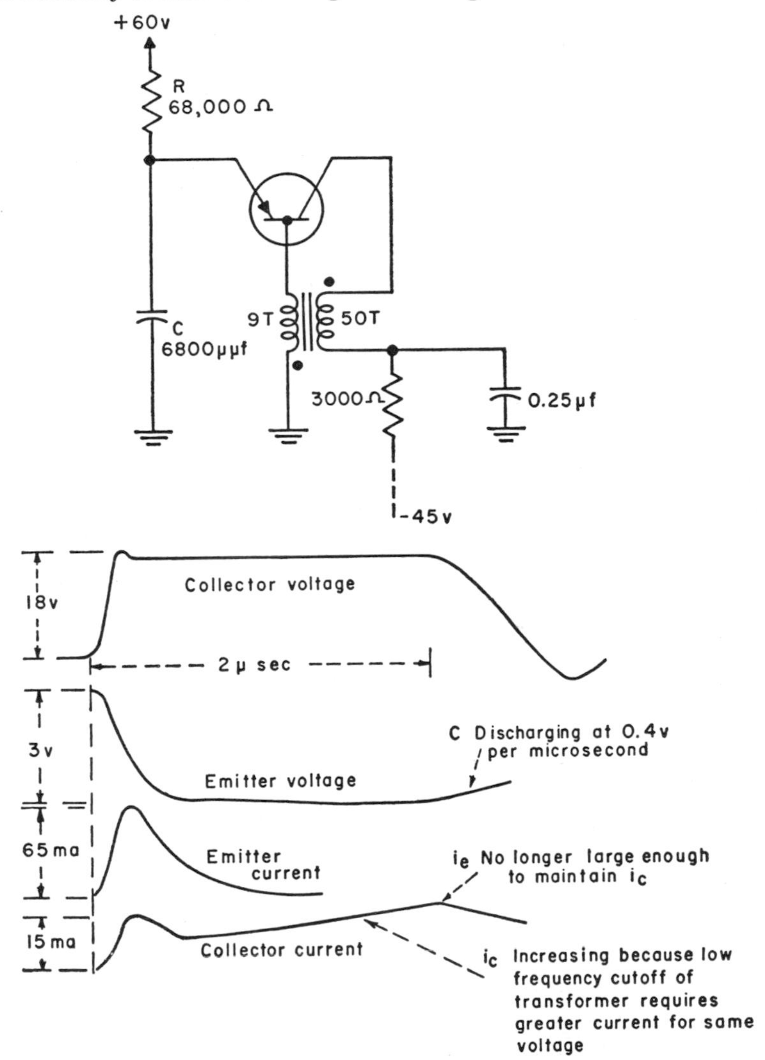

Fig. 19.7. Circuit and typical waveforms of a blocking oscillator utilizing an AN2891 point-contact transistor.

This circuit functions much like its vacuum tube equivalent. During conduction, the collector voltage is low, the pulse transformer keeps the base negative, and the emitter current charges the emitter capacitor negative almost to the value of the base voltage. During cutoff, the collector voltage is negative, the base potential is zero, and the emitter is held at a negative potential by the charge left in C.

For a more thorough explanation we may assume that the emitter capacitor has a negative charge and is now discharging through R toward the positive emitter supply voltage. The collector current is cut off until this capacitor rises to ground potential. Then emitter current starts with the release of holes to the collector. The collector current raises the collector potential, and the inverting transformer action decreases the base potential, increasing the emitter current. Depending on the individual transistor, in from one one-hundredth to several tenths of a microsecond, the emitter current increases from zero to a high current. Currently available transistors have less than 0.1 μsec rise times.

Throughout the rise time the emitter current charges C negatively, but the emitter current decreases because the emitter becomes less positive with reference to the base. While the emitter current declines, the transformer low-frequency cutoff or time constant causes the collector current, which maintains the negative pulse at the base, to increase. When the emitter current is no longer adequate to release the holes for the required collector current, the base voltage increases toward ground, causing a further decrease in emitter current, and the transistor regeneratively cuts itself off. Capacitor C is left charged negatively and the cycle repeats itself.

Capacitor C and the current supplied through R determine the recurrence rate. The transformer and C largely fix the pulse duration; the transistor has a minor effect.

Figure 19.8 is a test circuit developing a trigger pulse ahead of a main pulse which could be seen on an oscilloscope. Transistor No. 1 is a free-running blocking oscillator whose output is differentiated, delayed 0.15 μsec, and triggers transistor No. 2.

The free-running circuit with a Type AN2891 transistor has a 1.5 μsec pulse duration, a 0.15 μsec rise time, a 30 v collector pulse amplitude, and generates a 10 v signal across 560 ohms in the transformer tertiary. The negative tail occurring at the end of the pulse when the transformer is not fully loaded is clipped by the 400A crystal connected across the collector winding.

When 36 good transistors were tried in the second circuit, 9 had rise times of 0.03 μsec or less. The average pulse duration was 0.8 μsec with a standard deviation of less than 0.1 μsec.

Figure 19.9(A) shows the circuit of a transistor blocking oscillator employed to develop steep wave fronts. The collector voltage waveform is shown in Fig. 19.9(B). The collector output pulse when C is returned to the collector instead of ground is sketched in Fig. 19.9(C). The collector pulse is flattened but the fall time is increased by this circuit change.

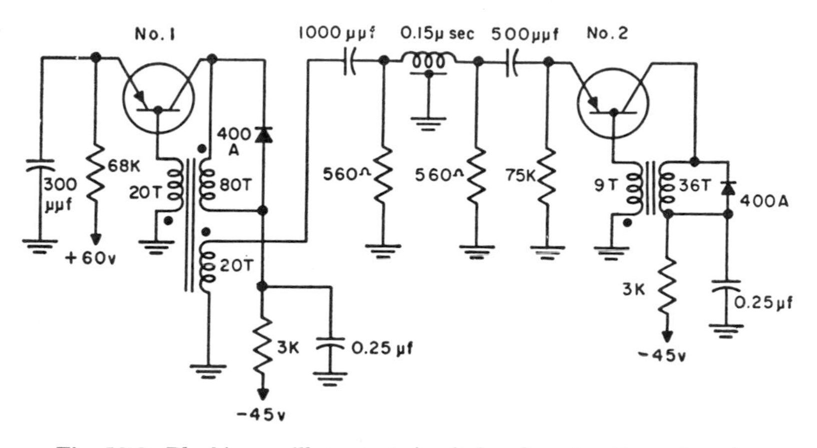

Fig. 19.8. Blocking oscillator test circuit for observing the main pulse.

These waveforms show that the transistor can generate pulse energy over a wide video band. It is possible that the transistor's low lead inductance and small shunt capacitances may make it a better generator of rapid pulses than the vacuum tube, even though the transistor has a limited linear amplifier bandwidth.

The circuit performance can be predicted in advance. Two types of transformer cores were tested for pulses of 0.5 to 2 μsec duration. A rectangular core of 4-79 Molybdenum Permalloy had a cross-sectional area of $\frac{1}{16}$ sq in. and over-all dimensions of 1 by $1\frac{1}{8}$ in. The other core was a $\frac{3}{4}$ in. ferrite ring with a cross sectional area of $\frac{9}{256}$ sq in. Although 0.01 μsec rise time was achieved with some transistors, it is possible that better transformers might have given even smaller rise times.

Good results were obtained with all transistors for a turns ratio of about five to one. Some units would not work with lower ratios.

A transformer consisting of the 4-79 Molybdenum Permalloy core, 3 turns for the base winding, and 16 turns for the collector winding, and a 430 $\mu\mu$f capacitor gave a $\frac{1}{3}$ μsec pulse. A 2200 $\mu\mu$f capacitor and a transformer having the same core, 9 turns for the base winding, and 50 turns for the collector winding produced a 1.5 μsec pulse. It is important to realize that the transistor may be burned out if C is made so large that an excessive emitter current is needed to charge it to the base potential.

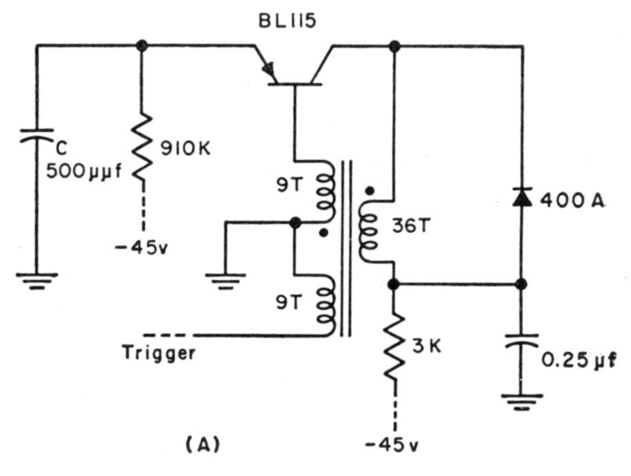

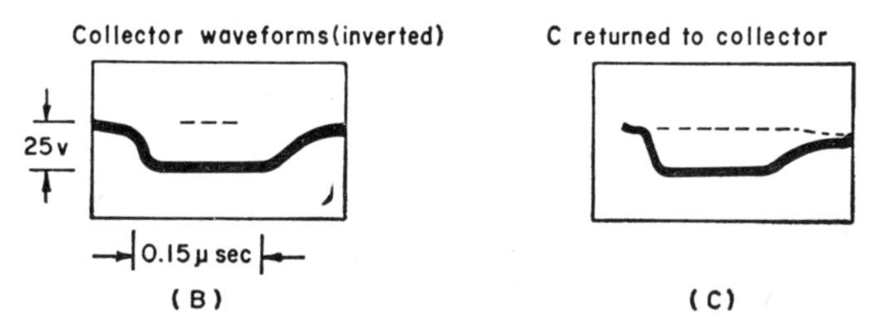

Fig. 19.9. (A) Blocking oscillator circuit generating steep wave fronts. (B) Collector voltage waveform. (C) Collector waveform with C returned to collector.

The emitter should be supplied with a constant current for predictable operation. This may be accomplished by returning the emitter resistor R to a large positive voltage E_e. If ΔE_e is the swing in emitter voltage during the pulse, the recurrence rate is

$$f_r = \frac{1}{RC\ \Delta E_e/E_e + \tau} \tag{7}$$

where τ is the pulse duration. The accuracy of this equation was found to be as good as oscilloscope readings. The emitter swing equals the base excursion, and is therefore approximately $\Delta E_c/N$, where ΔE_c is the collector swing and N is the transformer turns ratio. The swing in collector voltage nearly equals the battery voltage and is stable if N is 3 or larger and the collector winding is returned to a battery of E_c v. Hence the recurrence rate is approximately

$$f_r \approx \frac{1}{(E_c/E_e)(RC/N) + \tau} \tag{8}$$

Where a stable frequency is required, E_c should be supplied by a constant-voltage source instead of a series resistor. A circuit was designed by the above equation for a 14.5 μsec period. When 6 switching transistors were tested in this circuit, the measured periods were 14, 12, 12.5, 12.5, 12.5, and 14 μsec.

If a triggered oscillator is desired, the emitter should be returned to a negative voltage. The trigger is normally applied through an auxiliary transformer winding to obtain an output pulse. Rapid triggering rates may be produced with a 1200 ohm emitter resistor returned to -1.5 v. For small values of R and emitter capacitor C, the low-frequency cutoff of the transformer affects both the maximum triggering rate and the pulse duration.

3. *Gate, one-shot, or monostable circuits*

Figure 19.10 is the circuit of a one-shot emitter-coupled multivibrator[3] utilizing type 201 N-P-N junction transistors. The operation is similar to that of its vacuum tube counterpart. With no input trigger, transistor T_2 conducts because of the positive return of its base resistor R_b. Transistor T_1 is cut off by the voltage from its biasing network composed of resistors R_1 and R_2, which bias its base properly negative with reference to the common emitter voltage established by the conduction of T_2. A negative pulse coupled to the collector of T_1 by an isolating crystal diode can trigger the circuit. Triggering causes a rapid regeneration which turns T_2 off and T_1 on. Transistor T_2 remains off until capacitor C discharges enough to bring the base of T_2 to approximately the common emitter potential now established by the conduction of T_1. On reaching this point regeneration again occurs, restoring the circuit to its initial state, and hence completing a gate.

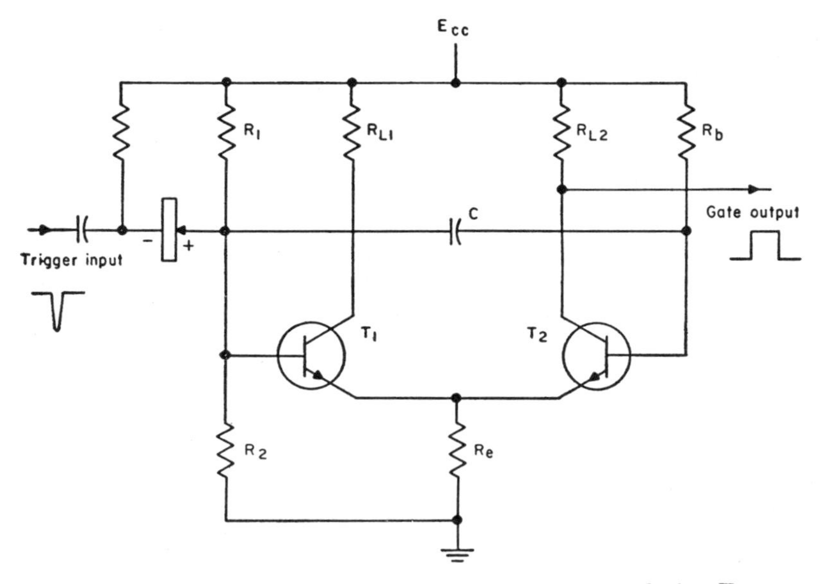

Fig. 19.10. One-shot emitter-coupled multivibrator employing Type 201 N-P-N junction transistors.

Assuming that T_1 is in its active region, its current gain α_1 is constant, impedances R_1 and R_2 are small enough to hold the base-to-ground potential of T_1 at $R_2E_{cc}/(R_1 + R_2)$, and the base-to-emitter voltage drop in T_1 is negligible, it can be shown that the gate width T is approximately

$$T \approx CR_b \log \left[\frac{1 + R_2/R_1}{1 + R_2/R_{L2}} + \left(\frac{R_2}{R_1}\right)\left(\frac{R_{L1}}{R_e}\right) \right] \qquad (9)$$

where $R_b \gg R_{L1}$, R_{L2}, and $\alpha_1 \approx 1$.

Resistor R_b has a maximum permissible value which places the initial operation of T_2 in its saturated region. Larger values of R_b move the operating point of T_2 to its active region. This would prevent rapid recovery after the gate because capacitor C should discharge through the comparatively low base-to-emitter impedance of T_2 in the saturated region. It can be shown that the maximum value of R_b is

$$(R_b)_{max} = \frac{R_{L2}(\alpha_2 E_{cc} + I_{co}R_e)}{(1 - \alpha_2)E_{cc} - I_{co}(R_e + R_{L2})} \tag{10}$$

where α_2 is the current gain of T_2, and I_{co} is the collector current of T_2 for zero emitter current. If $I_{co} \ll (1 - \alpha_2)E_{cc}/(R_e + R_{L2})$ then

$$(R_b)_{max} \approx \frac{\alpha_2 R_{L2}}{1 - \alpha_2} \tag{11}$$

Hence large values of α_2 or I_{co} permit high values of R_b. However, I_{co} must be kept small to prevent reducing the gate width T below the value of Eq. (9). The gate width should not depend upon I_{co} because I_{co} changes with different temperatures and transistors.

However, it is not desirable to make R_b much smaller than $(R_b)_{max}$. The comparatively smaller ratio of time constants for charging capacitor C during and after the gate will cause longer recovery time and gate width. The increased minority-carrier storage in a more heavily saturated T_2 will produce a slower rise time of the collector waveform of T_2.

For an experimental check of the theory the circuit values were $R_{L1} = 3300$ ohms, $R_{L2} = 2200$ ohms, $R_b = 33{,}000$ ohms, $R_e = 2200$ ohms, $R_1 = 3300$ ohms, $R_2 = 2200$ ohms, $E_{cc} = 15$ v, and $C = 0.1$ μf (actually 0.106 μf). For the Type 201 junction transistors, $\alpha > 0.95$ and $I_{co} < 10$ μa at room temperature. Equation (11) gives a value of 42,000 ohms for $(R_b)_{max}$, indicating that the above value of 33,000 ohms may be employed. Equation (9) gives the theoretical value of gate width T as 2100 μsec, whereas the exact equation gives 1800 μsec. These values compare with the measured gate width of about 1460 μsec $\pm$ 10 per cent for 14 different transistors in the circuit. This 20 per cent difference between the theoretical value of gate width from the exact equation and the measured value is caused by two factors. First, the change in the collector voltage of T_1 was about 15 per cent lower than the theoretical value, mainly because an average value should be employed for α_1, which varies with collector current and voltage. Second, the derivation of Eq. (9) neglected the several tenths of a volt between base and emitter of T_1 when T_1 is conducting.

The collector supply voltage E_{cc} should not affect the gate width T according to Eq. (9). The experimental variation with E_{cc} for a pair of average transistors was 1270, 1470, 1550, and 1600 μsec for E_{cc} voltages of 5, 10, 15, and 20 v, respectively.

When C was reduced from 0.1 μf to 0.005 μf (actually 0.0046 μf), the theoretical gate width from the exact equation became 80 μsec. The agreement between the theoretical and measured gate widths was essentially the same as before.

4. *Trigger, flip-flop, or bistable circuits*

Transistors have a number of advantages for trigger action.[5] They have low input and output capacitances of about 1 to 2 μμf. These in connection with a low emitter impedance give small RC time constants with the possibility of fast rise times and high repetition rates. In actual practice, the hole transit time from emitter to collector normally determines the transistor's high-frequency limit instead of the RC time constants. Other advantages are small physical size, low operating voltages, and no need for stand-by power. Point-contact transistors give a current gain larger than unity, and therefore a single unit will permit bistable operation.

Figure 19.11 is a basic single-unit trigger circuit. Figure 19.12 is the

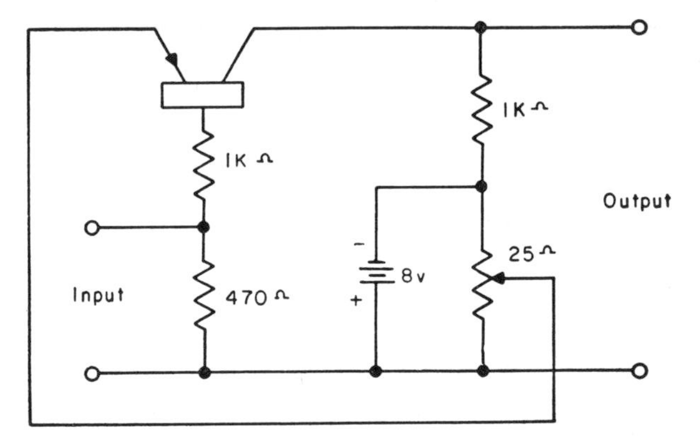

Fig. 19.11. Basic negative-resistance trigger circuit utilizing a point-contact transistor.

equivalent T network obtained by conventional circuit theory. If V_1 is the voltage applied to mesh 1, and V_2 is the potential applied to mesh 2, then R_{11} is the ratio of a change in V_1 to a change in I_1, R_{12} is the ratio of a change in V_1 to a change in I_2, R_{21} is the ratio of a change in V_2 to a change in I_1, and R_{22} is the ratio of a change in V_2 to a change in I_2.

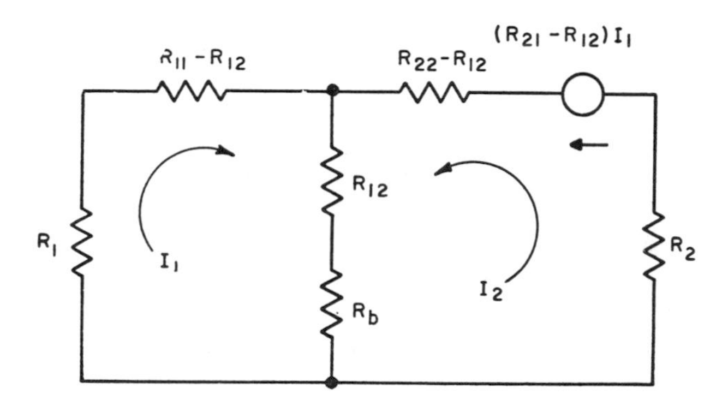

Fig. 19.12. Equivalent T network for the circuit of Fig. 19.11.

The condition for instability and therefore triggering is

$$(R_{11} + R_b + R_1)(R_{22} + R_b + R_2) < (R_{21} + R_b)(R_{12} + R_b) \quad (12)$$

Trigger action can occur anywhere within the possible operating range if this inequality is satisfied. This relationship shows that R_1 and R_2 work to stabilize the circuit, and that making $R_1 = R_2 = 0$ will aid triggering. However, practically, this mode of operation cannot be employed because of the current ratings of the transistor. For small values of R_1 and R_2 and a large R_b, inequality (12) becomes approximately

$$\frac{R_{21}}{R_{22}} = \alpha_{ce} > 1$$

because R_{22} and R_{21} are much larger than R_{11} and R_{12}. This indicates that a current gain larger than unity is required for triggering.

Inequality (12) also indicates that the insertion of resistance into the collector circuit should have little effect on circuit stability unless such resistance is comparable to R_{22}, or about 20,000 to 60,000 ohms. However, this reasoning does not hold true in actual practice because transistor characteristics are nonlinear. The effective collector-to-base voltage falls rapidly when current starts to flow through R_2 and the current gain decreases below unity. Collector-circuit resistances of about 1000 ohms raise the valley of the negative resistance characteristic as shown in Fig. 19.13. This difficulty is most troublesome in low-voltage circuits. Figure 19.14 gives a circuit which was devised

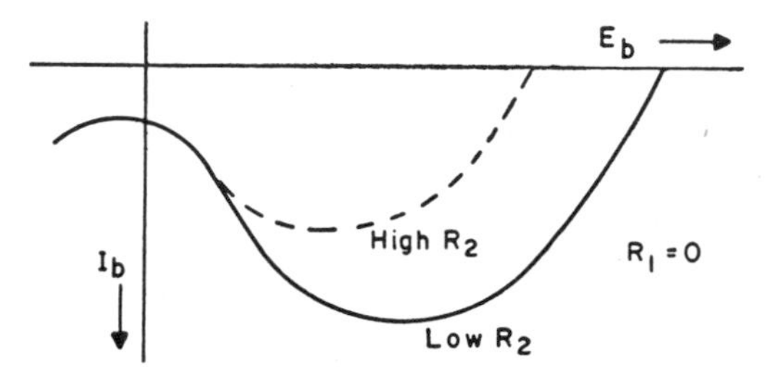

Fig. 19.13. Effect of collector-circuit resistance on negative resistance characteristic.

for supply voltages less than 10 v. Assuming the polarities defined in Fig. 19.12, a current equal to the sum of the emitter and collector currents flows through the 2000 ohm resistor, which consequently acts as a base resistance R_b. Out of ten transistors tested, nine units triggered reliably without changing the circuit components other than the bias adjustment. The circuit was tested for frequencies from direct current to 1 megacycle with a 6 v collector battery. An output voltage of 2 v with rise and fall times of about 0.1 μsec were achieved. We can apply trigger pulses either between emitter and base, as repre-

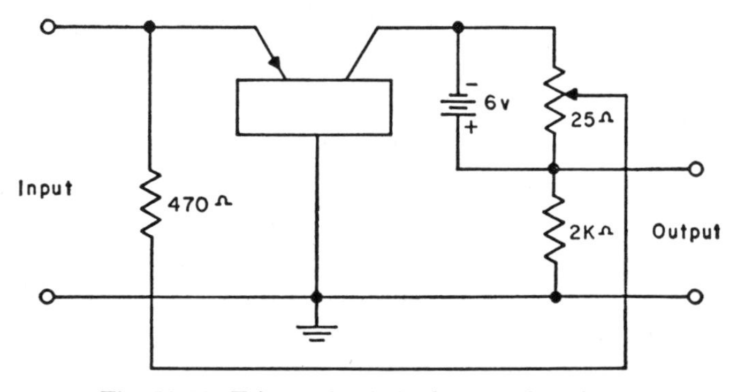

Fig. 19.14. Trigger circuit for low supply voltage.

sented in Fig. 19.14, or across the 2000 ohm base resistor. The replacement of the emitter-circuit resistance with a capacitor changes the device into a monostable circuit.

The circuit shown in Fig. 19.14 has the disadvantage of requiring trigger pulses of alternating polarity. One way of overcoming this is to introduce positive pulses alternately at the emitter and the base. A diode biased by a voltage from the proper point in the circuit can accomplish this commutation of pulses. Figure 19.15 is a successful circuit of this type. It gives a square-wave output of 30 v peak-to-peak amplitude for frequencies up to 600 kc/sec with reasonably good

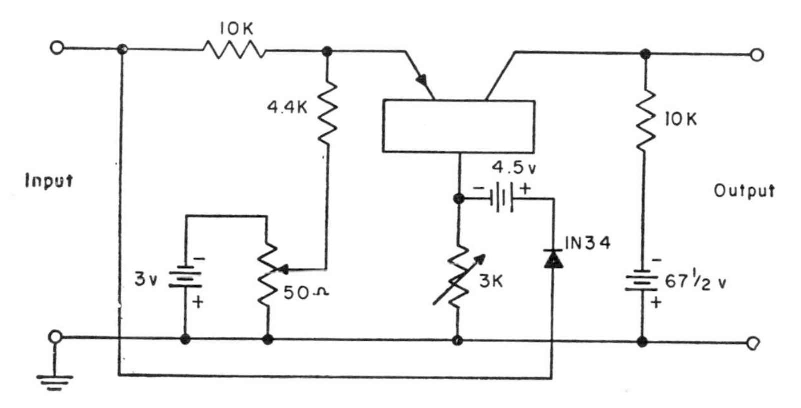

Fig. 19.15. Trigger circuit operating from single-polarity pulses.

wave shape up to 400 kc/sec. The wide range of collector current variation required to produce a base-voltage swing large enough to cut off the diode is probably the cause of the comparatively low upper frequency limit. Experiment demonstrates that the rise time increases with the output voltage.

Figure 19.16 illustrates a symmetrical flip-flop[3] employing Type 2N34 P-N-P junction transistors. This circuit bears a striking resemblance to the well-known Eccles-Jordan flip-flop vacuum tube circuit. The operation is also quite similar to that of its vacuum tube counterpart. The circuit has two stable states, transistor T_1 on and transistor T_2 off, and vice versa. The cross-coupling capacitors C_1 and the emitter by-pass capacitor C_e permit triggering from one state to the other.

We can make a helpful d-c analysis if we make several simplifying assumptions. If identical ideal junction transistors are assumed, then $\alpha = 1$, base current $= 0$, and base-to-emitter voltage $= 0$, when the transistors are turned on in their active regions. Likewise, all currents are zero when the transistors are turned off. Let I_o be the current in the "on" transistor, V_o the collector swing between "on" and "off"

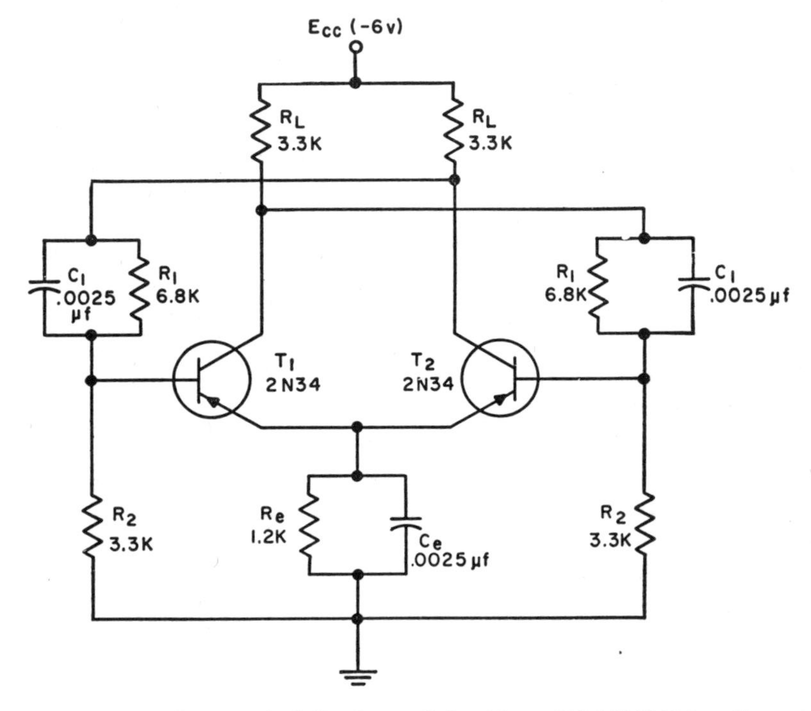

Fig. 19.16. Symmetrical flip-flop utilizing Type 2N34 P-N-P junction transistors.

states, V_b the base-to-emitter bias on the "off" transistor, and V_c the collector-to-emitter voltage of the "on" transistor. Then we can write the following equations:

$$I_o = \frac{R_2 E_{cc}}{R_e(R_L + R_1 + R_2)} \tag{13}$$

$$V_o = \frac{I_o R_L (R_1 + R_2)}{R_L + R_1 + R_2} \tag{14}$$

$$V_b = \frac{R_2 V_o}{R_1 + R_2} \tag{15}$$

$$V_c = \frac{(R_1 + R_2)E_{cc}}{R_L + R_1 + R_2} - I_o R_e - V_o \tag{16}$$

Expressions for the resistances, R_L, R_e, R_1, and R_2 in terms of E_{cc}, I_o, V_o, V_b, and V_c may be obtained by solving Eq. (13), (14), (15), and (16) simultaneously giving

$$R_L = \frac{E_{cc}(V_o - V_b)}{I_o(V_o + V_c)} \tag{17}$$

$$R_e = \frac{V_o + V_c}{I_o(V_o/V_b) - 1} \tag{18}$$

$$R_1 = \frac{E_{cc}(V_o - V_b)^2}{I_o[E_{cc}(V_o - V_b) - V_o(V_o + V_c)]} \tag{19}$$

$$R_2 = \frac{V_b E_{cc}(V_o - V_b)}{I_o[E_{cc}(V_o - V_b) - V_o(V_o + V_c)]} \tag{20}$$

The design of the practical circuit shown in Fig. 19.16 is based on the selected values of $E_{cc} = -6$ v, $I_o = 1.2$ ma, $V_o = 3$ v, $V_b = 1$ v, and $V_c = 0$ v. Actually V_c will be larger than zero to insure operation of the "on" transistor in the active region, because the transistors are not ideal. The values for R_L, R_e, R_1, and R_2 were calculated from Eq. (17), (18), (19), and (20), respectively, and then the nearest 5 per cent tolerance RMA values were employed for these resistors. From Eq. (13), (14), (15), and (16) the corresponding theoretical values are $I_o = 1.23$ ma, $V_o = 3.06$ v, $V_b = 1.00$ v, and $V_c = -0.02$ v. Five Type 2N34 and five each of Types RR14H and RR34H P-N-P junction transistors gave measured values of I_o (actually emitter current) = 1.0 to 1.04 ma, $V_o = 2.4$ to 2.7 v, $V_b = 0.5$ to 0.6 v, and $V_c = 0.6$ to 0.9 v. These 15 transistors had measured values of alpha varying from about 0.95 to 0.98 at the rated operating points. The higher alpha units gave the best agreement between the measured and theoretical values. All 15 transistors had low I_{co} and emitter characteristics with a sharp knee within 0.1 v base-to-emitter potential. Hence the actually measured V_b of 0.5 to 0.6 v was more than adequate to cut off the transistors.

Figure 19.17 is a triggering circuit to operate the flip-flop as a binary counter. The crystal diode connected to the base of the "off" transistor has a larger reverse bias than the crystal diode connected to the base of the "on" transistor. Hence the positive input pulse reaches the "on" transistor and begins the cumulative action that finishes in the other stable condition of the flip-flop. The next trigger likewise reaches the new "on" transistor and returns the flip-flop to its original state. The cycle repeats itself and binary-counter operation occurs. It is assumed that proper values have been selected for capacitors C_1 and C_e in Fig. 19.16. For transistors with higher alpha cutoff frequencies, these capacitors may have smaller values. The action of the flip-

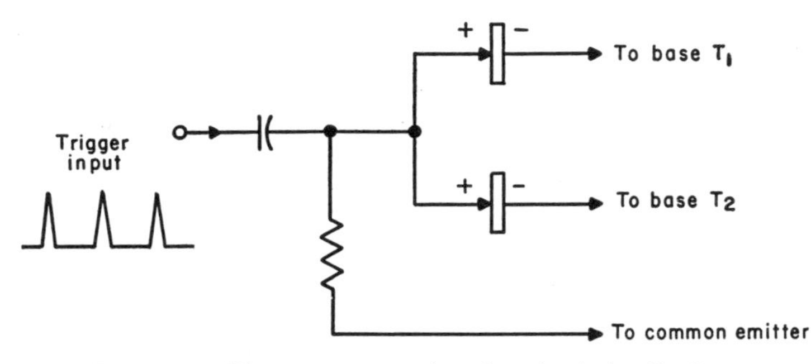

Fig. 19.17. Binary-counter triggering circuit for flip-flop.

flop is slowed by too great values. Values of C_1 and C_e equal to 0.0025 μf gave satisfactory triggering for transistors having alpha cutoff frequencies from 0.4 to 0.9 mc/sec. Trigger repetition rates up to about 100 kc operated the flip-flop connected as a binary counter. A scale of 8 was successfully operated by cascading three identical flip-flop stages, in which the collector waveform of T_2 of the first stage was connected to the input of the second stage, and so on.

References

1. G. E. McDuffie, Jr., "Pulse Duration and Repetition Rate of a Transistor Multivibrator," *Proc. IRE*, Vol. XL, No. 11, Nov. 1952, pp. 1487–1489.

2. *CBS-Hytron Transistor Manual, An Introduction to Transistor Theory, Data, and Applications, Bulletin E 212*, CBS-Hytron, A Division of Columbia Broadcasting System, Inc., Danvers, Mass.

3. Eugene W. Sard, "Junction-Transistor Multivibrators and Flip-Flops," *Convention Record of the IRE*, Vol. II, Part 2—Circuit Theory, 1954, pp. 119–124.

4. J. H. Felker, *A Transistor Blocking Oscillator*, Bell Telephone Labratories, Inc., New York, 1951.

5. Peter M. Schultheiss and Herbert J. Reich, "Some Transistor Trigger Circuits," *Proc. IRE*, Vol. XXXIX, No. 6, June 1951, pp. 627–632.

Chapter 20

COMPUTER APPLICATIONS OF TRANSISTORS

1. *Gating and switching circuits*[1]

Gating and level restoration are needed in numerous logic circuits in computers and switching systems. Normally needed in large quantities are the "threshold-two gates," or circuits where the production of an output signal requires the simultaneous presence of two input signals. The output signal may not be required to reproduce faithfully any input voltage when handling digital information or control signals employing pulse techniques. We may also desire gain or level restoration.

The basic circuit of a regenerative amplifier and its emitter input negative resistance characteristic are represented in Fig. 20.1. The active element is a Type 1698 point-contact transistor which has a current gain factor greater than unity in the positive emitter current region. If we connect an external resistor in series with the base element, we will obtain a negative resistance characteristic in the emitter circuit.

The electrode current flow and current amplification characteristics of the transistor can explain this negative resistance characteristic. The base current equals the algebraic sum of the emitter current and collector current. Because the collector current is negative and greater in magnitude than the emitter current in the positive emitter current region, the base current is normally positive. A positive increase of emitter current causes a larger increase of positive base current, which flows through the external base impedance, making the base more negative with respect to the emitter. This causes a further increase of emitter current, producing an even greater positive base current.

The negative resistance section of the characteristic results from this regenerative action. This process continues until, as controlled by the external circuit constants, the collector current saturates, and the characteristic slope once more becomes positive. Such a characteristic, however, does not have the required d-c stability. We especially desire a stable peak turning point in the neighborhood of zero emitter current.

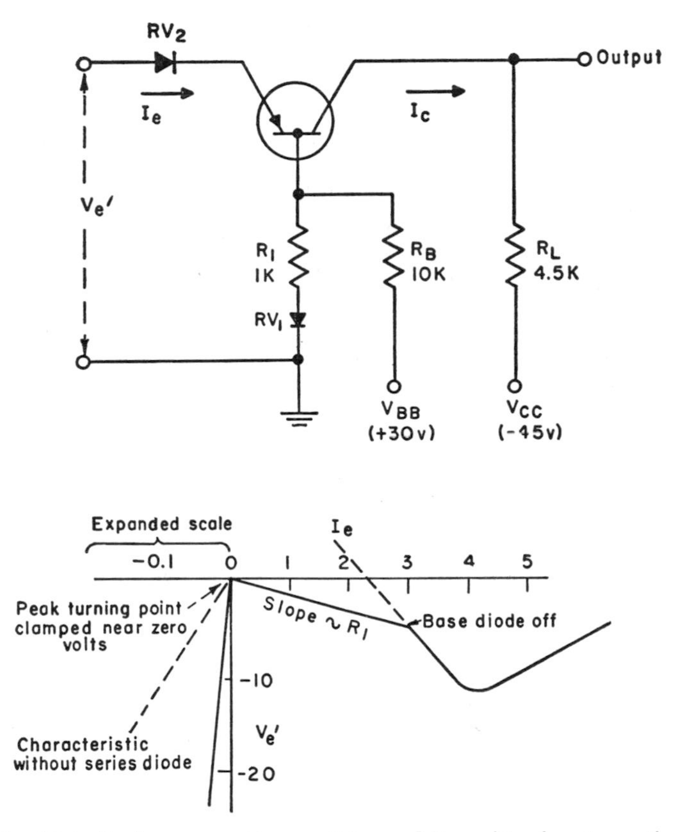

Fig. 20.1. Basic regenerative amplifier and its emitter-input negative-resistance characteristic.

A difficulty in point-contact transistors is that the collector current at a given collector potential and zero emitter current I_{co} may vary from 0.3 ma to 3.0 ma in good units. If a 5000 ohm base resistor is inserted to give negative resistance, the peak turning point may vary from 0.5 v to 15 v.

To eliminate these undesirable d-c variations, a diode RV_1, biased by the positive potential V_{BB} through resistor R_B, is connected in the base circuit. We adjust the biasing current to equal the largest I_{co} which we wish to compensate. When the transistor is turned off, the diode conducts and affords a low impedance to ground. When the transistor starts to conduct we have current gain, and the sum of the emitter and stabilizing currents exactly equals the collector current at some positive emitter current. Here the diode offers a high resistance, and the external base resistance is R_B in parallel with the large reverse resistance of the base diode. This clamps the peak turning point in the emitter input characteristic near to zero volts over a useful range of temperatures and for different acceptable transistors.

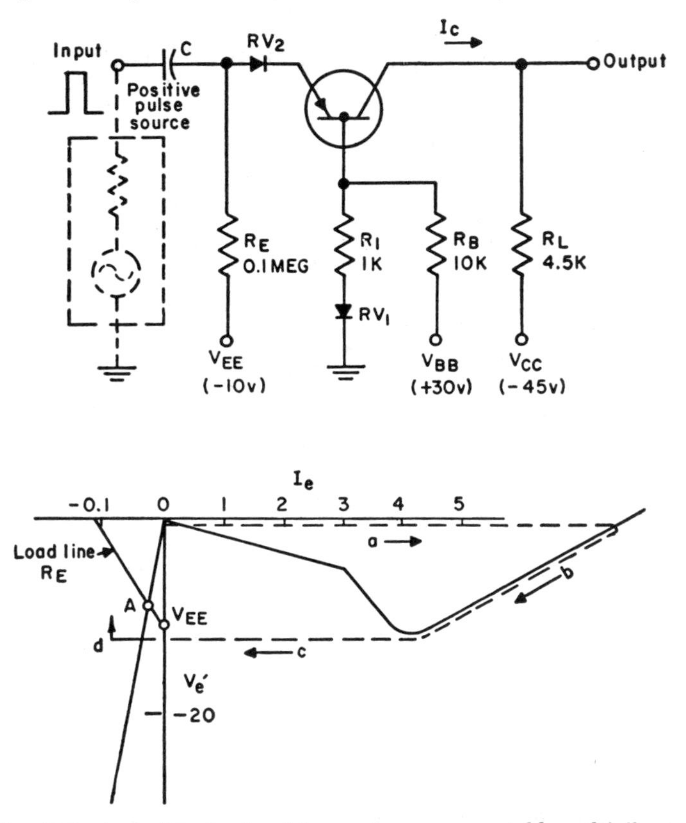

Fig. 20.2. An emitter load resistor produces a monostable multivibrator for pulse regeneration.

To secure a very high resistance in the negative emitter current region and to clamp the characteristic close to the voltage axis, a diode is also inserted in series with the emitter.

A monostable multivibrator for pulse regeneration may be obtained by connecting an emitter load resistance in the circuit as diagrammed in Fig. 20.2. The value of R_E largely determines the slope of the d-c load line. The load line intersects the characteristic only at point A, and therefore the circuit is monostable. Until the circuit is triggered, the triggering source sees a high input impedance of about 100,000 ohms.

The approximate operating path which the device follows is indicated as a-b-c-d in Fig. 20.2, and results in a positive output pulse at the collector. The capacitor C and the driving source impedance Z provide the dynamic load line for paths a and c. The given circuit constants produce a positive output pulse with an amplitude of about 30 v and a duration of 2 to 5 μsec.

To provide "and" gating, employing a step voltage input and a coincident positive pulse, we may connect the basic circuit as indicated in Fig. 20.3. When the step voltage varies between the negative potentials V_1 and V_2, the emitter load line R_E intersects the characteristic at points A and B, respectively.

When the step voltage is V_1 and the intersection of load line and characteristic is d-c stable at A, the input pulse amplitude is adequate to trigger the circuit. However, the triggering pulse amplitude will be inadequate to trigger the circuit and there will be no pulse in the collector circuit, when the step voltage is V_2 and the intersection of load line and characteristic is d-c stable at B.

This gated amplifier has a number of advantages. A high impedance of at least the emitter load resistance R_E is presented to the step voltage input signal source. Hence many of these gated amplifiers may be operated in parallel by the same signal source without loading it adversely. Except during a triggering period, the pulse input source also sees a high impedance. The output pulse in the collector circuit has a sharp positive going pulse wave front, since pulse regeneration takes place. The gated amplifier circuit constants fix the output pulse amplitude, which is independent of the input pulse amplitude. Voltage gains of about 10 to 20 db are achieved.

The operation of "and" gating with two coincident positive pulses may be performed by the modification of the basic circuit and characteristic as represented in Fig. 20.4. A source of negative biasing potential V_{EE} is supplied to the emitter load voltage divider R_1 and R_2.

Fairly rigid timing requirements and amplitude limitations are imposed upon the input pulses. The summed effect of the input pulses applied at terminals X and Y must trigger the amplifier, but the amplitude of the pulses applied at either terminal X or Y alone must be inadequate to trigger the devices.

If the pulse amplitude at X equals that at Y, it can be shown that

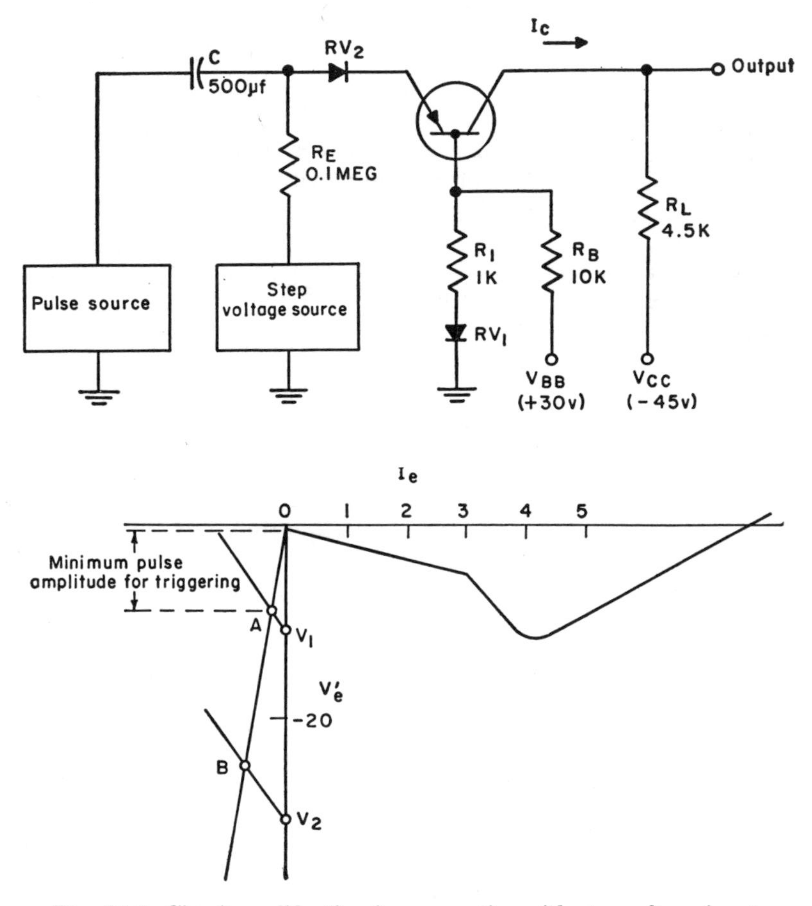

Fig. 20.3. Circuit modification for AND gating with step-voltage input and a coincident positive pulse.

$$V_{EE}\left(\frac{r'_{11} + RV_{2'}}{r'_{11} + RV'_2 + R_1 + R_2}\right) > X = Y > \frac{V_{EE}}{2}\left(\frac{r'_{11} + RV'_2}{r'_{11} + RV'_2 + R_1}\right) \quad (1)$$

where $r_{11'}$ is the slope of the emitter $V_{e'}$-I_e curve in the negative emitter current region, and $RV_{2'}$ is the reverse resistance of the emitter diode. Substituting the values for Fig. 20.4 gives the amplitude limits for pulses at X and Y as

$$17 > X = Y > 9 \quad \text{v peak approximately}$$

Therefore no output pulse will appear if pulses within the above amplitude limits are applied at either X or Y only. However, assuming

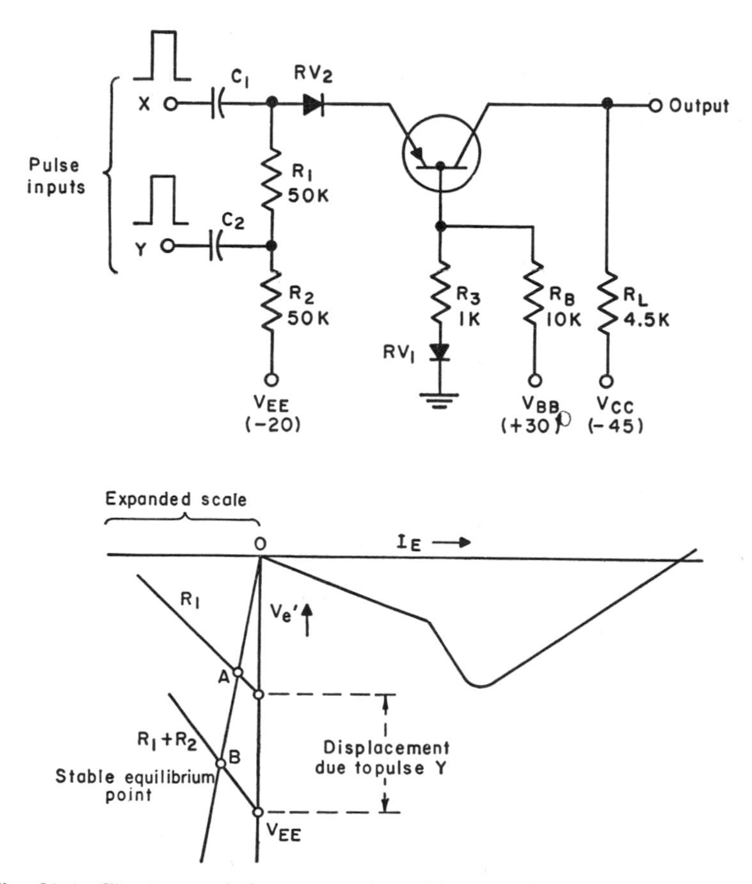

Fig. 20.4. Circuit permitting AND gating with two coincident positive pulses.

that a positive pulse is applied at input Y, the load line will rapidly move along the vertical axis to intersect the characteristic at A. Assuming that R_1 equals R_2, the slope of the load line is halved. If at the same time a positive pulse reaches input X, the amplifier will trigger and the output terminal will receive a pulse.

A gate, with two inputs and an output connected so that when inputs X and Y are applied at the same time no pulse reaches the output, performs the system operation of "but not" gating. However, an output pulse will appear if one of the signals, say X, is applied but not Y. An "inhibit" function is the name given to this type of control demonstrated by the Y input.

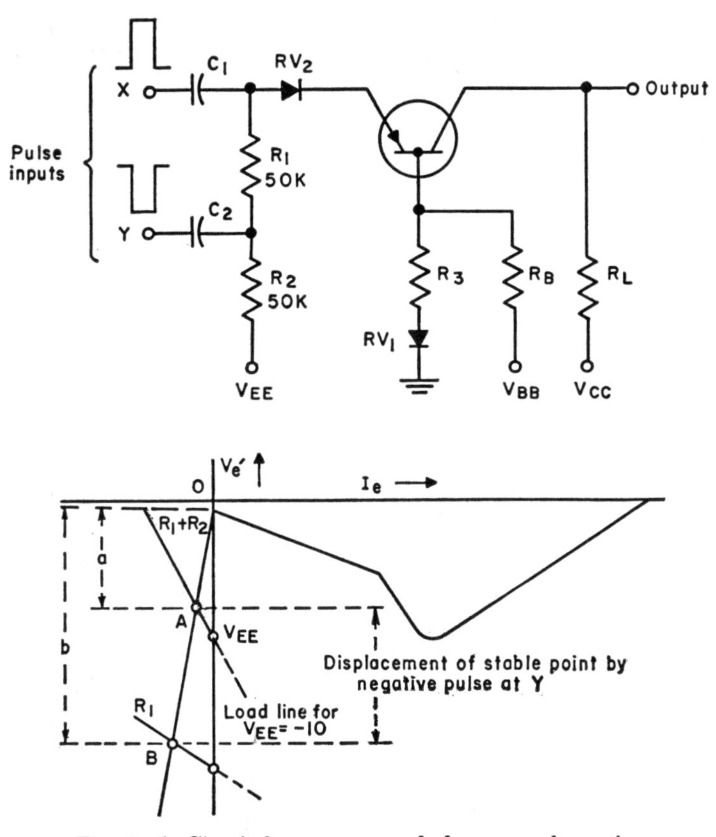

Fig. 20.5. Circuit for BUT NOT and also AND pulse gating.

Figure 20.5 presents a circuit which will perform this function, and also "and" pulse gating. The emitter load voltage divider is supplied by a small negative biasing potential V_{EE} determining a d-c stable "off" point A. A positive pulse of larger amplitude than a will trigger the circuit if no pulse is applied at input Y.

However, if a negative pulse simultaneously reaches input Y, and causes the load line to move rapidly down the vertical axis, point B becomes the stable equilibrium point instead of A. If the positive pulse applied at X is below the amplitude b now needed for triggering, no output pulse will result. The slope of the emitter load line at point B will be one-half that of point A, assuming that the Y input source impedance is small compared to R_2, and that R_1 equals R_2.

2. *A stabilized general purpose binary counter*[2]

A stabilized general purpose binary counter utilizing two Type A1698 point-contact switching transistors is diagrammed in Fig. 20.6. The circuit has two stable d-c equilibrium points, and pulses of the same polarity, applied to a common input terminal, trigger the counter from one stable point to the other.

Two balanced transistor stages are back coupled between collectors and bases by C_2 and R_4, and C_1 and R_5. Load resistor R_{12} provides direct d-c coupling and C_3 gives direct a-c coupling between emitters.

The couplings provide regenerative paths for a-c signals and also d-c paths to give stability after the transient effects have stopped. The transistor bases receive triggering pulses from a diode steering circuit composed of D_1 and D_2. The difference of potential between the bases, when one unit is "on" and the other is "off," directs the steering circuit.

The common emitter resistance R_{12} always passes the emitter current of the "on" stage to supply the biasing potential for the "off" stage, and thereby eliminates a separate bias supply for the emitters. The counter also employs base stabilization, which was discussed in the previous section, and insures low triggering.

If the correct steering diode polarity is provided, either positive or negative pulses may trigger this counter. Figure 20.6 shows the diodes connected for positive-pulse triggering. The difference of potential between "on" and "off" unit base connections accomplishes steering. The "on" unit base will receive a positive pulse from the input because

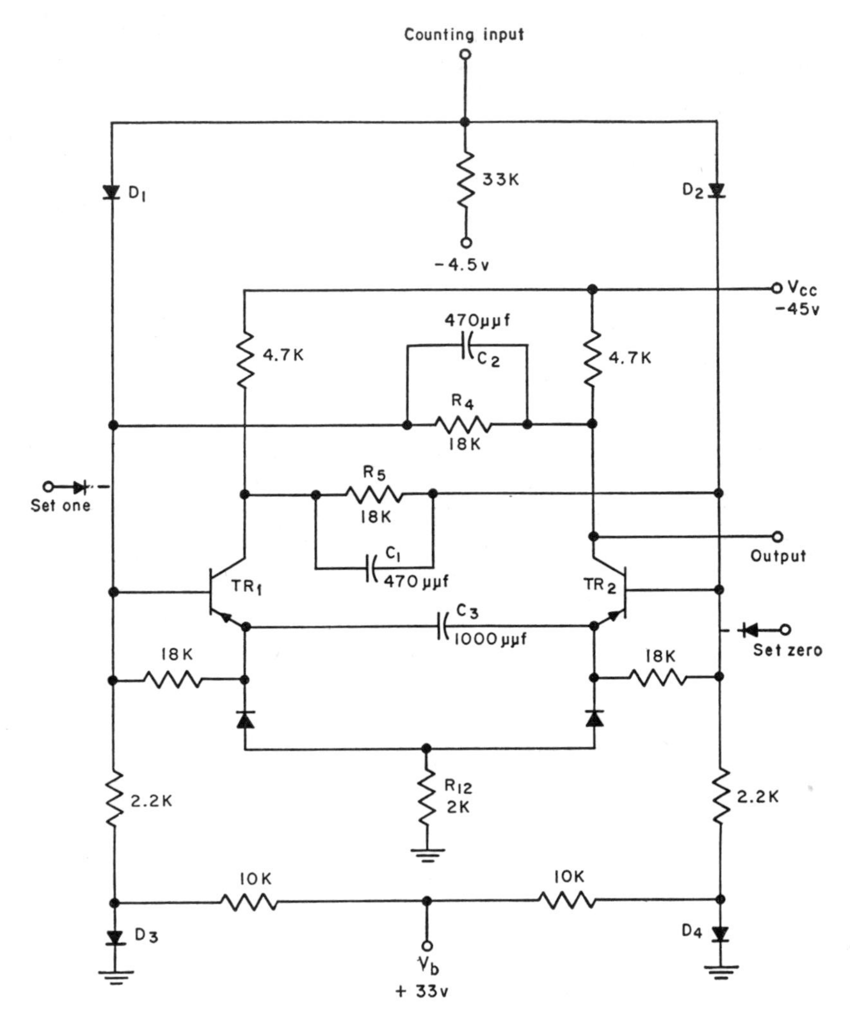

Fig. 20.6. Circuit of stabilized binary counter employing two A1698 point-contact transistors.

the "on" unit base is always 5 to 10 v more negative than the "off" unit base. The low impedance from base to emitter in the "on" state permits this pulse also to reach the emitter of the "on" unit.

The high impedance "off" unit emitter receives the pulse through coupling capacitor C_3. This triggers the "off" unit since it is stable at a point near the turning point of the characteristic. The triggering action causes a sharp pulse of 20 v amplitude and a 0.2 to 0.3 μsec rise time to appear at the collector of transistor TR_1. Capacitor C_1 passes this pulse back to the base of the "on" unit. The characteristic of the "on" unit moves suddenly in a positive direction.

The only stable point left is in the "off" stable region, provided that the characteristic moves such that the emitter load line does not intersect the characteristic. The collector voltage becomes more negative after the discharge of C_2 through resistor R_4. The upper limit on the repetition rate of the counter is fixed by this time constant R_4C_2.

Capacitor C_3 also provides a potential difference between the emitters during the triggering period. This keeps the steering diodes properly polarized until the completion of the transition interval. Reversing the steering diodes permits triggering with negative pulses. The base of the "off" unit then receives a negative pulse from the input.

The requirements for the counter triggering pulse are either positive or negative polarity, 3 to 6 v amplitude, and larger than 0.6 μsec duration. The repetition rate is 0 to 50 kc/sec. The output pulse has an amplitude of from 16 to 25 v, a rise time of 0.2 to 0.4 μsec, and a fall time of from 2 to 4 μsec. The power input is approximately 0.5 w.

3. *Transistor circuits for a shift register and serial adder*[3]

The binary cell consists of a symmetrical flip-flop as represented in Fig. 20.7 which consists of two point-contact switching type transistors and seven resistors. The advantages of such a symmetrical connection are that it simplifies logic circuits, and the power supply may have poor regulation since the power supply drain does not depend on stored information.

A positive pulse applied to the proper input terminal causes a change of condition. Since it is undesirable to apply a negative step to an input terminal, the connection of a diode in series with each input terminal can prevent such an occurrence. As indicated by the labels in parentheses on Fig. 20.7, a stored 1 is represented by the "on" condition of the left transistor, and 1 at the output is represented by the −30 v level.

The d-c power supply required by this flip-flop is −45 v at 8 to 10 ma. The two input voltages and equivalent internal resistances of the circuit are -9 v and 1000 ohms, and -5 v and 2000 ohms. The application of a positive pulse to the -9 v input produces a change of state. A minimum pulse of 10 v or about 2×10^{-8} coulomb is required. The output voltages and equivalent internal resistances are -10 v and 1500 ohms, or -30 v and 4000 ohms. The maximum permissible current in an output terminal is 1 ma, or larger when the current polarity is favorable. The preferable transition for an output is the negativeward transition.

Figure 20.8 shows the circuit of the regenerative pulse amplifier which is a simple and reliable monostable circuit utilizing a Type

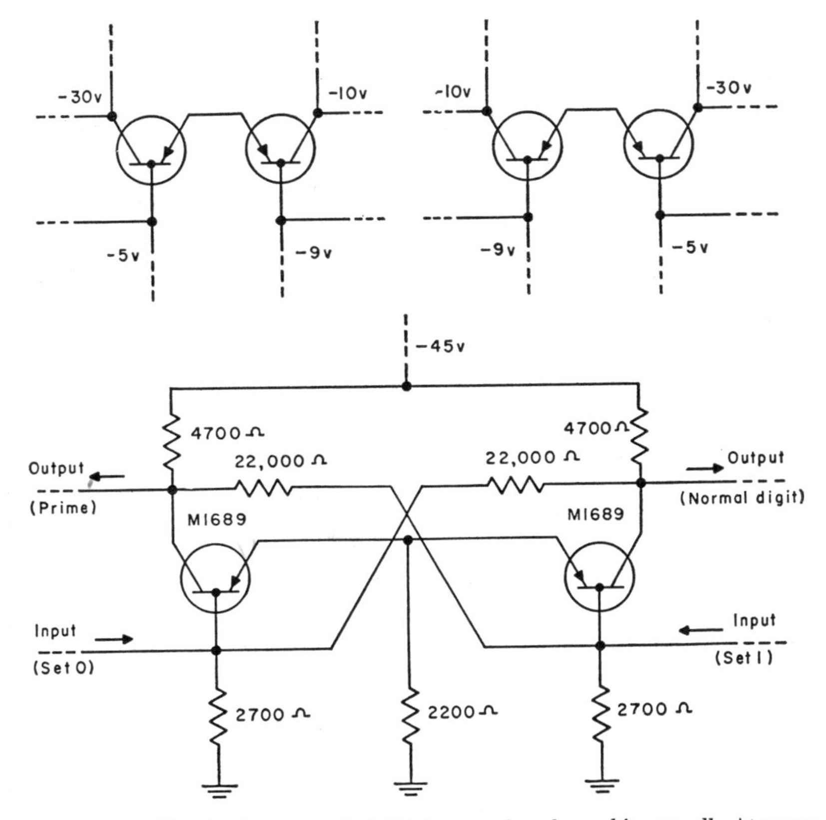

Fig. 20.7. Circuit of symmetrical flip-flop employed as a binary cell. At upper left, approximate terminal voltages with the left transistor OFF and the right transistor ON (cell storing 0). At upper right, approximate terminal voltages with the left transistor ON and the right transistor OFF (cell storing 1).

M1689 point-contact transistor. In this data system the amplifier is not required to preserve the original shape of a pulse. The amplifier may generate a pulse within itself. Therefore a triggered monostable circuit may be employed as an amplifier.

The circuit is ordinarily in the "off" position. When a trigger pulse switches it "on" it can supply a peak power of 1 w to a capacitively coupled load. Good reliability is achieved in this circuit by utilizing a step of 300 μa to trigger. The required input power is approximately $\frac{1}{3}$ mw. Hence the "power gain" is 3000, or much higher than the gain

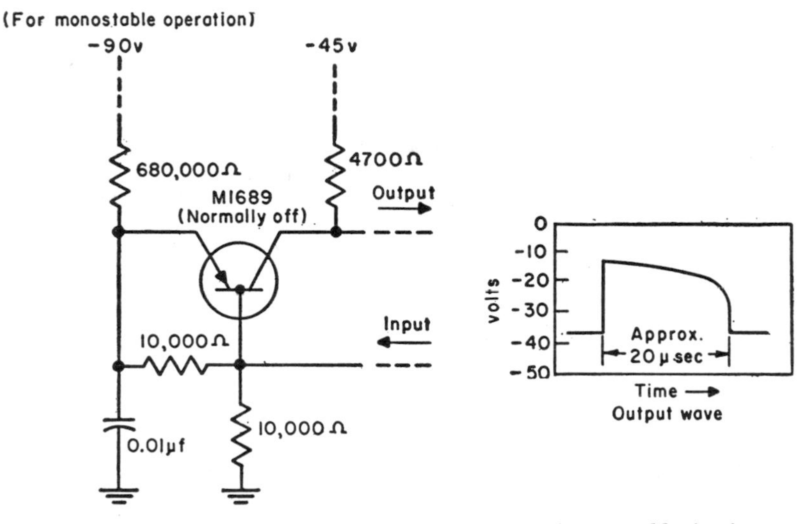

Fig. 20.8. Regenerative pulse amplifier consisting of monostable circuit.

of a linear amplifier with the same transistor. If the application is one in which we can adjust the resistances, the circuit can trigger with 10 μa or less.

The transistor switches "off" and the output pulse ceases when the emitter capacitor voltage is no longer sufficiently positive to sustain the "on" condition. The comparatively large capacitor permits a high-energy output pulse, but restricts the circuit triggering frequency. This, however, is of no importance here.

As required by the binary cell previously described, this amplifier receives a negative step for the input signal on the base, and produces a positive pulse as the output signal.

Remarkable switching times are achieved. The output signal has a total delay and rise time of approximately 0.1 μsec. Many transistors approach 0.02 μsec when the trigger signal is stronger than threshold value. This compares with a switch "off" time as long as 1 or 2 μsec unless the "on" time is short.

To achieve a fast-rising, high-power output pulse, we need a low internal output impedance in the "on" state. When "on," the output impedance consists primarily of the 0.01 μf emitter capacitor in series with the internal transistor emitter-to-collector path. Here the transistor acts as a good low-impedance switch with a voltage drop of only 2 or 3 v for currents of 10 to 100 ma. The usual static curves do not easily demonstrate this valuable transistor property. Although the dissipation in the transistor is relatively low, the low impedance permits a high-power output.

The terminal characteristics, especially in the "on" state, are more complex than those of the flip-flop. The input impedance in the "on" state is low, variable, and depends on the load. If this causes trouble, we can employ a resistance in series with the input. It is assumed that the 0.01 μf capacitor has small impedance at the operating frequencies. The d-c power supplies provide −90 v at 110 microamperes, and −45 v at 1.5 ma, which increases with frequent triggering. The input voltage and equivalent internal resistance in the "off" condition are −13 v and 4000 ohms. The signal required to trigger this monostable circuit is a negative current step of 300 μa or more with a rise time of 10 μsec or less. The maximum trigger rate for full sensitivity is 600 per second. The output voltage and equivalent internal resistance in the "off" state are −38 v and 4000 ohms. A negative current step as small as 900 μa is sufficient signal to trigger on the output terminal. The output pulse has an amplitude of 23 v with a pulse delay and rise time of 0.02 to 0.1 μsec, a pulse duration of 20 μsec, which is shortened by a load, and a maximum available charge per pulse of 0.1×10^{-6} coulomb.

A monostable circuit utilized for delay and regeneration is diagrammed in Fig. 20.9. This consists of a pulse amplifier followed by a simple normally "on" monostable circuit. The input trigger drives the base of the second transistor positive. The collector current rapidly switches from the emitter to the base. The transistor base-to-collector resistance remains at only a few hundred ohms for one or two microseconds. As the capacitors charge, the collector resistance increases, the current decreases to a small value, and the output terminal drifts in a negative direction. Then the first transistor cuts "off," the second turns "on," and the output terminal suddenly goes in a positive direction. As shown in Fig. 20.9, we can obtain a delayed positive pulse by differentiating the output wave with a series capacitor followed by a parallel-diode d-c restorer.

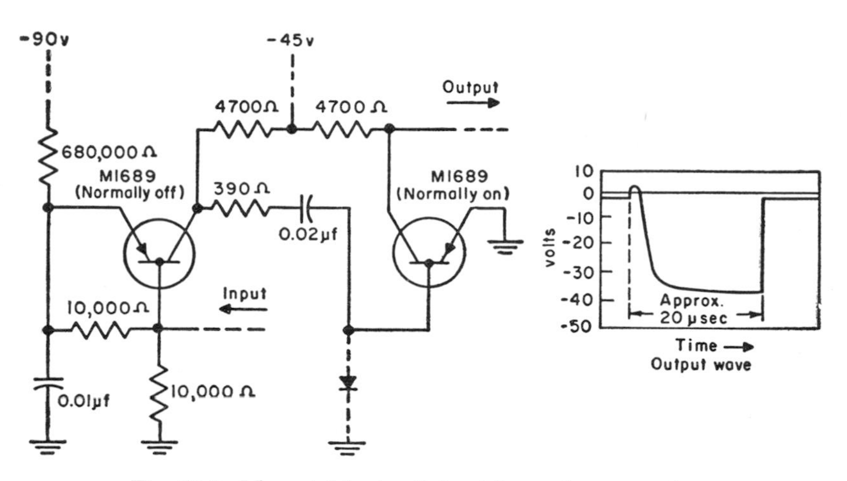

Fig. 20.9. Monostable circuit for delay and regeneration.

The circuit draws a comparatively high current, because one transistor is normally "on." Slow switch-off causes the positive step applied to the second transistor base to reach the load. A diode, added as in Fig. 20.9, can greatly reduce this effect at the load, if desired. The delay time is also somewhat reduced by this diode. The input characteristics are the same as those of the pulse amplifier previously described. The output has a fast switch "on" and a low internal impedance in the "on" condition like the pulse amplifier.

4. *A transistor pulse amplifier employing external regeneration*[4]

Figure 20.10 is the circuit of a pulse-regenerative amplifier which functions at a basic frequency of 3 mc/sec with a point-contact transistor. At this frequency its operation is comparatively unaffected by the slow recovery of reverse impedance which many diodes exhibit.

A germanium diode circuit and an external feedback path produce regenerated 0.17 μsec pulses with wave shapes practically independent of those of the input pulses. The output pulses are synchronized with a sinusoidal clock voltage. Transformer coupling provides d-c restoration.

The average 3 megacycle clock power dissipation is about 12 mw

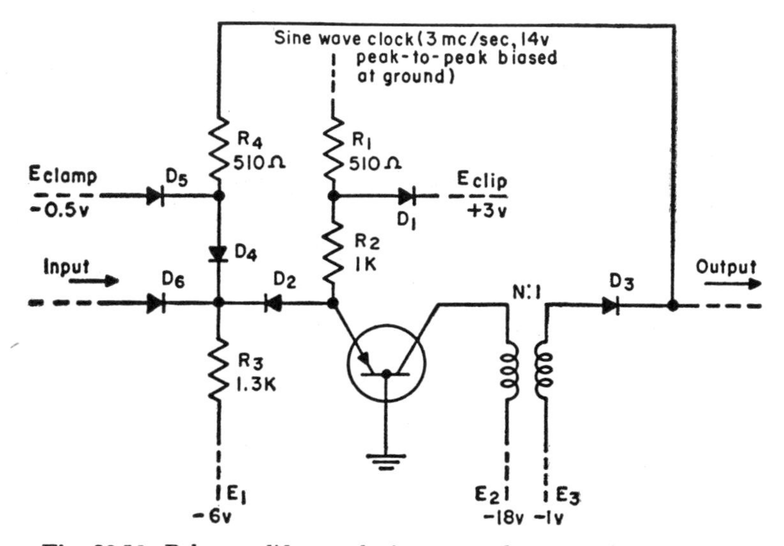

Fig. 20.10. Pulse amplifier employing external regeneration and point-contact transistor.

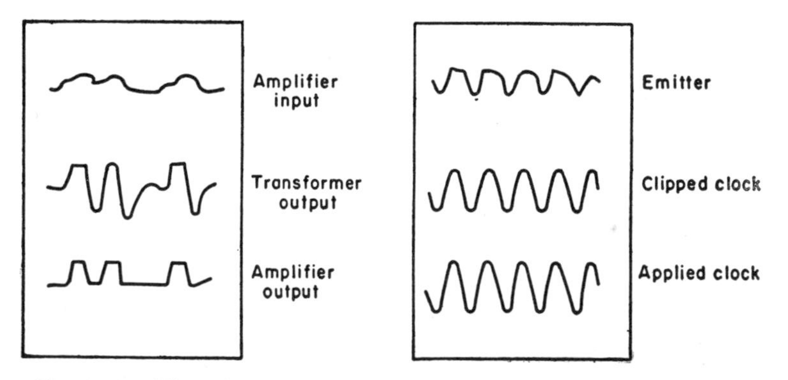

Fig. 20.11. Wave shapes at various points in the amplifier for a 500-ohm resistive load and a 3:1 transformer turns ratio.

per amplifier, regardless of whether or not the amplifier is pulsed. The d-c dissipation within the transistor closely equals the product of E_2 and I_{co}. It varies, therefore, with different transistors, but is normally less than 50 mw. The circuit dissipates an additional 25 mw of d-c power besides that of the transistor.

An input pulse causes the emitter current to change from a slightly negative value to a positive value of about 3.5 ma.

The wave shapes at various points in the amplifier are indicated in Fig. 20.11 for a 500 ohm resistive load and a 3 to 1 transformer turns ratio.

5. *The phase-bistable transistor circuit*[5]

This synchronized transistor switching circuit was designed for computer applications. Instead of being amplitude bistable, the circuit is phase bistable. Clock pulses operate a commutating ring which

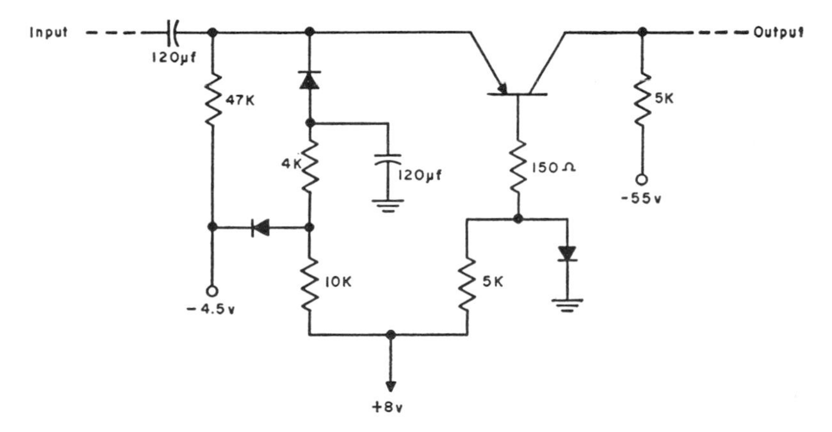

Fig. 20.12. Circuit of the one-shot multivibrator.

is sampled at one-half the repetition rate of the clock. An input pulse changes the phase of the ring with reference to the sample pulses. This is like an input pulse producing a change in the output amplitude of an ordinary amplitude bistable device. The one-shot multivibrator is the basic transistor circuit employed. This device was found to be more reliable than any amplitude bistable transistor circuit.

The one-shot multivibrator circuit is shown in Fig. 20.12. The cir-

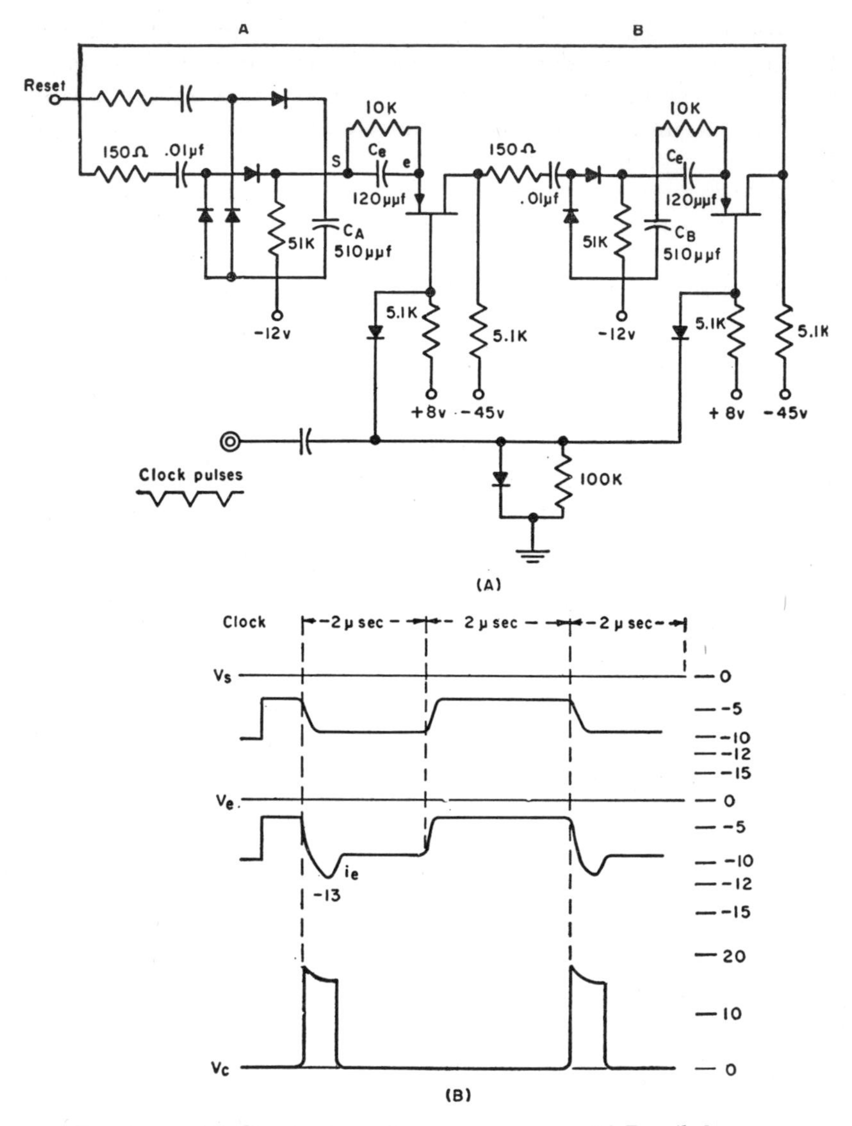

Fig. 20.13. (A) Circuit of the Commutating ring. (B) Detailed operation of the commutating-ring circuit.

cuit has a monostable load line. A high input impedance is provided by connecting the discharge capacitor in series with a diode between emitter and ground. The triggering requirements have been stabilized by utilizing base stabilization. Output pulse widths of 0.5 to 1 μsec are produced.

Figure 20.13(A) indicates the circuit of the commutating ring. One-shot multivibrators similar to that of Fig. 20.12 are employed for both units, except that we apply negative pulses to the base rather than positive pulses to the emitter to trigger the circuit. The clock pulses

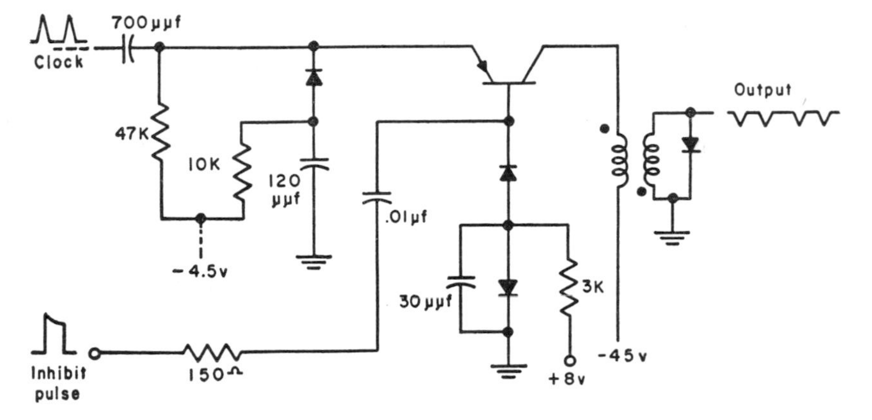

Fig. 20.14. Circuit of transistor inhibitor.

cannot trigger either stage because of the negative bias on both emitters. However, when we apply a positive reset pulse, we charge storage capacitor C_A and effectively reduce the bias of stage A. Stage A will then be triggered by the following clock pulse. Next capacitor C_A discharges and returns stage A to its previous highly biased condition. Meanwhile the storage capacitor of stage B receives the output pulse from A. Thus stage B is triggered by the next clock pulse, C_B is discharged, and C_A is charged. Stages A and B are alternately triggered by following clock pulses.

Figure 20.13(B) shows the detailed operation of the circuit. The potential at points e and s is about -10 v before we apply the reset of the pulse. A reset pulse charges capacitor C_A, and raises points e and s to about -3 v. The following clock pulse triggers stage A, lowering its emitter voltage to approximately -13 v in about 0.5 μsec so that the transistor switches off. Meanwhile, point *s* falls to about -8 v. The emitter voltage than rises with a time constant of 1.2 μsec (10,000 ohms $\times$ 120 $\mu\mu$f) to the voltage of point *s* (~ -8 v). This voltage stays practically constant because C_A discharges with a time constant of about 25 μsec which is much longer than the 2 μsec period of the clock pulses. The second clock pulse cannot override the bias on stage *A* but triggers stage *B*, whose bias had previously been decreased by the output pulse from stage *A*.

The inhibitor circuit is described in Fig. 20.14. This employs the basic one-shot multivibrator. We apply clock pulses to the emitter and inhibit pulses to the base. When there is no inhibit pulse present, a clock pulse triggers the multivibrator. An inhibit pulse raises the base potential to such a high value that the clock pulse cannot trigger the circuit. We can easily quantize the inhibit pulses in a synchronous system and make them of proper duration to mask the clock pulses entirely. Positive inhibitor operation is thus insured.

6. *Transistor shift registers utilizing high-speed bistable circuits*[6]

Shift registers normally consist of a chain of interconnected bistable elements. The device can perform such operations as sampling, coding, decoding, and storing.

Three different types of nonsaturating bistable circuits will be described here. A nonsaturating bistable circuit is one that has active points in the negative-resistance region. Two of these circuits may be employed as the bistable elements necessary to construct shift

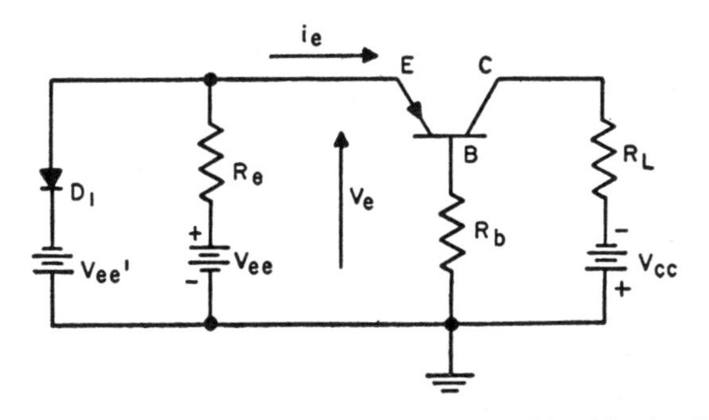

Fig. 20.15. High-speed negative-resistance bistable circuit.

registers. The third circuit provides a convenient method of building a sampling device such as a matrix switch. The shift-register logic is basically the same as that utilized with vacuum tubes, in that between each bistable stage there is a diode "and" gate which controls the state of the following stage.

The circuit[7] of Fig. 20.15 was devised to avoid the problems arising in saturated circuits. As shown in Fig. 20.16 the diode D_1 and resistor R_e, along with batteries V_{ee} and $V_{ee'}$, present the broken load line $R_{e'}R_e$ to the transistor emitter input characteristics. When the transistor is in the high conducting state at point b, the emitter voltage V_e

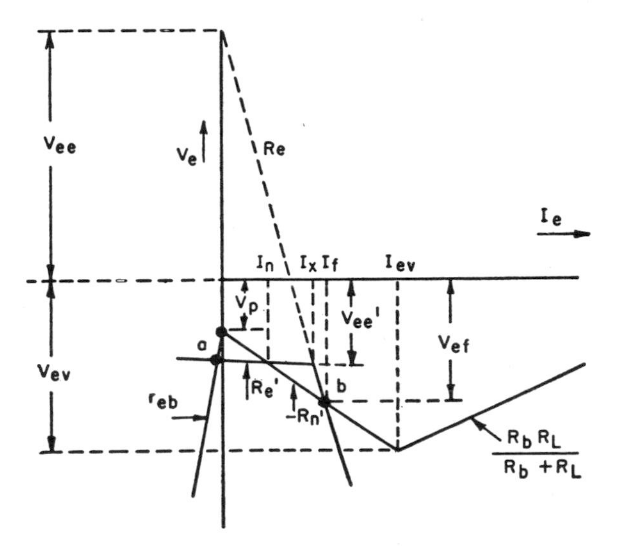

Fig. 20.16. Static emitter voltage-current characteristics for the circuit of Fig. 20.15.

equals V_{ef}. Since point b is short-circuit unstable, R_e must be larger than the negative transistor input resistance $-R_n$. Also we must keep the capacitance at the emitter small. The second point a occurs in the inactive region of the transistor. Thus we have a single-transistor bistable circuit with two nonsaturated stable states.

The two-transistor nonsaturating flip-flop circuit[8] shown in Fig. 20.17(A) was devised to avoid the effects of minority-carrier storage[9] that arise in saturated flip-flops. The circuit characteristics are more easily explained by breaking the circuit symmetrically as in Fig.

20.17(B) and plotting the input characteristics as in Fig. 20.17(C). Points a and b are the only stable points since the positive input resistance of the "off" transistor in parallel with R_e exceeds the negative input resistance of the "on" transistor.[7] Point c, where both transistors are "on," is unstable since both transistors have negative input resistances. We must keep the current I smaller than I_{ev} to avoid operation in the saturated region.

We can form a shift register from the single transistor bistable element by inserting diode gates between each stage. Fig. 20.18 shows the block diagram of such a shift register. The first stage is set, or

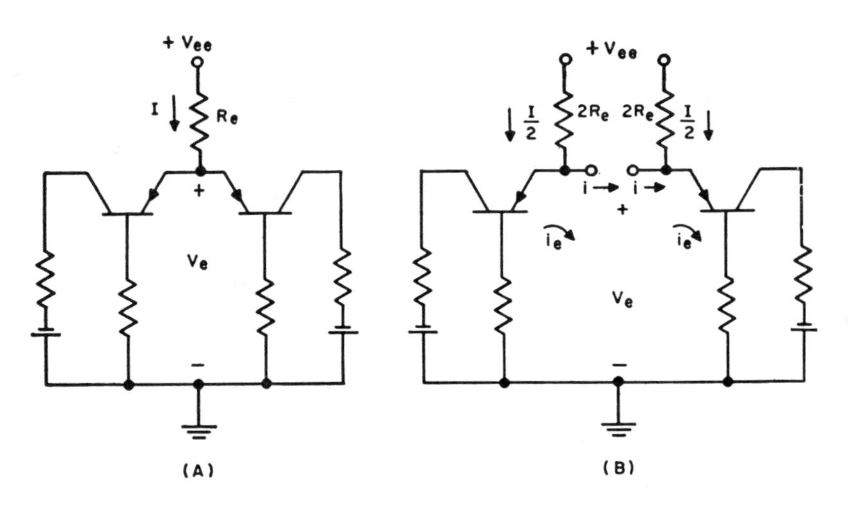

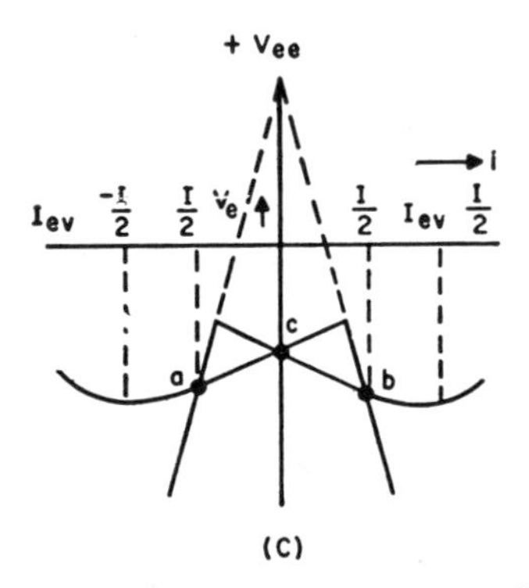

Fig. 20.17. The two-transistor nonsaturating flip-flop.

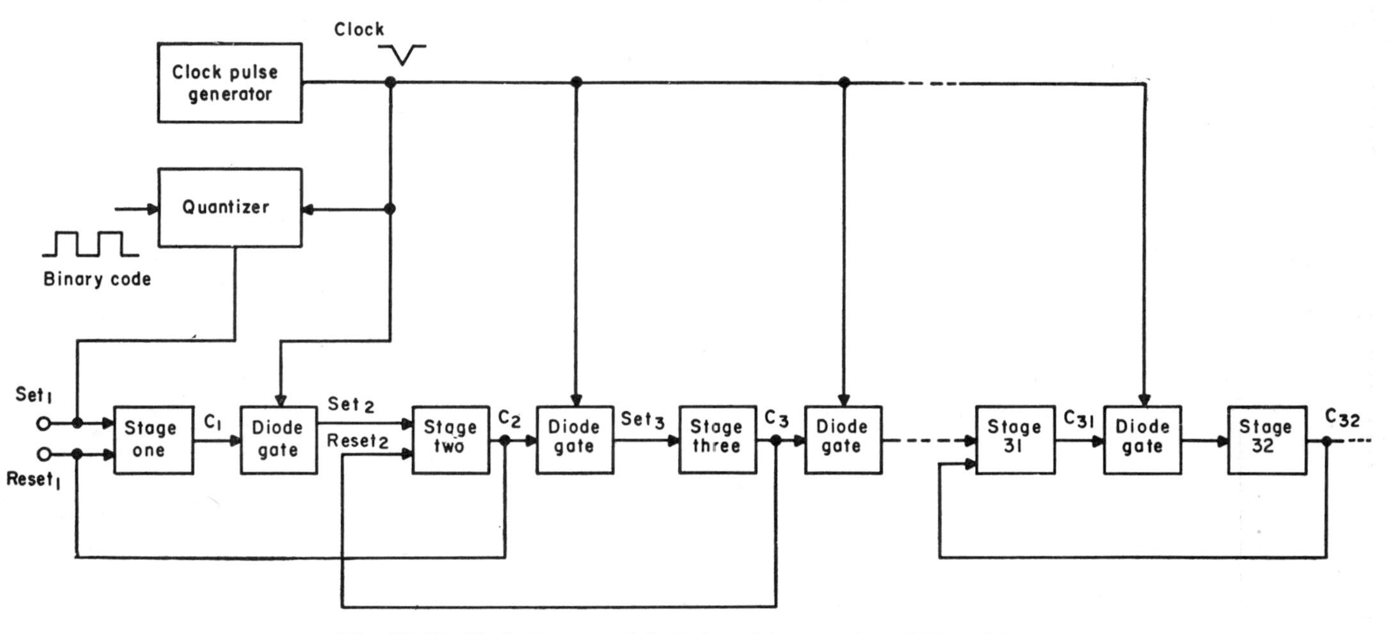

Fig. 20.18. Block diagram of single transistor-per-stage shift register.

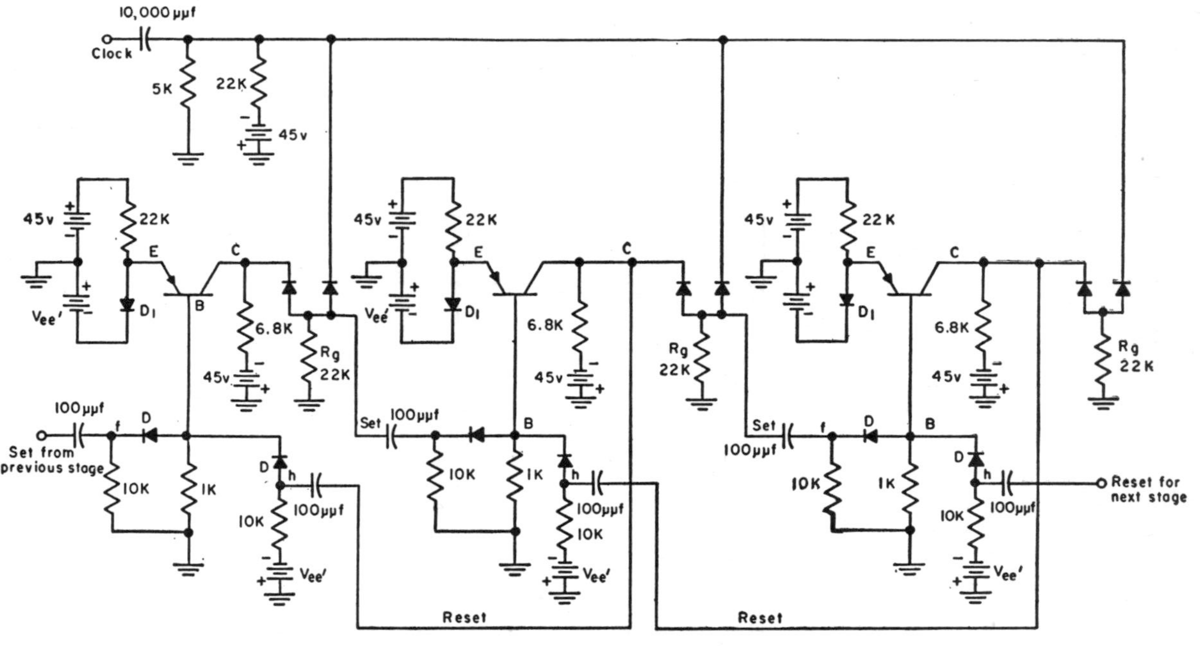

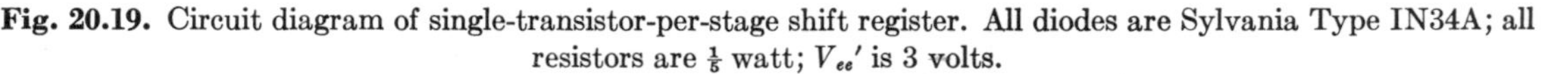

Fig. 20.19. Circuit diagram of single-transistor-per-stage shift register. All diodes are Sylvania Type IN34A; all resistors are $\frac{1}{5}$ watt; V_{ee}' is 3 volts.

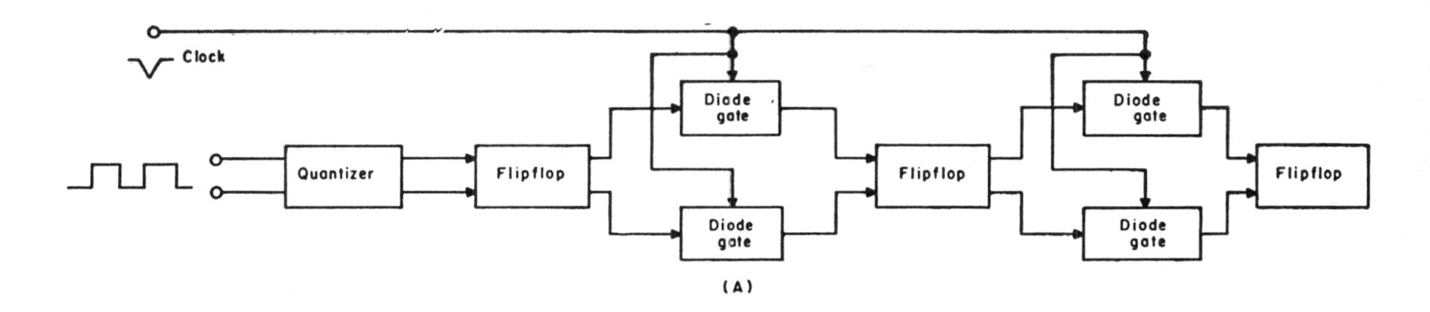

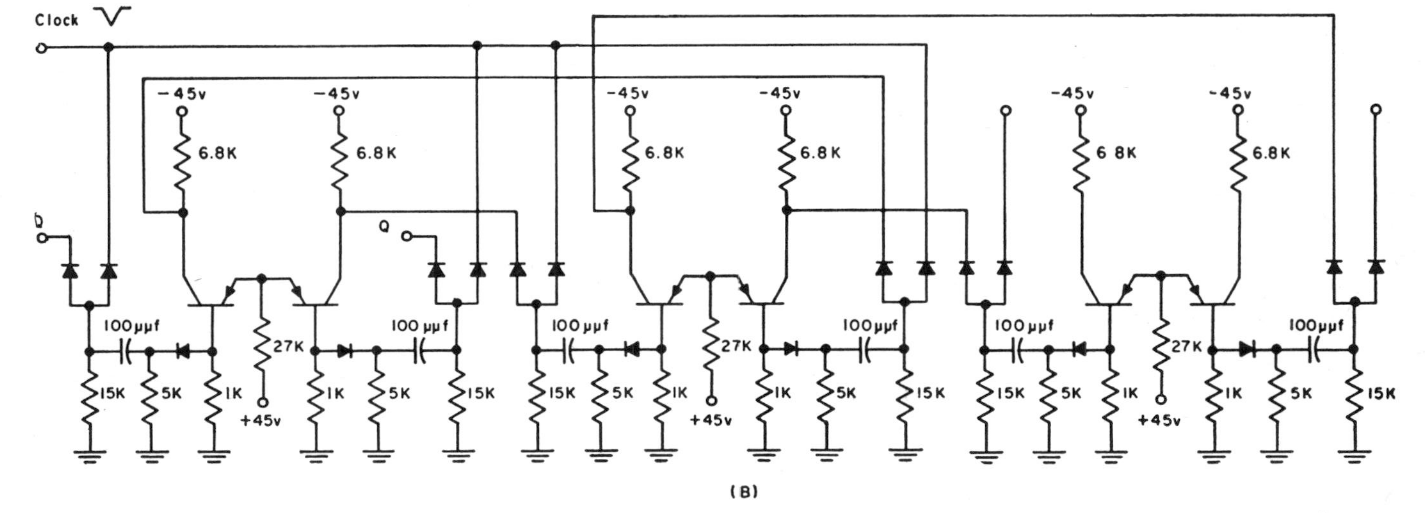

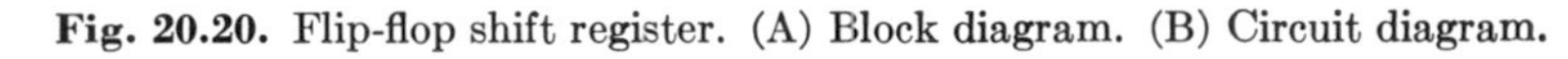

Fig. 20.20. Flip-flop shift register. (A) Block diagram. (B) Circuit diagram.

switched from point a to point b of Fig. 20.16, by clock pulses controlled by the input binary code. When Stage 1 is set, the diode gate permits a clock pulse to set the second stage. Stage 2 resets Stage 1 and allows the next clock pulse to set the third stage, etc. Thus the sense of the first stage transfers down the chain of bistable elements. A detailed three-stage circuit of the shift register is shown in Fig. 20.19.

We can form the flip-flop shift register from the bistable elements in the same way that we form vacuum tube shift registers; the inputs to a particular stage are the clock pulses that have been gated from the outputs of the previous stage. Figure 20.20 shows (A) the block diagram and (B) the circuit diagram of the flip-flop shift register.

From Fig. 20.19 it may be seen that the reset capacitor at point h must recover through a series combination of resistances. Hence to increase the maximum operating speed, we must make the triggering capacitors as small as possible. To determine the minimum value

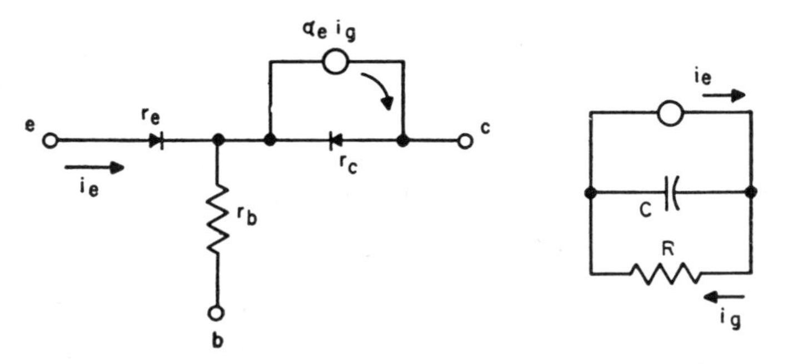

Fig. 20.21. Large-signal equivalent circuit for transistor dynamic characteristics.

capacitors that reliably will switch the nonsaturating bistable circuit, we must make a transient analysis. The model is that of the large signal equivalent circuit of Adler[10] with the dynamic interpretation shown in Fig. 20.21.

We are dealing with circuits whose "on" stable point is in the active region of the transistor characteristic. The transistor, looking from emitter to ground, displays a negative input resistance and is short-circuit unstable. For stability the external emitter resistance must be larger than the negative input resistance. Also, for a large external emitter resistance, C_e, the capacitance between emitter and ground must satisfy the relation

$$C_e < \frac{\tau}{R_n} = \frac{1}{2\pi f_{co} R_n} \tag{2}$$

where f_{co} is the transistor cutoff frequency.

We may consider the triggering requirements of the single transistor negative resistance bistable circuit with reference to Fig. 20.22. To be certain that this circuit will switch or change states reliably,

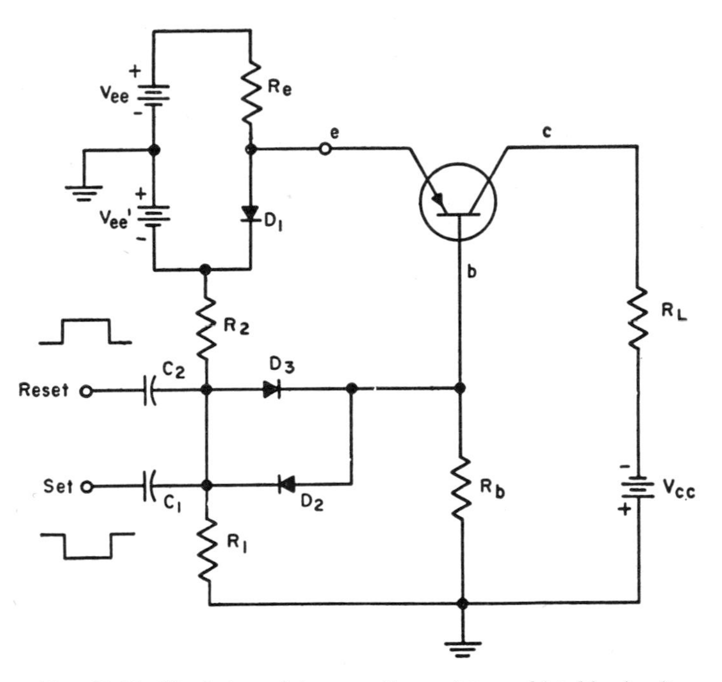

Fig. 20.22. Single-transistor negative-resistance bistable circuit.

the trigger pulse must exceed a given amplitude for a given period of time[7,11]. Also, the amplitude-width requirement varies with the state of the circuit[7,11] and the frequency response of the transistor.

The set or "turn on" function of the circuit shown in Fig. 20.22 will now be considered. The applied set pulse opens D_1. Resistor R_e is larger than R_n. The initial shape of i_e is a positive step, the amplitude of which depends upon the applied trigger voltage V_t, followed by a converging decay. Since i_g tries to follow i_e, the eventual circuit state depends upon the relative magnitudes of i_e and i_g as time progresses. When i_e decays to I_x of Fig. 20.16, diode D_1 closes and R_e becomes $R_{e'}$. Since $R_{e'}$ is smaller than R_n, the circuit is unstable. For the circuit still to switch on, even though i_e becomes less than I_x, the rate of change of i_e must be equal to zero at some time after t_x, the time at which i_e is equal to I_x.

The approximate criterion for triggering on is[7,11]

$$i_g(t_x) > I_n \quad \text{Turn on} \tag{3a}$$

$$i_g(t_x) < I_n \quad \text{Turn back off} \tag{3b}$$

Figure 20.23 shows the values of C_1 versus the trigger voltage V_t that satisfy condition (3a). The results are in good agreement with experimental data.

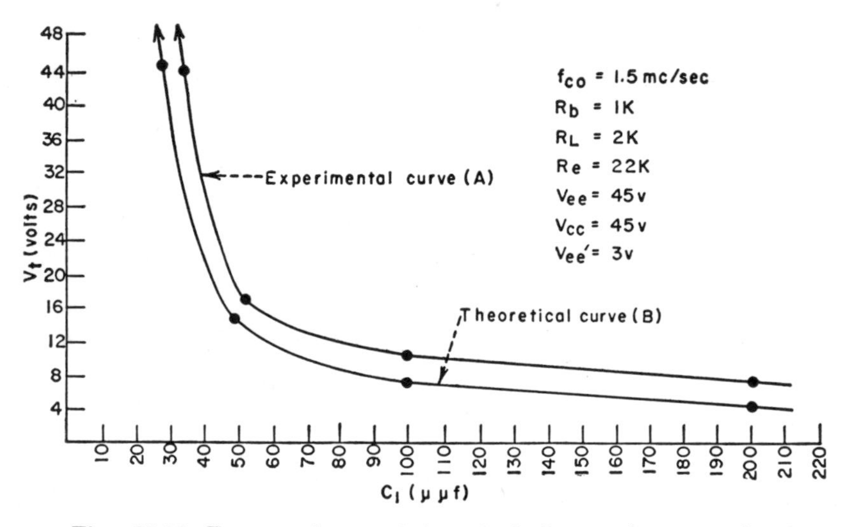

Fig. 20.23. Turn-on characteristics of single transistor negative-resistance bistable circuit.

We can employ the same approach to determine the "turn off" trigger requirement as for the "turn on" function. We draw the appropriate equivalent circuit, solve the pertinent loop equations, define the turn off criterion, and solve for the minimum trigger voltage that will switch the circuit.

Since we turn off the circuit by applying a positive pulse to the base, as indicated in Fig. 20.22, this instantaneously switches off the transistor emitter and starts C_2 charging. When the base voltage decays below $V_{ee'}$, current i_e starts increasing. Once again, for the circuit to switch off, i_e must go to zero. As before, the triggering diode D_3 will open when the rate of change of i_e equals zero. Therefore at this time t_Δ,[7,11]

$$i_g(t_\Delta) > I_n \quad \text{Turn back on} \tag{4a}$$

$$i_g(t_\Delta) < I_n \quad \text{Turn off} \tag{4b}$$

The plot of V_t as a function of C_2 is given in Fig. 20.24. The theoretical curve compares well with the experimental data.

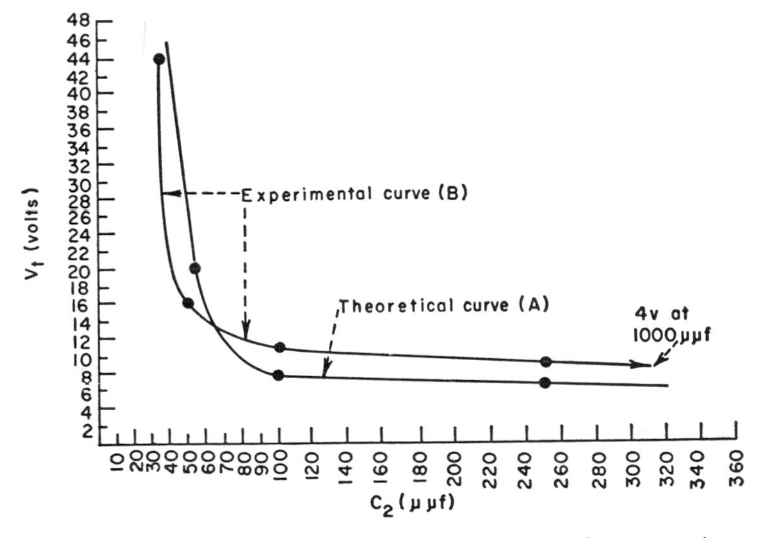

Fig. 20.24. Turn-off characteristics of single-transistor negative-resistance bistable circuit.

The two transistor nonsaturating flip-flop may be analyzed by the same techniques described above. The solutions for the various current equations will be of the same form, although slightly more complex because of the circuit configuration. As before, the triggering requirements have a definite minimum amplitude-width relationship. This analysis is made elsewhere.[12] However, it is important to realize that the two-transistor flip-flop will trigger on narrower pulses than the single-transistor negative-resistance bistable circuit. This is because, although we are triggering at the base of the first transistor of Figures 20.17 and 20.20, and the same conditions apply as when triggering the single transistor, the second transistor is being triggered at the emitter. Since the circuit is short-circuit unstable at the emitter,

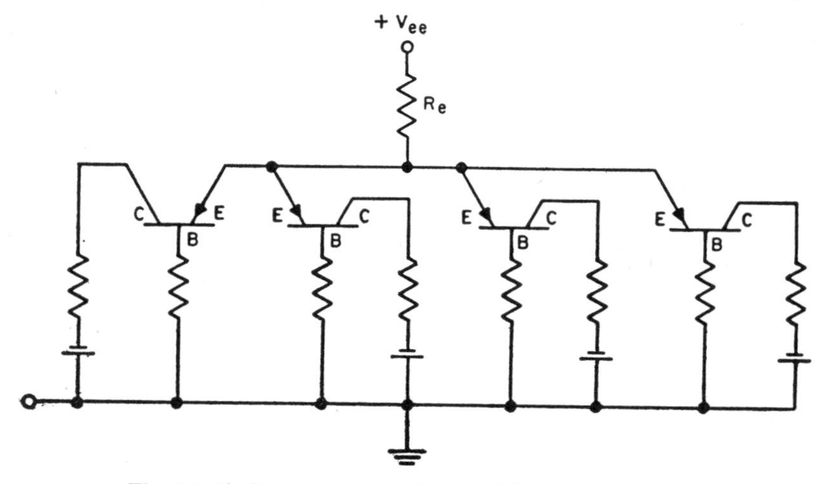

Fig. 20.25. Four-transistor circuit with four stable states.

the currents in the second transistor decay (or increase) with positive exponentials. This causes the second transistor to switch faster, which results in faster switching of the circuit.

Fig. 20.25 shows a multistage circuit where several transistor stages have their emitters tied to a common load resistor as a logical exten-

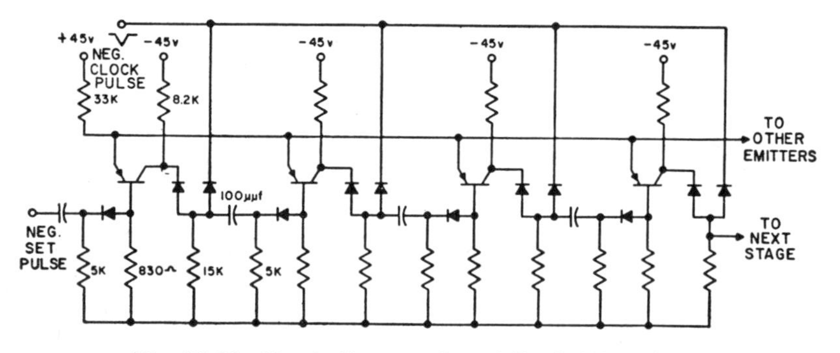

Fig. 20.26. Circuit diagram of specialized shift register.

sion of the circuit of Fig. 20.17(A). As in the two-transistor connection, only one transistor can conduct at a time, since any state with more than one transistor in the negative-resistance region is unstable.

Figure 20.26 is the circuit of a specialized shift register based on this idea. Assume that a negative pulse is applied to the base of the first stage. This stage will then conduct, whereas the others are nonconducting. The sense of this first stage may then be propagated down the register by clock pulses gated to the stages in sequence.

Two factors limit the number of stages that we may connect together. First, we must keep the total accumulated capacitance between emitter and ground small enough to render each transistor stable in accordance with relation (2). Second, we must keep the resistance between emitter and ground, which the addition of more transistors reduces, large enough to render each transistor's "on" operating point in the negative-resistance region.

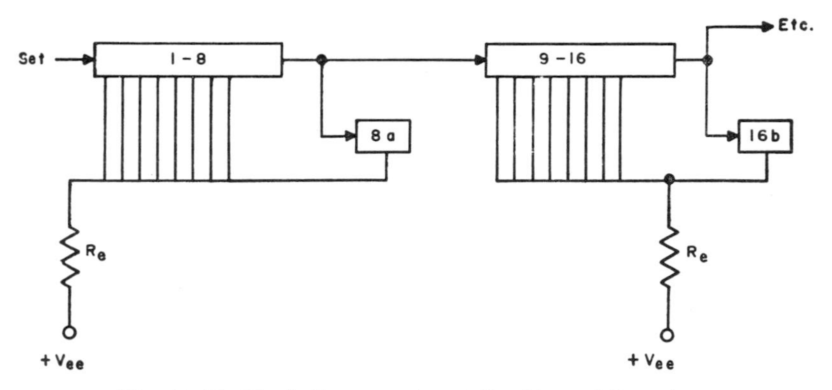

Fig. 20.27. Block diagram of specialized long-shift register.

We may connect as many as ten transistors in this manner with little or no difficulty. When we desire to employ more transistors in a long register, we may construct it as indicated in Fig. 20.27.

An over-all analysis of the shift register circuits reveals the following points. First, a point-contact transistor switching circuit requires a definite, predictable, minimum pulse-height width relationship that depends upon the transistor frequency response and the circuit configuration. Second, the maximum speed of operation of a system constructed with these circuits is limited, not by the switching time of the circuits, but by the recovery time of the associated triggering capacitors. Therefore when designing high-speed systems, we should employ circuits with as high imput impedance, and as low recovery resistance as possible for the triggering-capacitor circuits.

Each of the shift registers described above has undergone exhaustive tests. The two-transistor flip-flop works reliably with 80 per cent of BTL 1698 transistors at rates up to 5 μsec per shift pulse. The single transistor negative-resistance bistable circuit operates up to 6 μsec per stage. However, at these fast rates which require small coupling capacitors, this shift register is less reliable than the flip-flop unit. At lower rates, we can have larger coupling capacitors with greater reliability. The specialized shift register provides good reliability up to 3 μsec per shift pulse when we connect a maximum of nine stages to the common bias resistor R_e. We should arrange longer registers as shown in Fig. 20.27.

References

1. R. L. Trent, "Gating and Switching Circuits Employing Transistors," *Electronic Design*, Vol. I, No. 10, Oct. 1953, pp. 10–11.
2. R. L. Trent, *A Stabilized General Purpose Two-Transistor Binary Counter*, Bell Telephone Laboratories, 1951.
3. James R. Harris, "A Transistor Shift Register and Serial Adder," *Proc. IRE*, Vol. XL, No. 11, Nov. 1952, pp. 1597–1602.
4. J. H. Vogelsong, "A Transistor Pulse Amplifier Using External Regeneration," *Proc. IRE*, Vol. XLI, No. 10, Oct. 1953, pp. 1444–1450.
5. R. H. Baker, Irwin L. Lebow, Robert H. Radiker, and I. S. Reed, "The Phase-Bistable Transistor Circuit," *Proc. IRE*, Vol. XLI, No. 9, Sept. 1953, pp. 1119–1124.
6. R. H. Baker, I. L. Lebow, and R. E. McMahon, "Transistor Shift Registers," *Proc. IRE*, Vol. XLII, No. 7, July 1954, pp. 1152–1159.
7. I. L. Lebow, R. H. Baker, and R. E. McMahon, *The Transient Response of Transistor Switching Circuits*, Technical Report No. 27, Lincoln Laboratory, M.I.T., July 1953.

8. A. W. Carlson, *A Transistor Flip-Flop With Two Stable Nonsaturating States, AFCRC Report,* Dec. 1952.

9. R. A. Bradbury, *Hole Storage or Turn Off Time,* AFCRC, Dec. 1952.

10. R. B. Adler, *A Large Signal Equivalent Circuit for Transistor Static Characteristics,* M.I.T., R.L.E. Transistor Group Report T-2, Aug. 1951.

11. R. H. Baker, *Transistor Shift Register,* M.S. Thesis, M.I.T., June 1953 (E. E. Dept.)

12. R. E. McMahon, I. L. Lebow, and R. H. Baker, *A Two Transistor Shift Register,* Lincoln Laboratory, M.I.T., M24–20, May 1953.

Chapter 21

MISCELLANEOUS APPLICATIONS OF TRANSISTORS

1. *Transistor microammeter*[1]

The circuit of a transistor microammeter employing a CK722 junction transistor is shown in Fig. 21.1. This current amplifier produces a gain of 10 with an input current of approximately 100 μa applied to the emitter. A range of 0–100 μa full scale can be measured with a 0–1 ma meter connected to the output of the transistor. Thus weak currents can be measured with an inexpensive, rugged instrument.

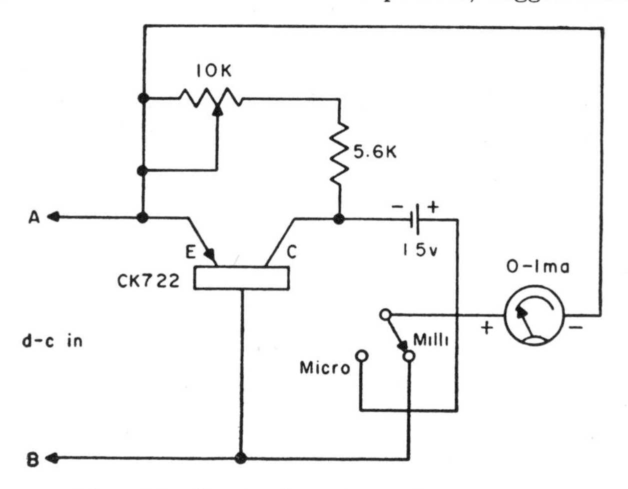

Fig. 21.1. Circuit of transistor microammeter.

The circuit provides two current ranges. When the switch is thrown to MICRO the 10-to-1 current amplifier is utilized with the meter, giving a range of 0–100 μa. When the switch is in MILLI position, the meter is connected across the input and the range is 0–1 ma. When the meter is not being used the switch should be left at MILLI, which is an off position for the battery.

The transistor amplification varies somewhat over the scale, being less than 10 near the bottom of the scale and slightly higher than 10 near full scale. A compensating circuit is added to minimize this error. The variable resistor should be adjusted to give an exact reading near 0.8 on the meter scale. Then the reading will be accurate over most of the range. The error is about 2 to 3 per cent for the range of 0.2 to 1.0 ma on the meter, corresponding to 20–100 μa input. Greater error occurs for readings near zero, but this is no great disadvantage.

For the microammeter connection, *A* is the positive input terminal which connects to the emitter. However, for the milliammeter circuit, *B* is the positive terminal, and although the transistor input circuit is connected across terminals *A* and *B*, negligible error results.

2. *A transistor bridge null detector*[2]

Figure 21.2 is the circuit of a transistor bridge null detector which is more convenient for an impedance or capacitance bridge than headphones. This transistor circuit has the advantages over a vacuum tube null detector circuit of requiring no long warm-up time or separate power supply. The 6 v battery normally included in the impeddance bridge supplies the power for this circuit.

This null detector is composed of two grounded-emitter amplifier stages employing CK722 junction transistors, a rectifier *W*, and a 0–500 microammeter. The rectifier *W* consists of a bridge instrument rectifier or four germanium diodes connected in a bridge circuit. The

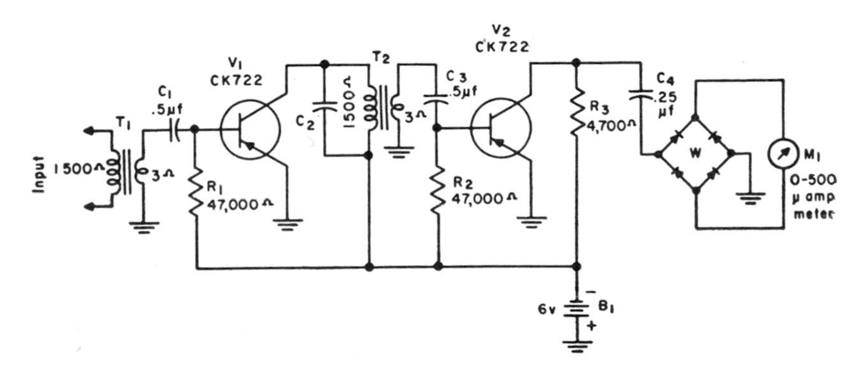

Fig. 21.2. Transistor bridge null detector circuit.

sensitivity, though somewhat less than for headphones, is still adequate for most purposes.

The circuit has an input impedance of approximately 20,000 ohms. The stages may be coupled by conventional miniature output transformers. Capacitor C_2 tunes the primary of transformer T_2 to the 1000 cps signal. The value of C_2 depends on the individual transformer, but normally falls within the range of about 0.002 to 0.005 μf.

Just before the needle of the meter goes off scale, the second stage should saturate. Resistor R_2 fixes the emitter bias current, which determines the overload level. Each transistor employed in the second stage may require a different value of R_2. When a more sensitive microammeter is utilized, R_2 should be appropriately increased.

3. *A transistorized megohmmeter*[3]

The circuit of a two-range megohmmeter with a transistor high-voltage generator is given in Fig. 21.3. This electrostatic megohmmeter measures only 6 in. by 4 in. by 3 in. and is powered by a small hearing-aid battery. The two ranges are 3 to 1500 megohms and 35 to 22,000 megohms.

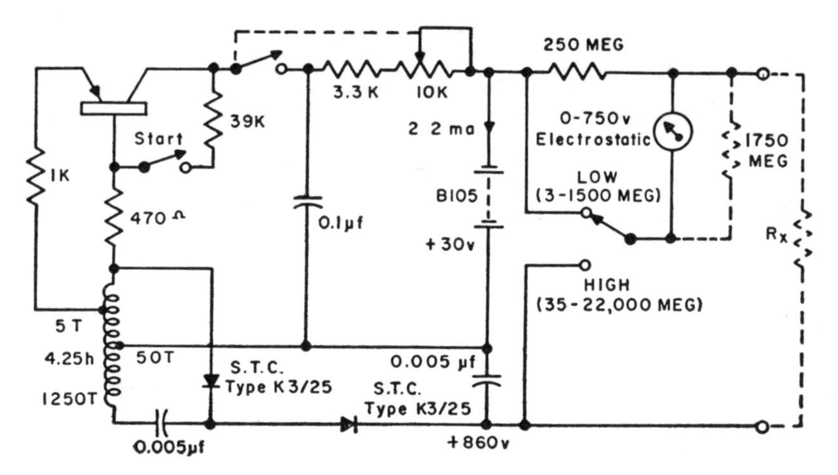

Fig. 21.3. Circuit of two-range megohmmeter with transistor high-voltage generator.

The 750 v electrostatic meter has a leakage of 1750 megohms. A value of 250 megohms is employed for the standard resistor.

The maximum power required for the low range is 750 v at 3.4 μa and for the high range 815 v at 3.25 μa. The effective source impedance must be small compared with the standard for proper regulation. The effective source impedance measured 14 megohms.

The high voltage is supplied by a battery-driven transistor oscillator with a step-up transformer to a selenium rectifier system. The transistor operates more like an astable multivibrator than as an amplifier with positive feedback. This triggering mode of oscillation has the advantage of low collector dissipation both during conduction and cutoff. The switch should be rapid, however, since the dissipation is large during the transition. Class B operation gave satisfactory results.

We can consider the transistor as a switch which connects the tuned circuit to the battery during each negative alternation. The peak-to-peak voltage developed across the tuned circuit then becomes twice the battery voltage. This is the voltage the collector is required to withstand at the peak of the cutoff alternation. Since a safe peak collector voltage is 33 v, we must restrict the battery voltage to 16.5 v.

Actually a 30 v battery supplies 16.5 v to the transistor through a decoupling series resistance. A fixed limiting resistor and a variable resistor ganged to the ON-OFF switch constitute this resistance. The variable resistor precisely controls the high voltage and compensates for battery aging. It also reduces the current to a small value before switching off so that it prevents dangerous inductive surges.

Oscillations may not start in cold weather. Unlike a vacuum tube, a transistor has no gain at zero bias. Only the small collector leakage current flowing through the base bias resistor biases the emitter. Since high-purity germanium has a negative coefficient of resistance with temperature, this current is small when the crystal is cold. After being turned on, the collector current increases slowly as the transistor warms up. Seconds or even minutes may elapse before the circuit breaks into oscillation. A fixed resistor of approximately 39,000 ohms connected between the collector and base can cause quick starting. However, this wastes current and loads the tuned circuit. A push-button starting switch is utilized to connect this resistance.

An auto transformer, which has a step-up ratio of $830/33 = 25/1$

approximately, supplies the 830 v d-c from the peak-to-peak rectifier system. The battery voltage adds in series to produce the desired no-load total output of 860 v.

The auto transformer is wound on a four-section polystyrene form with a small pair of "Ferroxcube" E cores (FX 1105/A4) without gaps for a total of 1250 turns of No. 38 AWG vinyl acetal enameled grade M (medium thickness) wire. Taps are placed at 5 turns for the emitter and 50 turns for the positive battery terminal. The entire transformer winding has a total inductance of 4.25 h with a Q of 50 at the self-resonant frequency of 32 kc/sec. The stray capacitance of the rectifier system lowers the frequency of oscillation to approximately 20 kc/sec. The waveform consists of a distorted sine wave on which higher-frequency damped oscillations are superimposed. The several leakage inductances resonating with stray capacitance generate these high-frequency ripples during the switching transitions. Leakage inductance should be kept to a minimum, lest the switching transients should exceed the maximum safe collector dissipation.

The collector-to-base leakage within the transistor causes a large percentage of the power loss. The home-made point-contact transistor employed in this megohmmeter was formed to an I_{co} of 0.6 ma at 30 v to obtain the low current consumption of 2.2 ma. The average commercial point-contact transistor has an I_{co} of 1 to 2 ma at E_c = 30 v.

A wooden box houses the complete unit with high-grade insulation where needed. Terminals are avoided by bringing out the polythene test leads to crocodile clips. Because few switches have adequate insulation, the meter is switched by plug and socket.

For the low range, the zero is fixed by short-circuiting the test leads and adjusting the variable resistor to give full-scale deflection on the meter. For the high range, infinity is set by separating the test leads and adjusting the variable resistor again for full-scale deflection.

No shock can be felt when handling the test leads, since the meter has a high internal impedance.

Large low-leakage capacitors require considerable time for testing. For instance, it requires more than 15 min to measure a 1 μf capacitor. If the standard resistance is momentarily short-circuited, this time could be cut down to about 1 min. However, a large charged capacitor is extremely dangerous and should be carefully discharged after measuring.

This transistor megohmmeter has given three months of reliable service without any loss of efficiency or output.

In addition to the megohmmeter, the high-voltage generator could supply the high voltage for Geiger-Muller radiation counters, image-converter tubes, flash bulbs, or small cathode-ray tubes.

4. *A transistor organ*[4]

Figure 21.4 shows the circuit of a toy electronic organ. A Type CK722 junction transistor functions as a modified grounded-emitter "Hartley" oscillator. The emitter is connected through push-button

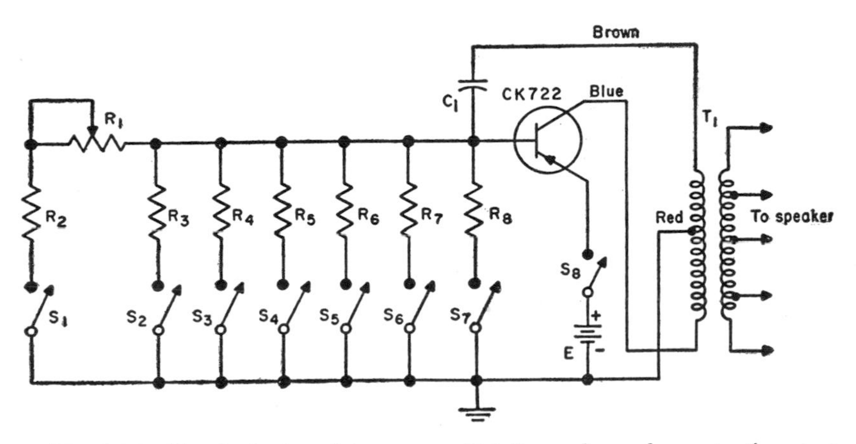

Fig. 21.4. Circuit of a transistor organ. R_1 is 2 megohm carbon potentiometer; R_2 is 8200 ohm, $\frac{1}{2}$ w resistor; R_3, R_4, R_5, R_6, R_7, R_8 are $\frac{1}{2}$ w carbon resistors; C_1 is 0.01 μf disc ceramic capacitor; T_1 is output transformer, single or push-pull plates, 4000–10,000 ohms to v.c. (Stancor A-3856 or equivalent); S_1 is S.P.S.T. toggle switch; S_2, S_3, S_4, S_5, S_6, S_7, S_8, are S.P.S.T. push-button switches; E is 15 v hearing-aid battery (Burgess U-10); speaker is 3 in. PM loudspeaker; CK722 is junction-type transistor (Raytheon).

switch S_8 to the positive terminal of a small hearing-aid type battery, and the collector is connected through one-half of the transformer primary winding to the negative terminal of this battery. The necessary feedback signal is obtained from the other half of the transformer primary winding, which is connected through coupling condenser C_1 to the base of the transistor.

Resistors R_3 to R_8 serve as base return resistors, with the desired resistance selected by depressing push-buttons S_2 to S_7 respectively. If toggle switch S_1 is closed, the base return resistance becomes R_1 and R_2 in series. Since R_1 is variable we can adjust the total resistance from the value of R_2 to the sum of R_2 and R_1 or from 8200 ohms to more than 2 megohms.

The 3 in. PM loudspeaker is connected to the proper taps on the secondary winding of the transformer. Transformer T_1 thus serves both as an oscillator coil and as an output transformer.

In operation, one of the resistor switches, S_1 to S_7, and the power switch S_8 are thrown simultaneously. Battery current then flows over two paths. Part of the current flows through the base return resistor and the base-emitter of the transistor, establishing the bias current for the transistor. The amount of bias current depends on the battery voltage and the total resistance of the resistor plus the internal base-emitter resistance of the transistor. Since the external resistor is normally much larger than the internal base-emitter resistance of the transistor, the base current depends primarily on the size of the base return resistor. Current also flows over the path including half of the transformer primary winding and the collector-emitter resistance of the transistor. This is the collector current and its value depends primarily on the base current and also on the battery voltage.

Any changes in collector current induce an a-c voltage in the top half of the primary of transformer T_1. This voltage is coupled through condenser C_1 to the base of the transistor, adding an a-c component to the d-c base current, and causing corresponding changes in collector current. Thus we have the basic condition for oscillation, positive feedback from output to input along with amplification.

The frequency of operation depends on the transistor characteristics, the transformer, the value of coupling condenser C_1, and the size of the base return resistor. If we vary any of these factors, we will change the frequency. In practice, it was found easiest to vary the size of the base return resistance, hence a selection of resistors R_3 to R_8 with corresponding switches S_2 to S_7.

When we utilize the continuously variable resistor R_1, we can easily change the frequency over wide ranges. Specifically, we can vary the output frequency continuously from about 20 cps to approximately 10 kc/sec simply by adjusting R_1.

The frequency of operation varies inversely with the size of the base return resistor. In other words, when we reduce this resistor value, we increase the frequency of operation. Also, we increase the base current and therefore the collector current. Thus, at high frequencies the battery current drain is several times larger than at low frequencies. This characteristic makes it necessary to provide the fixed resistor R_2 in series with the continuously variable control. Although R_2 limits the maximum frequency of operation when we utilize the variable control, resistor R_2 also limits the maximum base and collector currents and hence protects the transistor from damage.

Since the circuit oscillates by "brute force" feedback instead of a tuned circuit, the output signal is not a sine wave but is extremely rich in harmonics. The waveform varies with frequency, and also with the characteristics of the transformer and transistor.

This transistor organ was assembled in a standard ICA sloping front cabinet with a black push-button for the power key S_8 and red push-buttons for the tone keys S_2 to S_7. Thus six notes were provided, plus a continuously variable tone controlled by R_1.

Other arrangements of keys and case may be employed. For example, the keys of a toy piano could be modified to serve as switches for the transistor organ, and the other components assembled inside the case of the piano. Space permitting, the loudspeaker could be mounted inside the toy piano case. Otherwise it could be mounted separately such as in a sloping panel meter case.

The transformer is of the universal replacement type with a multitapped secondary winding. The loudspeaker connections to the different taps should be experimented with to find the pair giving the best results.

The sizes of the base return resistors R_3 to R_8 are determined experimentally after the unit is wired and tested. If the completed unit is to be primarily a toy, the resistor values may be chosen arbitrarily without regard to the notes obtained. In accordance with this method, resistors of 150 k, 170 k, 190 k, 210 k, and 260 k ohms were selected for this unit.

However, if the completed unit is to play actual tunes, we should adjust each key to give the desired musical note. We can do this with a potentiometer to determine the proper resistor value and then permanently install a fixed resistor, or incorporate a rheostat for each resistor. The latter method permits readjustment at any time, but is more expensive since it requires a separate potentiometer for each note.

To sound a particular note, the desired tone key of S_2 to S_7 and the power key S_8 are depressed simultaneously. They are held down long enough to sound the desired interval, such as a quarter note, half note, or full note, and then released together.

The toggle switch S_1 is thrown to activate the continuously variable control. One note at a time may be sounded by rotating the knob on the side of the case to the desired position, and then depressing and releasing the power key. To obtain a continually changing note, the power key is held down while the control knob is rotated back and forth.

Unusual tonal effects can be achieved by depressing two or more of the tone keys simultaneously. This essentially connects two or more resistors in parallel, reduces the resistance, and increases the frequency or pitch of the note.

5. *Transistorized ukulele*[5]

The amplifier circuit for a transistorized ukulele is given in Fig. 21.5. The output stage utilizes both a P-N-P and an N-P-N junction transistor in a complementary symmetry push-pull amplifier. The first stage is a voltage amplifier whose input comes from the ukulele magnetic pickup, whereas the second stage provides a low-impedance driving source for the output stage. Power is supplied by two small 22.5 v batteries, one connected to give a negative voltage with reference to ground, and the other positive. This is required by the push-pull output stage which loads each battery equally with a current drain of about 7 ma.

The first stage utilizes a P-N-P junction transistor in a stabilized grounded-emitter circuit. A voltage divider of 10,000 ohms and 43,000 ohms keeps the base of the transistor at a constant voltage.

The biasing network of the second stage is similar to that for the first stage except that the emitter resistance is not by-passed. This stage is operated as a grounded-collector amplifier and the output is taken from the emitter. A potentiometer is employed as the emitter resistor, and serves as a gain control.

An auxiliary foot-pedal volume control for special harmonium effects or for convenient volume control may be plugged into a jack provided for this purpose. This foot pedal may be a modified commercial model, or an experimental unit may be constructed by wrap-

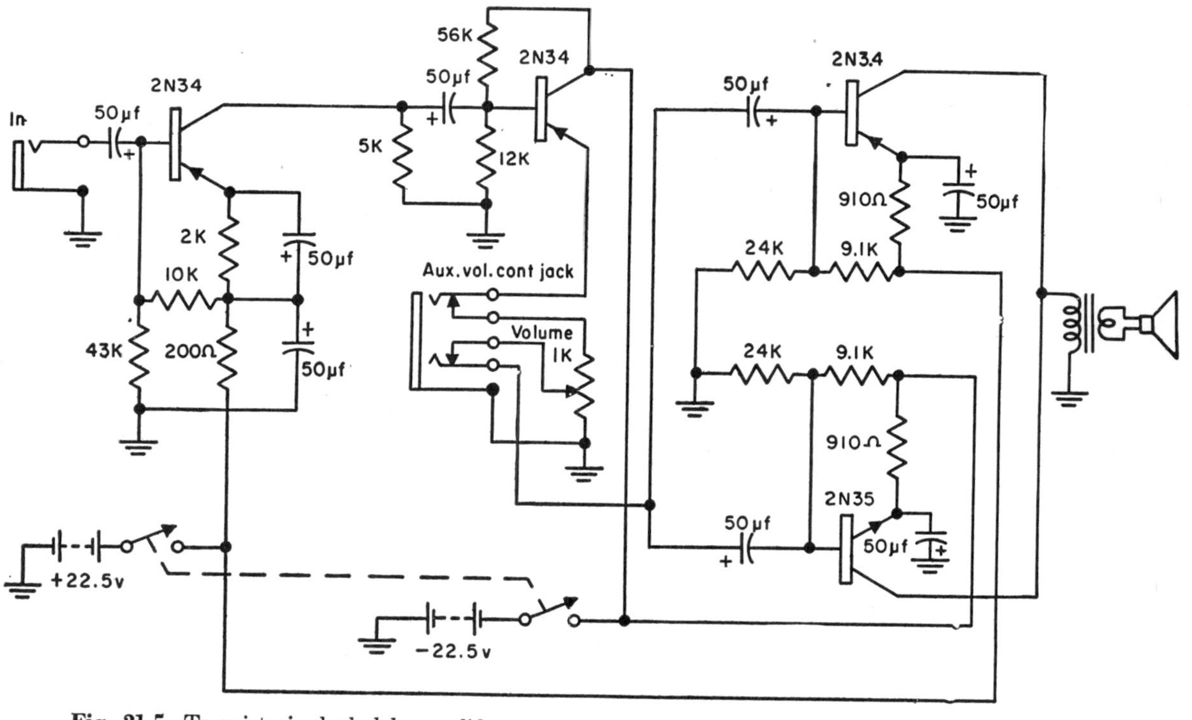

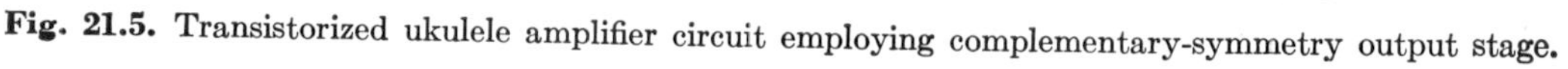
Fig. 21.5. Transistorized ukulele amplifier circuit employing complementary-symmetry output stage.

ping a piece of heavy string around an enlarged 1000 ohm potentiometer shaft and connecting the ends to a suitably mounted pedal.

The output transformer is a 1000 ohms-to-voice coil type.

The maximum power output of this ukulele amplifier is limited by the acoustic feedback rather than the transistors. Too much output causes self-oscillation. However, the modified instrument has considerable volume, and a sustained tonal quality.

6. *The transistor in hearing aids*[6]

A typical hearing-aid circuit employing junction transistors is shown in Fig. 21.6. Either a crystal microphone or a magnetic microphone may be utilized with this circuit. Because of its high imped-

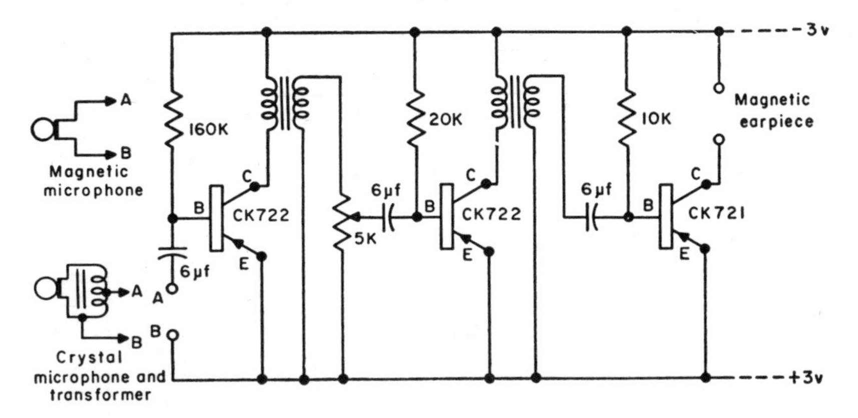

Fig. 21.6. A typical hearing-aid circuit employing junction transistors.

ance, a crystal microphone requires a matching transformer. A two-element parallel crystal wlll operate successfully with a coupling transformer having a primary inductance of about 20 h. The exact value is chosen to resonate with the microphone crystal capacitance at the low-frequency end of the audio range where the response is down 3 db. This is 750 cps for hearing aids. The turns ratio is selected to give maximum power transfer at 1000 cps and results in a fairly uniform frequency response with a decrease of 6 db per octave below 750 cps. An autotransformer is utilized to save space and consists of 6000 turns of No. 50 AWG wire with a tap at 600 turns.

The sensitivity of the microphone and transformer is −100 db referred to 1 w per dyne per cm² at 1000 cycles and can easily be maintained to 6 kc/sec as indicated in Fig. 21.7.

A magnetic-type microphone can easily be constructed with its coil wound to give the proper source impedance for matching the input impedance of the transistor. The power sensitivity of such a unit is about the same as that of the crystal microphone. However, the high-frequency response generally cuts off rapidly above the chief resonant frequency of about 2500 cps.

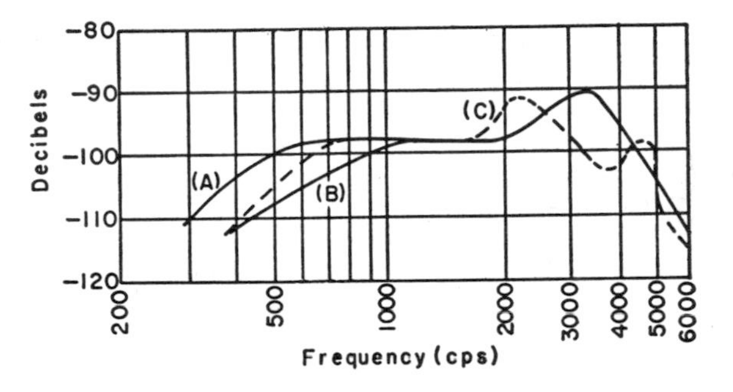

Fig. 21.7. Frequency response of parallel-connected crystal microphone with transformer operating into 1000 ohm load. (A) 4000 μμf microphone capacitance. (B) 2000 μμf microphone capacitance. (C) Typical magnetic microphone response.

The earpiece magnetic telephone receiver has high-power sensitivity, good low-frequency response, and low distortion. However, in most units the peak sensitivity is at about 2 kc/sec with a rapid decrease in sensitivity above 2.5 to 3 kc/sec. The magnetic receiver can be wound to match the output impedance of a transistor. An output greater than +120 db referred to a threshold level of 0.0002 dyne per cm² can be achieved for 2 mw input power. This is normally sufficient for most hearing-aid requirements.

Careful adjustment of the base bias resistor is necessary to obtain maximum power output without exceeding the maximum rated values of the transistor. This resistor normally has values between 5000 ohms and 30,000 ohms. However, once the optimum value has been determined, it will not have to be changed during the life of the transistor unless the latter is subjected to temperatures above about 60° C. This resistance should be adjusted until the collector current is about

2 to 2.2 ma, although for greater power output it may be as high as about 4 ma. This reduces the input impedance of the transistor and the coupling transformer turns ratio must be changed accordingly.

The second stage is not critical, but the adjustment of the base resistor can cause a large change in the over-all gain. A value of 20,000 ohms has proved satisfactory.

Generally the first transistor has to be chosen carefully for noise, and the base bias resistor should be varied for optimum results; a value of about 160,000 ohms was the best compromise between maximum signal-to-noise ratio and maximum gain.

Miniature coupling transformers are employed. Each unit measures 0.375 in. by 0.375 in. by 0.25 in. The core cross-sectional area is 0.096 in. by 0.096 in., and consists of a stack of 0.008 in. thick Mu-

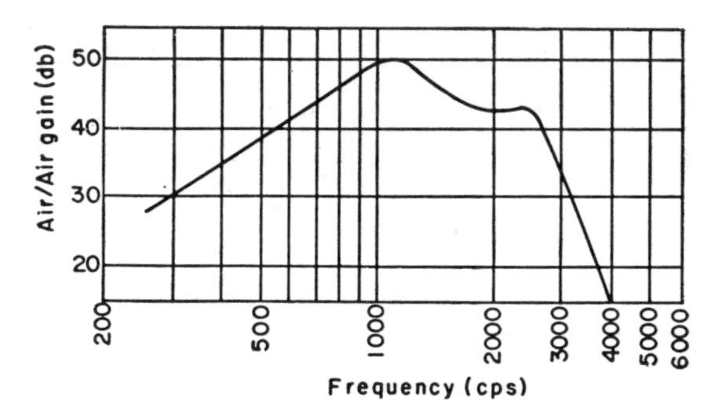

Fig. 21.8. Air-to-air overall gain for the hearing aid of Fig. 21.6.

metal laminations. The bobbin is a 0.25 in. cube. The primary is wound with 3500 turns of No. 48 AWG wire and the secondary with 800 turns of the same size wire. The transformer has an insertion loss of 2.7 db at 3000 cps under operating conditions. The primary inductance is 6 h for 0.1 v, alternating, across it.

The maximum operating gain is about 80 to 85 db, and is flat from about 500 cps to 15,000 cps. With care, the noise level can be kept within 20 db of Johnson noise.

Figure 21.8 is the air-to-air over-all gain of the entire hearing aid. The amplifier itself is quite flat in the high-frequency region, and the earpiece telephone receiver mainly causes the rapid decrease for frequencies above the peak. The microphone circuit is designed to give a low-frequency cutoff at a rate of 12 db per octave in accordance with

British Medical Research Council Report No. 261 to give optimum articulation efficiency for deaf people.

7. *A single channel transistor remote amplifier*[7]

A compact single-channel remote amplifier operating from battery power and utilizing two Type 2N34 junction transistors is shown in Fig. 21.9. The operating points of the transistors are so stabilized that different 2N34 transistors will work in either socket.

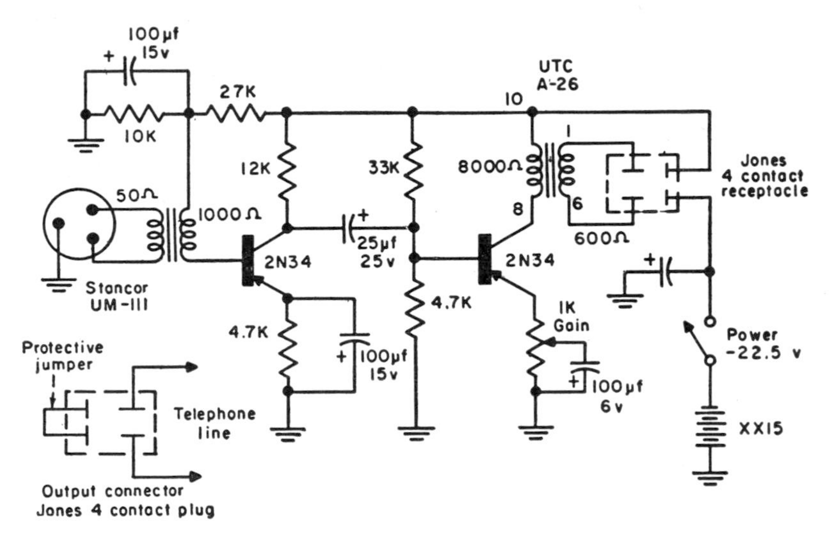

Fig. 21.9. Circuit of single-channel transistor remote amplifier.

The first stage is designed to have a low noise level. For this type of transistor this occurs with a collector current of 1 or 2 ma and a collector-emitter voltage of 1 or 2 v.

A Stancor UM-111 transformer matches a 50 ohm microphone to the 1000 ohm input impedance of the first common-emitter stage. The two stages are coupled by a resistance-capacitance network. The degenerative gain control is in the emitter circuit of the output stage, and maximum gain occurs when the negative terminal of the capacitor connects to the emitter.

The amplifier was designed to give 1 mw undistorted output. The quotient of the collector-emitter voltage divided by the collector current closely approximates the collector load impedance for maximum power output. Therefore the output stage has a load impedance of 8000 ohms. A UTC A-26 transformer matches this impedance to the 600 ohm telephone line.

The transformers, rather than the transistors, limit the frequency response. With the announcer about 1 ft from a Shure 55S microphone, the noise level is about 30 to 40 db below average signal level. The background noise in a remote location almost always obscures this low noise level.

A Burgess XX15 battery supplies 20 v at 4 ma for the amplifier. A battery lasts about 50 hours for 1 hour daily operation. The connector to the telephone line has a jumper which also connects the battery to the amplifier and prevents accidental battery drain when the amplifier is not in use. An aluminum box measuring 3 by 4 by 5 in. houses the complete amplifier including the battery.

The amplifier is extremely simple to operate, since the power switch is the only control. The gain control is only a service or setup adjustment. It is adjusted so that the output never exceeds 1 mw. The average signal level can be 10 to 20 db below 1 mw without troublesome line noise.

8. *A transistor clamp circuit*[8]

Figure 21.10 indicates a symmetrical transistor connected as a clamp circuit. A P-N-P transistor requires a single negative pulse, whereas an N-P-N transistor needs a single positive pulse, which prac-

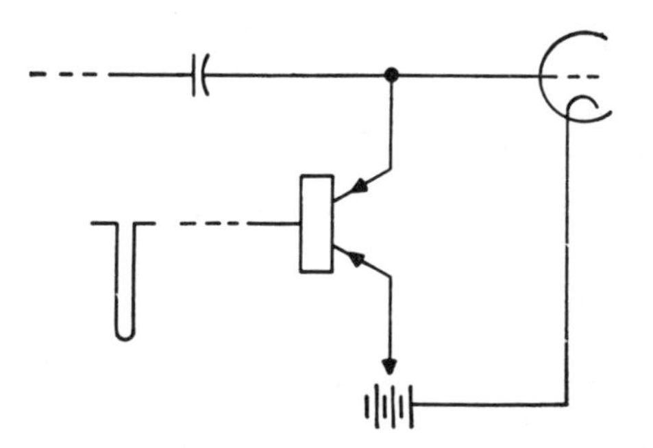

Fig. 21.10. A transistor clamp circuit utilizing a symmetrical transistor.

tically short-circuits the emitter-collector path during the clamping interval.

9. *A transistor phase detector*[8]

A phase detector employing a symmetrical transistor and curves indicating its operation are sketched in Fig. 21.11. When signal source *A* is in phase with signal source *B*, the transistor conducts only during the negative alternation, and a negative voltage drop appears across the load, as shown in curve *a*. When source *A* lags source *B* by 90°, the output wave has the form of curve *b* and the average or d-c output

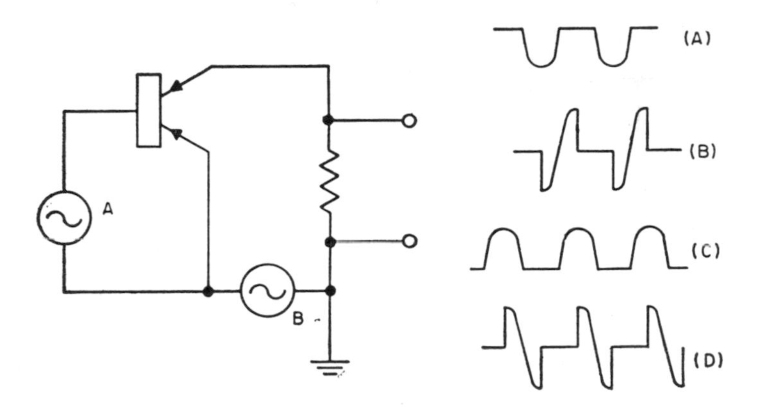

Fig. 21.11. A phase detector employing a symmetrical transistor.

is zero. Between 0° and 90° the ratio of the negative and positive swings and the d-c output vary gradually. Between 90° and 180° a similar relation exists with the opposite polarity. When the two sources are 180° out of phase, the collector is positive. When the base is biased negatively, the output waveform is that of curve *c* and the d-c output is positive. For a phase difference of 270° the waveform is that of curve *d*, whose sequence makes it easy to distinguish from curve *b* for 90°. A direct calibration can be made of the amplitude ratio of negative and positive waves and the d-c output.

This phase detector can also provide automatic phase control in television-synchronizing circuits by detecting the time relationship of a sawtooth and a pulse.

10. *A transistorized radarscope display unit*[9]

Figure 21.12 shows the circuit of a transistorized radarscope display unit. Replacing the vacuum tubes in a standard airborne radar indicator with four Type 1698 point-contact transistors and a crystal diode reduced the power drain from 10 w to 1 w without sacrificing

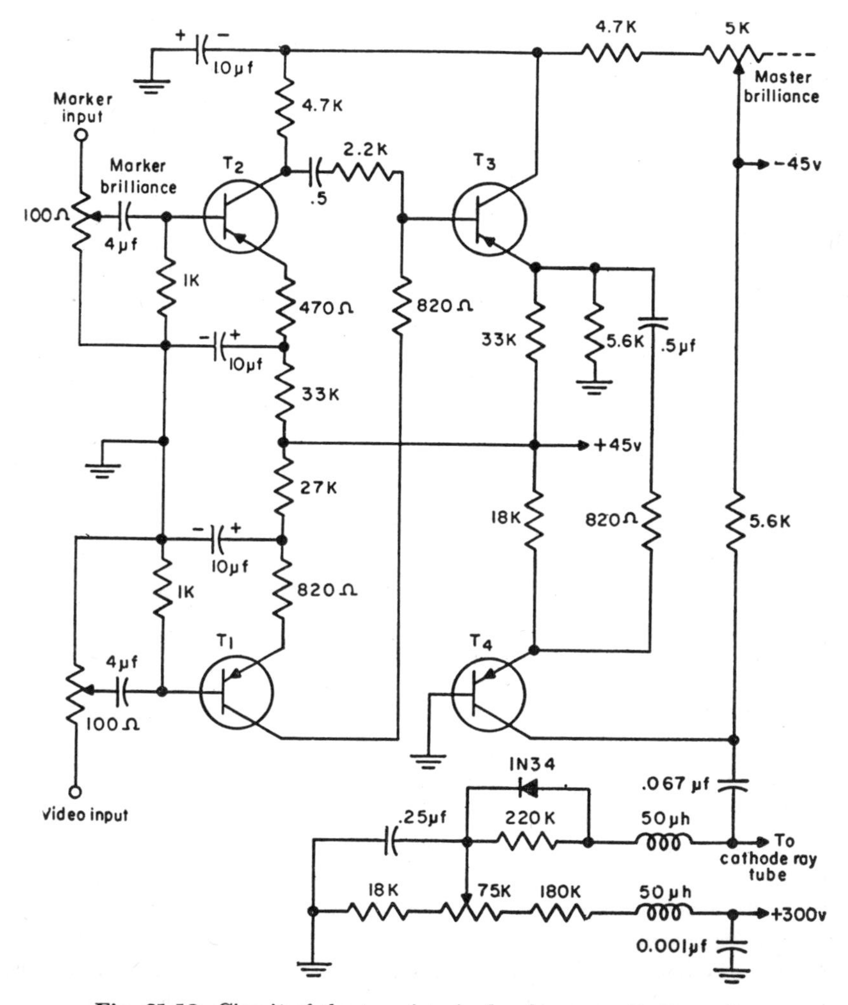

Fig. 21.12. Circuit of the transistorized radar-scope display unit.

performance. Other advantages are increased physical ruggedness and reduction in size and weight.

The unit was designed for a maximum input peak positive pulse of 2 v, and to drive the cathode of a 5BP7 display scope requiring about 20 to 30 v for blooming. Two 45 v batteries supply power to the indicator. The original unit utilized four tubes performing six functions, including two d-c restorers. The transistorized version requires only one d-c restorer. The marker and video signals are amplified separately, then combined, again amplified, and coupled to the cathode ray tube.

The unit is basically a video voltage amplifier with a 4 megacycle bandwidth. Video mixing and the required 180° phase shift are accomplished by two common-emitter amplifiers operating into a common load impedance consisting of the input impedance of the common-collector stage. The marker input stage is a-c coupled to the base of the common-collector stage, but the video input stage is direct coupled. This reduces the collector dissipation of the common-collector stage and facilitates setting optimum working points for the various stages. Isolating resistors were required in the respective collector circuits because of the mutual loading between the common-emitter stages. Since this caused a reduction of the gain, a more efficient mixing system utilizing a diode-coupling network was required.

The collector potential of both the marker common-emitter stage and the common-collector stage are adjusted by the master brilliance control. Although this gives a somewhat nonlinear variation, it is the simplest scheme having no signal on the control itself and is highly stable.

The common-collector stage works into a load consisting of the input impedance of the grounded-base stage in parallel with the series emitter resistance, which fixes the saturation level with a 3 ma emitter-current bias. This final stage produces a voltage gain of 16 db, and can deliver a peak pulse of about 25 v magnitude to the cathode ray tube.

A cable terminated in 100 ohms conveys the video signal to the indicator. Tantalum capacitors of high capacitance, low voltage rating, and small size a-c couple this cable to the 300 ohm input impedance of the common-emitter stage.

This indicator was tested according to standard temperature specifications. At 70°C the operating point shifted, decreasing r_c and increasing alpha, and the gain fell off 18 db. The common-emitter and common-collector stages experienced the greatest change, as expected. There was essentially no change in the grounded-base stage up to about 60°C. The maximum temperature rating of this indicator is 50°C.

11. *A transistorized grid-dip meter*[10]

The transistor makes possible the construction of a grid-dip meter having the advantages of portability, a self-contained power supply, compactness, and one hand operation. Such a device will be very handy to take readings and adjust the elements of a parasitic array at the top of a steel tower. It also has many uses in the amateur's "shack" or the engineer's laboratory.

Figure 21.13 shows the circuit of the "Transdipper," as the device is named. The frequency of oscillation is determined by L_1 and C_3. The indicating circuit consists of a conventional crystal probe with a

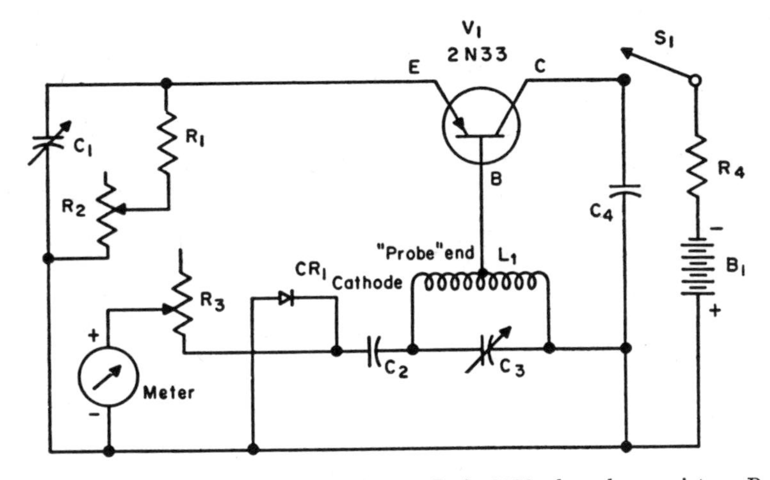

Fig. 21.13. Circuit of the Transdipper. R_1 is 3900 ohm, $\frac{1}{2}$ w resistor; R_2 is 10,000 ohm potentiometer (IRC Type Q); R_3 is 250,000 ohm potentiometer (IRE Type Q); R_4 is 4700 ohm, $\frac{1}{2}$ w resistor; C_1 is 2.7–30 $\mu\mu$f trimmer capacitor; C_2 is 10 $\mu\mu$f mica capacitor; C_3 is 50 $\mu\mu$f midget variable capacitor (Hammarlund HF-50); C_4 is 500 $\mu\mu$f mica capacitor; CR_1 is 1N34-A crystal diode; meter is 0–100 μa microammeter (International Instrument Co.); S_1 is S.P.S.T. toggle switch; B_1 is $22\frac{1}{2}$-v B-battery (RCA VS084); V_1 is 2N33 point-contact transistor (RCA); L_1 is plug-in coil (see text).

microammeter in the output connected across the tuned tank circuit to indicate the r-f voltage. When the tank circuit is loaded, the r-f voltage drops giving the desired dip in the meter reading.

The unit is housed in a $2\frac{1}{4}$ in. by $2\frac{1}{4}$ in. by 5 in. ICA "Flexi-Mount" case. This is a two-piece metal case such that upon completion of construction and adjustment, the two pieces are snapped or screwed together to provide the proper shielding and protection.

Since a suitable dial for the "Transdipper" was not commercially available, a home-made dial was cut from a one-eighth inch sheet of Lucite. This dial protrudes from the upper front sides of the case for easy manipulation. The dial is read through a cut-out hole in the case. A brass bushing about $\frac{3}{4}$ in. in diameter and $\frac{1}{4}$ in. thick having a $\frac{1}{4}$ in. hole and set screw was fastened to the Lucite disc by two countersunk machine screws. A piece of white drawing paper was cemented to the upper surface to complete the dial.

Lengths of wire should be soldered to the terminals before mounting any of the components, because it may be difficult to reach the terminals with a soldering iron after the components are mounted. Since space is limited, the circuit should be wired as each component is installed.

To obtain a compact design, the coils were wound on Amphenol 24-5H forms. It is important that the coils have a reasonably high Q to help obtain a good dip. Powdered-iron slugs are provided for four of the five coils to improve the Q. Holes are drilled and tapped in the bottom of the coil form and each slug is screwed into position with a lock washer and nut. The top of the slug is lined up approximately with the probe end of the coil. The specifications for making the coils covering the five low-frequency amateur bands are as follows: The coil for 1.7 to 3.6 mc/sec consists of 93 $\frac{1}{2}$ turns of No. 28 enameled wire with a $\frac{1}{2}$ in. diameter, 1 in. long slug; for 3.1 to 5.9 mc/sec, 43 $\frac{1}{2}$ turns of No. 24 enameled wire with a $\frac{1}{2}$ in. diameter, 1 in. long slug; for 5.4 to 10.9 mc/sec, 22 $\frac{1}{2}$ turns of No. 24 enameled wire with a $\frac{1}{2}$ in. diameter, $\frac{1}{2}$ in. long slug; for 10.6 to 20.5 mc/sec, 10 $\frac{1}{2}$ turns of No. 24 enameled wire with a $\frac{1}{2}$ in. diameter, $\frac{1}{4}$ in. slug; for 16.7 to 33.0 mc/sec, 10 $\frac{1}{2}$ turns of No. 24 enameled wire spaced to fill a 1 in. winding length. All coils are closewound, except for 16.7 to 33.0 mc/sec, and center-tapped on Amphenol 24-5H $\frac{3}{4}$ in. diameter plug-in forms. The slugs are National Moldite Co. products. There is no slug for the 16.7 to 33.0 coil. It is convenient to color-code the coils to match the colored frequency scales on the dial. The coils should be coated with a plastic spray to hold the wire in place.

The circuit wiring should be double-checked, since transistors are expensive. It is especially important that the battery connections have the correct polarity. Although transistors are extremely rugged mechanically, they can easily be damaged electrically.

Before assembling the case, connect the device to a d-c source of the proper voltage. The total battery current as read on a low-range d-c milliammeter should read about 3.5 ma. The switch should be turned off before inserting one of the coils. Adjust the meter control knob for maximum resistance and apply power. The Transdipper microammeter should show a reading indicating that the oscillator is working. The oscillator signal should now be checked with a receiver with its beat-frequency oscillator turned on. Incidentally, the 2N33 transistor should not be inserted into or withdrawn from the socket with the power turned on, because high transient currents may cause permanent damage to the transistor. When the signal is located with the receiver, the signal should be checked for frequency stability and tone. Tap the device. If the circuit has been wired correctly, good solder connections made, and the components rigidly mounted, the frequency should not change more than a few cycles.

We should next adjust capacitor C_1. The emitter resistor R_2 should be set at maximum resistance when this adjustment is made. The low frequencies require a larger value for C_1 to sustain oscillations than the high frequencies. To eliminate continual adjustments of this screwdriver control, we should employ the minimum value of capacitance required to sustain oscillation at the lowest frequency of operation. This minimum value of capacitance is also suitable for the high frequencies, although better output and dip are obtained when this capacitor is adjusted for maximum output on each tuning range. The adjustment of C_1 may be eliminated by a small fixed capacitor in the base of each coil connected to the two unused pins on the coil form. The optimum value of capacitance for each coil range should be selected.

Grasp the probe end of the coil and observe the meter reading. If the instrument is operating properly there should be a noticeable dip in current. The case may now be assembled and all coils checked for operation, proper frequency range, and overlap.

Because the primary purpose of a grid-dip oscillator is to determine, conveniently and quickly, the approximate resonate frequency of a tuned circuit, the accuracy of the tuning dial is generally not considered too important. Therefore we can calibrate the dial with the station receiver. Calibration of the dial is accomplished by providing a suitable reference line above the dial and, starting with the lowest frequency coil, placing a dot on the paper scale below the reference line with a pencil and marking in the frequency. For easy reading of the dial, utilize the innermost arc for the lowest frequency coil and progress outward during the calibration of the other coils. We can now ink the dial and protect it with a coat of plastic spray.

To determine the resonant frequency of an unknown circuit, insert a coil which you think will be suitable. Turn the switch on, adjust the emitter resistor for maximum output, and then set the meter needle to about three quarters of full scale with the meter control potentiometer. Couple the coil of the Transdipper tightly with the circuit under test and swing the tuning dial slowly over its range. A large dip will occur at resonance. The tight coupling, however, will throw the dial calibration off slightly; back the instrument away until only a small dip is observed.

If difficulty is experienced with false dips, readjustment of the emitter condenser or the emitter resistance will help. Locate the largest false dip and maximize the output on that frequency. When reasonably high-Q circuits are checked, the real dip at resonance is unmistakable provided that the coupling is tight.

Like the conventional grid-dip oscillator, the Transdipper may be employed as a wavemeter, signal generator, field-strength-meter, and for the determination of L or C when one set of values is known. When the Transdipper is utilized as a wavemeter, turn the switch "on" and gradually approach the source of r-f. The meter will peak sharply at resonance.

The input to the oscillator is about 25 mw.

References

1. Nathaniel Rhita, "Transistor Microammeter," *Radio-Electronics*, Vol. XXIV, No. 6, June 1953, p. 49. Copyright 1953 by Gernsback Publications.
2. Louis D. Carcano, "A Transistor Bridge Null Detector," *Radio and Television News*, Vol. L, No. 4, Oct. 1953, p. 132.

3. P. B. Helsdon, "Transistorized Megohmmeter," *Wireless World*, Vol. LX, No. 3, March 1954, pp. 121–123.

4. Louis E. Garner, Jr., "A Transistor Electric Organ," *Radio and Television News*, Vol. L, No. 1, July 1953, pp. 64–65.

5. G. B. Herzog, "Transistorized Ukulele," *Radio-Electronics*, Vol. XXV, No. 2, Feb. 1954, pp. 30–32. Copyright 1954 by Gernsback Publications.

6. S. Kelly, "The Transistor in Hearing Aids," *Wireless World*, Vol. LX, No. 2, Feb. 1954, pp. 56–59.

7. Robert Flory, "Single Channel Transistor Remote Amplifier," *Tele-Tech and Electronic Industries*, Vol. XIII, No. 3, March 1954, p. 114.

8. George Clifford Sziklai, "Symmetrical Properties of Transistors and Their Applications," *Proc. IRE*, Vol. XLI, No. 6, June 1953, pp. 717–724.

9. Raymond Markowitz, "Transistorized Radar-Scope Display Unit," *Philco Tech Rep Division Bulletin*, Vol. III, No. 7, July 1953, pp. 3–6.

10. C. A. West, "The Transdipper," *Radio & Television News*, Vol. L. No. 4, Oct. 1953, pp. 60–62.

APPENDIX

*I. IRE standards on electron devices: definitions of semiconductor terms, 1954**

Acceptor (in Semiconductor)—See *Impurity, Acceptor.*

Barrier (in a Semiconductor) (Obsolete)—See *Depletion Layer.*

Base Electrode (of a Transistor)—An *ohmic* or *majority carrier contact* to the *base region.*

Base Region—The interelectrode region of a *transistor* into which *minority carriers* are injected.

Boundary, P-N—A surface in the transition region between *P*-type and *N*-type material at which the *donor* and *acceptor* concentrations are equal.

Carrier—In a semiconductor, a mobile *conduction electron* or *hole.*

Collector (of a Transistor)—An electrode through which a primary flow of carriers leaves the interelectrode region.

Conduction Band—A range of states in the energy spectrum of a solid in which electrons can move freely.

Conductivity Modulation (of a Semiconductor)—The variation of the conductivity of a semiconductor by variation of the charge *carrier* density.

Conductivity, N-type—The conductivity associated with *conduction electrons* in a semiconductor.

Conductivity, P-type—The conductivity associated with *holes* in a semiconductor.

Contact, High Recombination Rate—A semiconductor-semiconductor or metal-semiconductor contact at which thermal equilibrium *carrier* densities are maintained substantially independent of current density.

Contact, Majority Carrier (to a Semiconductor)—An electrical contact across which the ratio of *majority carrier* current to applied voltage is substantially independent of the polarity of the voltage while the ratio of *minority carrier* current to applied voltage is not independent of the polarity of the voltage.

* Reprinted with permission of The Institute of Radio Engineers, Inc.

Crystal Pulling—A method of crystal growing in which the developing crystal is gradually withdrawn from a melt.

Depletion Layer (in a Semiconductor)—A region in which the mobile *carrier* charge density is insufficient to neutralize the net fixed charge density of *donors* and *acceptors.*

Diffusion Constant (in a Homogeneous Semiconductor)—The quotient of diffusion current density by the charge *carrier* concentration gradient. It is equal to the product of the *drift mobility* and the average thermal energy per unit charge of *carriers.*

Diffusion Length—In a homogeneous semiconductor, the average distance to which *minority carriers* diffuse between generation and recombination.

Diode, Semiconductor—A two-electrode *semiconductor device* having an asymmetrical voltage-current characteristic.

Donor (in a Semiconductor)—See *Impurity, Donor.*

Doping—Addition of *impurities* to a semiconductor or production of a deviation from stoichiometric composition, to achieve a desired characteristic.

Doping Compensation—Addition of *donor impurities* to a *P-type semiconductor* or of *acceptor impurities* to an *N-type semiconductor.*

Drift Mobility (in a Homogeneous Semiconductor)—The average drift velocity of *carriers* per unit electric field.

Note: In general, the mobilities of electrons and holes are different.

Electrode (of a Semiconductor Device)—An element that performs one or more of the functions of emitting or collecting electrons or *holes*, or of controlling their movements by an electric field.

Electrons, Conduction—The electrons in the *conduction band* of a solid, which are free to move under the influence of an electric field.

Element (of a Semiconductor Device)—Any integral part of the *semiconductor device* that contributes to its operation.

Emitter—See *Emitter, Majority* and *Emitter, Minority.*

Emitter, Majority (of a Transistor)—An *electrode* from which a flow of *majority carriers* enters the interelectrode region.

Emitter, Minority (of a Transistor)—An *electrode* from which a flow of *minority carriers* enters the interelectrode region.

Energy Gap (of a Semiconductor)—The energy range between the bottom of the *conduction band* and the top of the *valence band.*

Extrinsic Properties (of a Semiconductor)—The properties of a semiconductor as modified by *impurities* or *imperfections* within the crystal.

Fermi Level—The value of the electron energy at which the Fermi distribution function has the value one-half.

Forming, Electrical (Applied to Semiconductor Devices)—Process of applying electrical energy to a semiconductor device in order to modify permanently the electrical characteristics.

Generation Rate (in a Semiconductor)—The time rate of creation of electron-hole pairs.

Hall Constant (of an Electrical Conductor)—The constant of proportionality R in the relation

$\mathbf{E_h} = R\,\mathbf{J} \times \mathbf{H}$, where

$\mathbf{E_h}$ = Transverse electric field (Hall field)

$\mathbf{J}$ = Current density

$\mathbf{H}$ = Magnetic field.

Note: The sign of the *majority carrier* can be inferred from the sign of the Hall constant.

Hole—A mobile vacancy in the electronic valence structure of a semiconductor which acts like a positive electronic charge with a positive mass.

Imperfection (of a Crystalline Solid)—Any deviation in structure from that of an ideal crystal.

Note: An ideal crystal is perfectly periodic in structure and contains no foreign atoms.

Impurity, Acceptor (in a Semiconductor)—An impurity which may induce hole conduction.

Impurity (Chemical)—An atom within a crystal which is foreign to the crystal.

Impurity, Donor (in a Semiconductor)—An impurity which may induce electronic conduction.

Impurity, Stoichiometric—A crystalline imperfection arising from a deviation from stoichiometric composition.

Intrinsic Properties (of a Semiconductor)—The properties of a semiconductor which are characteristic of the pure, ideal crystal.

Intrinsic Temperature Range (in a Semiconductor)—The temperature range in which the electrical properties of a semiconductor are essentially not modified by *impurities* or *imperfections* within the crystal.

Junction (in a Semiconductor Device)—A region of transition between semiconducting regions of different electrical properties.

Junction, Alloy (in a Semiconductor)—A junction formed by alloying one or more *impurities* to a semiconductor crystal.

Junction, Collector (of a Semiconductor Device)—A junction normally biased in the high-resistance direction, the current passing through which can be controlled by the introduction of *minority carriers*.

Junction, Emitter (of a Semiconductor Device)—A junction normally biased in the low-resistance direction to inject *minority carriers* into an interelectrode region.

Junction, Fused (in a Semiconductor)—A junction formed by recrystallization on a base crystal from a liquid phase of one or more components and the semiconductor.

Junction, N-N (in a Semiconductor)—A region of transition between two regions having different properties in *N*-type semiconducting material.

Junction, P-N (in a Semiconductor)—A region of transition between *P*- and *N*-type semiconducting material.

Junction, P-P (in a Semiconductor)—A region of transition between two regions having different properties in *P*-type semiconducting material.

Junction (Semiconductor), Diffused—A junction which has been formed by the diffusion of an *impurity* within a semiconductor crystal.

Junction (Semiconductor), Doped—A junction produced by the addition of an *impurity* to the melt during crystal growth.

Junction (Semiconductor), Grown—A junction produced during growth of a crystal from a melt.

Junction (Semiconductor), Rate-grown—A *grown junction* produced by varying the rate of crystal growth.

Lifetime, Volume—The average time interval between the generation and recombination of *minority carriers* in a homogeneous semiconductor.

Majority Carrier (in a Semiconductor)—The type of *carrier* constituting more than half of the total number of *carriers*.

Minority Carrier (in a Semiconductor)—The type of *carrier* constituting less than half of the total number of *carriers*.

Mobility—See *Drift Mobility*.

Mobility, Hall (of an Electrical Conductor)—The quantity μ_H in the relation $\mu_H = R\sigma$, where R = *Hall constant* and σ = conductivity.

Ohmic Contact—A contact between two materials, possessing the property that the potential difference across it is proportional to the current passing through.

Photovaristor—A varistor in which the current-voltage relation may be modified by illumination, e.g., cadmium sulphide or lead telluride.

Point Contact—Pressure contact between a semiconductor body and a metallic point.

Primary Flow (of Carriers)—A current flow which is responsible for the major properties of the device.

Recombination Rate, Surface—The time rate at which free electrons and *holes* recombine at the surface of a semiconductor.

Recombination Rate, Volume—The time rate at which free electrons and *holes* recombine within the volume of a semiconductor.

Recombination Velocity (on a Semiconductor Surface)—The quotient of the normal component of the electron (*hole*) current density at the surface by the excess electron (*hole*) charge density at the surface.

Semiconductor—An electronic conductor, with resistivity in the range between metals and insulators, in which the electrical charge *carrier* concentration increases with increasing temperature over some temperature range. Certain semiconductors possess two types of *carriers*, namely, negative electrons and positive *holes*.

Semiconductor, Compensated—A semiconductor in which one type of *impurity* or *imperfection* (e.g., *donor*) partially cancels the electrical effects of the other type of *impurity* or *imperfection* (e.g., *acceptor*).

Semiconductor Device—An electron device in which the characteristic distinguishing electronic conduction takes place within a semiconductor.

Semiconductor Device, Multiple Unit—A semiconductor device having two or more sets of electrodes associated with independent *carrier* streams.

Note: It is implied that the device has two or more output functions which are independently derived from separate inputs, e.g., a duo-triode transistor.

Semiconductor Device, Single Unit—A semiconductor device having one set of electrodes associated with a single *carrier* stream.

Note: It is implied that the device has a single output function related to a single input.

Semiconductor, Extrinsic—A semiconductor with electrical properties dependent upon *impurities.*

Semiconductor, Intrinsic—A semiconductor whose electrical properties are essentially characteristic of the pure, ideal crystal.

Semiconductor, N-type—An *extrinsic semiconductor* in which the *conduction electron* density exceeds the *hole* density.

Note: It is implied that the net ionized *impurity* concentration is *donor* type.

Semiconductor, P-type—An *extrinsic semiconductor* in which the *hole* density exceeds the *conduction electron* density.

Note: It is implied that the net ionized *impurity* concentration is *acceptor* type.

Space Charge Region (Pertaining to Semiconductor)—A region in which the net charge density is significantly different from zero. See also *Depletion Layer.*

Thermistor—An electron device which makes use of the change of resistivity of a semiconductor with change in temperature.

Transistor—An active *semiconductor device* with three or more electrodes.

Transistor, Conductivity Modulation—A *transistor* in which the active properties are derived from *minority carrier* modulation of the bulk resistivity of a semiconductor.

Transistor, Filamentary—A *conductivity modulation transistor* with a length much greater than its transverse dimensions.

Transistor, Junction—A *transistor* having a *base electrode* and two or more *junction* electrodes.

Transistor, Point-contact—A *transistor* having a *base electrode* and two or more *point-contact* electrodes.

Transistor, Point-junction—A *transistor* having a *base electrode* and both *point-contact* and *junction* electrodes.

Transistor, Unipolar—A *transistor* which utilizes charge *carriers* of only one polarity.

Transition Region—The region, between two homogeneous semiconductor regions, in which the *impurity* concentration changes.

Valence Band—The range of energy states in the spectrum of a solid crystal in which lie the energies of the valence electrons which bind the crystal together.

Varistor—A two-electrode *semiconductor device* having a voltage-dependent nonlinear resistance.

Zone Leveling (*Pertaining to Semiconductor Processing*)—The passage of one or more molten zones along a semiconductor body for the purpose of uniformly distributing *impurities* throughout the material.

Zone Purification (*Pertaining to Semiconductor Processing*)—The passage of one or more molten zones along a semiconductor for the purpose of reducing the *impurity* concentration of part of the ingot.

II(a). Manufacturers of transistors discussed in the text, with abbreviations as used in Table II(b)

AE Amperex Electronic Corp., 230 Duffy Avenue, Hicksville, N.Y.

BTL Bell Telephone Laboratories, 463 West Street, New York 14, N.Y.

CBS CBS-Hytron, Division of Columbia Broadcasting System, Danvers, Mass.

GE General Electric Co., Electronics Park, Syracuse, N.Y.

GP Germanium Products Corp., 26 Cornelison Avenue, Jersey City 4, N.J.

MH Minneapolis-Honeywell Regulator Corp., 2747 Fourth Avenue South, Minneapolis, Minn.

RCA Radio Corporation of America, Tube Dept., Harrison, N.J.

RR Radio Receptor Co., 251 West 19th Street, New York 11, N.Y.

RM Raytheon Manufacturing Co., 55 Chapel Street, Newton, Mass.

SEP Sylvania Electric Products Co., 1740 Broadway, New York 19, N.Y.

TI Texas Instruments, Inc., 6000 Lemmon Avenue, Dallas 9, Texas.

TP Transistor Products, Inc., Snow & Union Streets, Boston 35, Mass.

WE Western Electric Co., Inc., 195 Broadway, New York 7, N.Y.

II(b). Essential characteristi

Number	Manufacturer	Type	Maximum Ratings							Characteristics							
			Collector			Emitter											
			Dissipation, mw	Volts	Current, ma	Dissipation, mw	Current, ma	Voltage	Ambient temp., °C	Current amp. factor	R_{11}, ohms	R_{12}, ohms	R_{21}, kilohms	R_{22}, kilohms	r_e, ohms	r_b, ohms	kilohms
IN188	TP	Jct. P-N	*Photodiode*							(Light sensitivity, 10 μamp/ML)							
2N32	RCA	Pt. cont.	50	−40	−8		3	−40	40	2.2	400	140		31			
2N33	RCA	Pt. cont.	30	−8.5	−7		0.8		40	2.3	370	350		12			
2N34	RCA	Jct. P-N-P	50	−25	−8				50	40							
2N35	RCA	Jct. N-P-N	50	25	8				50	40							
2N36	CBS	Jct. P-N-P	50	−20	−8				50	45							
2N37	CBS	Jct. P-N-P	50	−20	−8				50	30							
2N57	MH	Jct. P-N-P	20 w	−60	800	5 w									1	40	
3N21	SEP	Pt. cont.	100	−60				*−50	50	2.5	*500	*350		25			
A1698	WE	Pt. cont.	120	−100	−15		15	−40	55	2.3	350	190	60	26			
A1723	WE	Pt. cont.															
A1729	WE	Pt. cont.	200	50	20		15			2.5	195	75	37.6	15.1	120	75	1
A1768	WE	Pt. cont.	120	−30	−25	25	15	−20	50	2.5	150	110		6.5			
A1858	WE	Jct. N-P-N															
AN2891	WE	Pt. cont.															
BL115	BTL	Pt. cont.															
CK716	RM	Pt. cont.	100	−40	−4		+10			1.5							
CK721	RM	Jct. P-N-P	33	−22	10		10		50	45					25	700	200
CK722	RM	Jct. P-N-P	33	−22	10		10		50	12					25	250	200
CK727	RM	Jct. P-N-P	30	−6	10		10		50	35					50	500	200
G11	GE	Pt. cont.	100	30	7		3	50	40	2.2					275	200	2
M1689	BTL	Pt. cont.	80	50	40		40								800	500	1
M1729	BTL	Pt. cont.	200	50	20		15			2.5	195	75	37.6	15.1	120	75	1
M1740	BTL	Jct. P-N	100	200	10				80	*Photocell*							
M1752	BTL	Jct. P-N-P	50	50	5		5			.98	275	240	4750	5000	25	240	500
M1768	BTL	Pt. cont.	120	−30	−25	25	+15	−20	40	2.4	155	75	16	6.8			
M1832	BTL	Pt. cont.															
OC51	AE	Pt. cont.	100	−50	−15		12	−35	55	2.2	280	150	44	22			
PT2A	CBS	Pt. cont.	100	−40	−10		5	−40	55	1.5					300	200	1
PT2S	CBS	Pt. cont.	100	−40	−10		5	−40	55	2						400	
RR14H	RR	Jct. P-N-P	70	−25					50	28					30	550	100
RR34H	RR	Jct. P-N-P	70	−25					50	15					30	400	100
TA153	RCA	Jct. P-N-P		−20						.95							50
TA154	RCA	Jct. N-P-N		20						.95							50
TA165K	RCA	Pt. cont.		−50	−8		3	−50	50	2.2	400	140			260	140	3
TA166	RCA	Pt. cont.							50	2.0	250	100				100	1
TA172	RCA	Pt. cont.	50	10						2.3	370	350				350	1
TI210	TI	Jct. P-N-P	50	30	5				50								

* Either emitter.

transistors

Collector voltage	Collector current, ma	Emitter current, ma	Input resistance, ohms	Load resistance, kilohms	Power gain, db	Power output, mw	Cutoff frequency, f_c (mc/sec)	Noise factor, db	Ambient temperature, °C	Circuit	Rise time, μsec	Turn-off time, μsec	Application	Number
	Typical Operating Characteristics													
40	(Dark current, 20 μamp max.)								25				Light detector	IN188
25		.5	500	10	21		2.7		25				Pulse, switching	2N32
−8	3.3	.3	500	10	22	1.0			25				50 mc/sec oscillator	2N33
−6		1	500	30	40				25	GE			Amplifier	2N34
6		−1	500	30	40				25	GE			Amplifier	2N35
−6		1	1000	30	40			21	25	GE			High-grain amplifier	2N36
−6		1	1000	30	36			18	25	GE			High-grain amplifier	2N37
28		360			20	5 w	.02		21	GE			Class B amplifier, 2 units	2N57
Tetrode transistor											.2	.5	Switching, mixer	3N21
30		1.0					2.7		25				Switching	A1698
													A-f oscillator	A1723
30	5/7	1/2	190	15	20/18	50		54					Audio and carrier	A1729
−5		1.5					.35		25				General	A1768
													Audio amplifier	A1858
													Blocking oscillator	AN2891
													Blocking oscillator	BL115
15	2.5	1.0					.1	65					Amplifier, switching	CK716
−6		1	1500	20	41		.8	22 max.	27	GE			General purpose	CK721
−6		1	500	20	36		.8	30 max.	27	GE			General purpose	CK722
1.5		.5	1000	20	36		.8	10 max.	27	GE			Low noise	CK727
25		.5	500	20	17		2	57	25				Amplifier, oscillator	G11
			800	10									Switching	M1689
30	5/7	1/2	190	15	20/18	50		54					Audio, carrier	M1729
90				200	(Dark current, 20 μamp max.) (Light sensitivity, 30 μamp/ML)								Photo detection	M1740
			25	13									General purpose	M1752
−5	−5	1.5	155	6.8	21	5	.4	48	25				Low-voltage audio oscillator	M1768
													106 mc/sec r-f oscillator	M1832
-35		1					1.5		25				Switching	OC51
-30		1	300	20	19		2	57	25				Amplifier	PT2A
-30		1							25			1.0	Switching	PT2S
1.5		.5	1000	30	36			19	25	GE			Audio amplifier	RR14H
1.5		.5	1000	30	32			19	25	GE			Audio amplifier	RR34H
−6		1	500	30	38				25				Audio amplifier	TA153
6		−1	500	30	38				25				Audio amplifier	TA154
-25		.5	500	10	21		3.5		25	GB			R-f or i-f amplifier	TA165K
-20	3.3	.5					3		25	GB			i-f or video amplifier	TA166
8	2	.3				.5			25				50 mc/sec oscillator	TA172
2.5	2		500	10	39	12			25	GE			Audio amplifier	TI210

II(b). Essential characteristic

Number	Manufacturer	Type	Maximum Ratings							Characteristics							
			Collector			Emitter											
			Dissipation, mw	Volts	Current, ma	Dissipation, mw	Current, ma	Voltage	Ambient temp., °C	Current amp. factor	R_{11}, ohms	R_{12}, ohms	R_{21}, kilohms	R_{22}, kilohms	r_e, ohms	r_b, ohms	r_c, kilohms
TI222	TI	Jct. N-P-N	50	30	5				50								
TI233	TI	Jct. N-P-N	50	30	5				50								
X15	TI	Jct. N-P-N†	1 w	50	100				85								
X25	TP	Jct. N-P-N	60	*Phototransistor*													
X47	TP	*Photoconducting cell*					(Dark resistance, 1800–2000 ohms)										
X78	TP	Jct. P-N-P	1 w	45	50												
200	TI	Jct. N-P-N	50	30	5				50	9 min.					22	150	40[illegible] mi[illegible]
201	TI	Jct. N-P-N	50	30	5				50	19 min.					22	170	40[illegible] mi[illegible]
700	TI	Jct. N-P-N	50	30	*Tetrode transistor*					.95					30	1000	100[illegible]
903	TI	Jct. N-P-N†	75	30	10					.93							
904	TI	Jct. N-P-N†	75	30	10					.96							
904A	TI	Jct. N-P-N†	75	30	10					.95							
905	TI	Jct. N-P-N†	75	30	10					.975							
1698	BTL	Pt. cont.	120	−100	−15		15	−40	55	2.3	350	190	60	26			
1729	BTL	Pt. cont.	200	50	20		15			2.5	195	75	37.6	15.1	120	75	1[illegible]
1734	BTL	Pt. cont.															
1768	BTL	Pt. cont.	120	−30	−25	25	15	−20	50	2.5	150	110		6.5			
2517	GP	Jct. N-P-N	50	30	10		−10		75	.93					25	100	300[illegible]

† Silicon transistor.

of transistors (cont'd.)

Typical Operating Characteristics														
Collector voltage	Collector current, ma	Emitter current, ma	Input resistance, ohms	Load resistance, kilohms	Power gain, db	Power output, mw	Cutoff frequency, f_c (mc/sec)	Noise factor, db	Ambient temperature, °C	Circuit	Rise time, μsec	Turn-off time, μsec	Application	Number
22.5	.7		750	70	35				25	GE			Neutralized 262 kc/sec i-f amplifier	TI222
22.5	.7		300	60	20				25	GE			Oscillator and mixer	TI233
35		45		2	14	1 w			25	GE			Med. power class B push-pull amplifier	X15
				10		60	>0.25						Relay operation	X25
(Dark resistance, 1800–2000 ohms)													Light detector	X47
45	90		10	2	>10	>2 w	>.01		25	GE			Push-pull class B amplifier	X78
5		−1	500	20	37	2.15	.9	26	25	GE			High-gain audio amplifier	200
5		−1	500	20	40	2.30	1.1	23	25	GE			High-gain audio amplifier	201
5		−1							25	GE			Low-frequency automatic gain control	700
5		−1					3	23		GB			High gain, low level	903
5		−1					3	23		GB			High gain, low level	904
5		−1					8	23		GB			High gain, low level	904A
5		−1					3	23		GB			High gain, low level	905
−30		1.0					2.7		25				Switching	1698
−30	5/7	1/2	190	15	20/18	50		54					Carrier frequency oscillator	1729
													22 mc/sec i-f amplifier	1734
−5		1.5					.35		25				General purpose	1768
4.5		−1			38		1	20	25	GE	.1	.2	Amplifier, switching	2517

AUTHOR INDEX

SUBJECT INDEX